Instrumentation Training Course

Vol. 1

Pneumatic Instruments

Edited by The Howard W. Sams
Technical Staff

HOWARD W. SAMS & CO., INC.
THE BOBBS-MERRILL CO., INC.
INDIANAPOLIS · KANSAS CITY · NEW YORK

FIRST EDITION

SIXTH PRINTING—1977

International Standard Book Number: 0-672-20621-8
Library of Congress Catalog Card Number: 68-20568

Preface

This work has evolved over the last ten years. Initially it was a collection of lecture notes developed and used in a variety of training situations. The need then, and now, was for a systematic and orderly structure that would reduce the maze of instrumentation to a coordinated and integrated entity. The method that evolved was to start with a series of basic components that are common to all pneumatic and mechanical instruments, then combine these into subassemblies that are then arranged into the fundamental instrument types. These fundamental instruments are idealized, and each represents a basic instrument type. Given such a structure, the learner can relate each instrument being studied to the fundamental instrument. New instruments, as they appear on the market, then can readily be fitted into the basic structure.

Accordingly, a very careful attempt has been made to reduce each instrument being studied to a chain of functional components and to show how that instrument relates to fundamental instruments it exemplifies. Once the basic components and elementary instruments are understood, it becomes a relatively easy way to fit each new instrument studied into the basic structure. This approach has proven to be much more fruitful than a direct comparison of instruments.

Contents

CHAPTER 32

Proportioning Response—Integral Response—Derivative Response—Combined 3-Mode Response

CHAPTER 33

What Does Control Mean?—"Open" Versus "Closed-Loop" Control—Control in a Practical Plant

Chapter 1

Basic Lever Mechanisms and Adjustments

LINK AND LEVER MECHANISMS

Industrial instruments used for recording are all quite similar in principle. Except for some electrical instruments, almost all recorders consist of rather elementary arrangements of links and levers. In this chapter, link/lever mechanisms will be discussed and their limitations will be examined.

Components

The mechanism of a typical instrument consists of:

1. An "input" lever (Fig. 1-1).
2. An "output" lever (Fig. 1-2).
3. A "link" connecting a lever to an input, or connecting two levers.

We shall define a lever as a member that rotates about a point, or pivot. Levers may have either two sides or one side. An example of a two-sided lever is the child's "see-saw." The handle on a rotary wall-mounted can opener is an example of a one-sided lever.

NOTE: In certain respects, the one-sided lever is more nearly a wheel and axle mechanism. In our work, however, the one-sided lever shall, in all cases, travel less than 180 degrees—usually about 15 or 20 degrees —which makes the mechanism more nearly a lever than a wheel.

Arrangements

The input lever may be one- or two-sided. In a one-sided lever, the input to the mechanism comes through the shaft about which the lever rotates. That is, the input causes the shaft to rotate, and the lever that is attached to the shaft rotates with it. The "link" is attached to this lever. (See Fig. 1-1A.)

If the input lever is two-sided, the input comes to one side of the lever, causing the lever to rotate about its pivot, moving the second side of the lever to which the link is attached. (See Fig. 1-1B.)

The link attached to the input lever is connected to the output lever. The motion of the input lever is passed by the link to the output lever, causing the output lever to rotate. This lever is solidly attached to a shaft that rotates with the lever. Attached to this shaft is the pen (or indicator). Also attached to this shaft are the levers that feed the integrators, controllers, contacts, etc.

Links are almost always straight; thus, the levers connected by the link must be in the same plane. That is, they must be the same distance from the back (or the front) of the instrument case. If they are not in the same plane, levers will be "offset."

Principle of Operation

The input to the mechanism causes the input lever (or shaft) to rotate. This rotation is transferred to the output lever by the link. The rotation of the output lever causes the output shaft to rotate, which, in turn, causes the pen to move. Other levers that drive the controller, integrator, alarm contacts, etc., depending on the particular instrument, may also be attached to the output shaft.

The movement of the input lever in the actual instrument is usually small compared to the movement of the output lever. In order to get the input lever to drive the output lever through its proper travel, the movement of the input lever must be multiplied. For example, suppose the angular rotation of the input lever is 10 degrees, and the angular rotation of the output lever is 40 degrees. This means that the input must be multiplied by a factor of 4. (10 degrees × 4 = 40 degrees.) This multiplication of motion

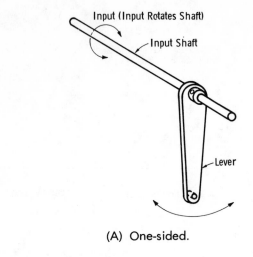

(A) One-sided.

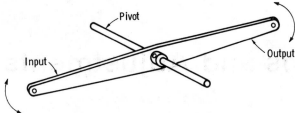

(B) 180-degree two-sided.

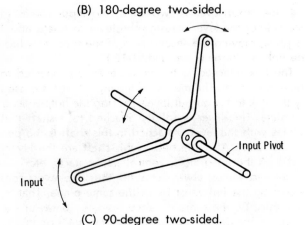

(C) 90-degree two-sided.

Fig. 1-1. Link levers.

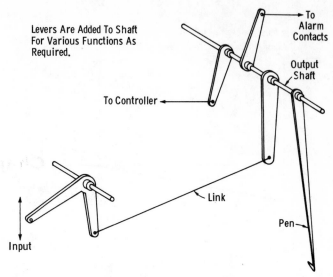

Levers Are Added To Shaft For Various Functions As Required.

(A) Link connecting two levers.

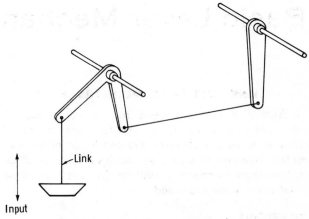

(B) Link connecting input to lever.

Fig. 1-2. Link levers.

1. The "physical" levers are not necessarily the "actual" levers.
2. The "actual" levers are not necessarily the "effective" levers.

is obtained by adjusting the ratio of the length of the input lever to the length of the output lever. The multiplication factor can be changed by changing the length of the levers. For our work, it can be said that the input angle multiplied by the length of the input lever must equal the output angle multiplied by the length of the output lever. For example: Suppose the rotation of the output lever is 40 degrees, the length of the input lever is 3 inches, and the rotation of the input lever is 30 degrees. Then,

$$30 \times 3 = 40 \times X$$

$$X = \frac{90}{40} = 2\frac{1}{4} \text{ inches} \qquad \text{See Fig. 1-3.}$$

Physical, Actual, and Effective Levers

The operation of the link/lever mechanism is not as straightforward as it might appear at first glance for two reasons:

The physical lever, the lever one sees in the mechanism, may take rather unusual shapes. (See Fig. 1-4.)

The actual lever is identified by connecting a straight line from the point of rotation to the point at which the link is attached. This line represents the actual lever and in many mechanisms falls outside the physical lever. It is important that this mental image of the actual lever be retained when working on link/lever mechanisms.

The effective lever is the line originating at the point of rotation and connecting the link so that it forms a 90-degree angle with the link. The effective lever changes length as the lever rotates. We have already seen that the lengths of the levers determine their travel. When the ratio of the input/output travel changes with rotation (that is, when the effective lever is not the actual lever) an angularity error occurs. (See Fig. 1-5.) The point in the link/lever mechanism where the actual and the effective levers coincide is the only

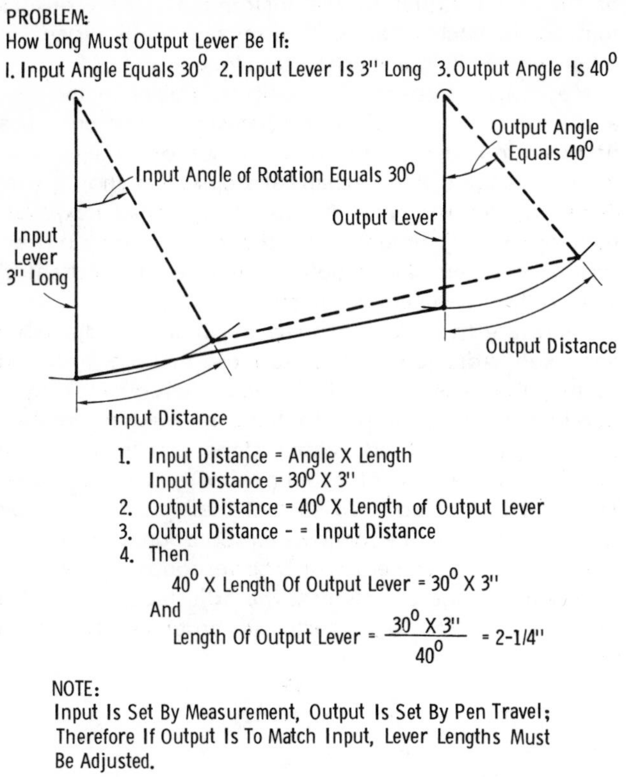

PROBLEM:
How Long Must Output Lever Be If:
1. Input Angle Equals 30° 2. Input Lever Is 3" Long 3. Output Angle Is 40°

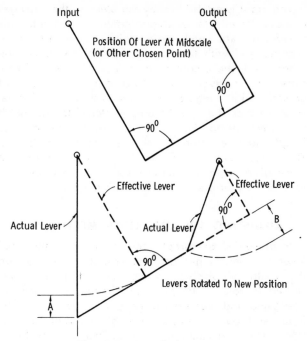

1. Input Distance = Angle X Length
   Input Distance = 30° X 3"
2. Output Distance = 40° X Length of Output Lever
3. Output Distance - = Input Distance
4. Then
   40° X Length Of Output Lever = 30° X 3"
   And
   Length Of Output Lever = $\dfrac{30° \times 3"}{40°}$ = 2-1/4"

NOTE:
Input Is Set By Measurement, Output Is Set By Pen Travel; Therefore If Output Is To Match Input, Lever Lengths Must Be Adjusted.

Fig. 1-3. Link lever calculations.

point where the mechanism is absolutely correct. This point can be at any location on scale, but is usually either at mid-scale or at the critical point. If the critical point is not given, then the mid-scale is selected as the point for making the effective and actual levers coincide. (See Fig. 1-5.)

Angularity

A completely accurate relationship between input and output is obtained only under the most ideal conditions, namely:

1. The input lever is the same length as the output lever.
2. The length of the link causes the output lever to be parallel to the input lever.

In actual practice, these ideal conditions almost never exist. First, the introduction of different lengths of input and output levers results in angularity error.

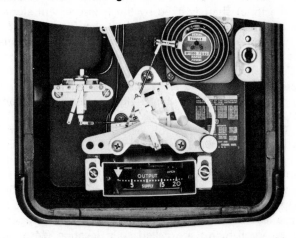

Fig. 1-5. Angularity error.

Methods to minimize this error will be considered in a later lesson. Also, as the levers travel over different distances, they may not remain parallel. The link/lever mechanism of a Foxboro Model 41A indicating controller is shown in Fig. 1-6.

Fig. 1-6. Link/lever mechanism of a Foxboro Model 41-A indicating controller.

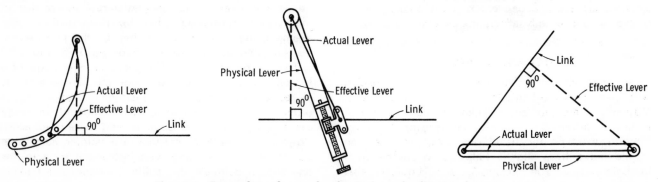

Fig. 1-4. Examples of actual, physical, and effective levers.

The input is established by the element that changes a measurement to a proportionate movement. This movement varies with the magnitude of measurement changes and with the specific input element. On the other hand, the output (pen or index travel) is fixed, since it must travel a fixed distance, namely, the chart or scale width, regardless of the magnitude of measurements or the specific output elements. To match measurements to different distances, the input lever length must be different than the output lever length. The introduction of different lever lengths results in mechanisms with angularity errors. Our task shall be to keep any errors within acceptable limits.

ADJUSTING THE LINK/LEVER MECHANISM

In preceding paragraphs, the operation of the link/lever mechanism has been described. It was shown that as the input shaft rotated, the output shaft was caused to rotate. The problem of angularity was investigated and was seen to be emphasized when the input and output levers were of different lengths. Under standard calibration procedures, an absolutely correct reading occurs only when the levers are parallel and at a 90-degree angle with the link. As the levers rotate, no longer will they be parallel nor will they form a 90-degree angle with the link. This creates an error (the angularity error) that can be minimized by an adjustment procedure that we shall describe.

It was further emphasized that the angular rotation of the input shaft is fixed by the measurement signal, and the rotation of the output shaft should be sufficient to cause the pen to travel the chart. To accomplish this, the length of levers must be adjusted. This second adjustment will be called the span adjustment. When you adjust span, you are adjusting the ratio of output to input in a system, whether the system be mechanical, pneumatic, or electronic.

The final adjustment of a link/lever mechanism is to match the input shaft to the output shaft so that when the input is at a known angle of rotation, the output shaft is at a corresponding known angle. For example, when the input shaft has rotated the first 10 percent of its travel, then the output shaft should have also rotated the first 10 percent. The adjustments to accomplish this are called span location (zero) adjustments.

These three adjustments (angularity, span, and span location) are not independent of each other, since a change in one usually affects the others.

MECHANICAL STOPS

An extremely important consideration in working with instrument mechanisms are the mechanical stops. Mechanical stops are any mechanical interference that makes it impossible for the mechanisms to move through their proper travel. For example, the pen should move from slightly below zero on the chart to slightly above 100 percent. Suppose, however, that it can move to only 98 percent on the chart, regardless

of the input signal to the instrument. This indicates that some mechanical part is restraining the pen. In other words, it is a mechanical stop.

Mechanical stops act at particular points in the low and high portions of a mechanism movement. The first step in investigating the operation of a mechanism is to investigate the mechanical stops. This should precede any adjustments. All too frequently, however, mechanism adjustments are changed to obtain performance when the problem involves a mechanical stop, rather than faulty adjustment.

There are two types of mechanical stops: adjustable and fixed. Adjustable stops are those that are arranged so that they can be easily moved, thereby making it possible to select the point where the mechanism shall stop. Examples of adjustable stops are those which limit the movement of a bellows or a Bourdon tube. These stops are mounted so that their position can be changed to limit the bellows or Bourdon tube movement to that movement which corresponds to the measurement change of interest. The adjustable stops of a Bristol Series 760 Dynamaster Recorder are shown in Fig. 1-7.

Fig. 1-7. Adjustable stops on a Bristol Series 760 Dynamaster recorder.

Fixed stops, on the other hand, are those stop points which cannot be changed since they are due to mechanisms contacting other fixed mechanisms. For example, the pen travel is limited by the pen mechanism striking the pen-shaft supporting mechanisms.

The mechanical stops may serve as overrange protection. The purpose of overrange mechanical stops is to restrain the travel of an instrument component in order to prevent damage to the component. In many cases, such stops are obvious and easily adjusted. However, in other cases, they are neither adjustable nor obvious. In working with instrument mechanisms one should cultivate the ability to detect mechanical stoppage.

Mechanical stops also arise from the fact that each mechanism needs only a limited amount of travel. For example, the mechanism driving a pen needs to rotate 40 degrees to cause the pen to stroke the chart. In general, the pen-driving mechanism will be designed to rotate 44 degrees, thus allowing the pen to "overtravel". However, the mechanism might be out of adjustment so much that the 4 degrees of overtravel is all on "one side", with the result that the pen may be able to travel to 111 percent of the chart but can drop only to 1 percent of chart, unable to go to zero.

ADJUSTMENT PROCEDURES

Linearity (Angularity) Adjustment

Examination of the relation of the levers to each other and the links to the levers at mid-travel (or the critical point) will show how well the mechanism is adjusted for angularity.

Under standard calibration procedures, the link/lever mechanism is absolutely correct only when:

1. The actual levers are parallel.
2. The link forms a 90-degree angle with the actual lever.

The linearity adjustments are those which put the levers parallel and the link at 90-degree angles to the levers. To make this adjustment, change the length of the link, and/or rotate the levers relative to their shafts, and/or shift the axis of rotation of the input lever.

Not all instruments provide for all three adjustments but some combination of the three is usually possible. In Fig. 1-8 a span adjustment and a zero adjustment are shown. It is also possible to adjust the length of the measurement link for linearity.

Span Adjustment

As the input shaft is rotated through its angle of rotation, observe the output shaft to see whether its rotation is such as to cause the pen to travel a distance equal to the chart width. If the input rotation does not cause adequate rotation of the output, the lengths of levers must be adjusted. Changing the length of a lever will change the ratio of input rotation to output rotation so as to obtain the correct span. Additionally, for some instruments, span can be adjusted by changing spring constants. This method will be considered later under the pertinent instruments.

Span Location (Zero) Adjustment

Span location adjustment is accomplished by shifting the output lever relative to the output shaft, or by shifting the input lever relative to the input shaft. By shifting one or the other, the output shaft is made to assume the proper position of rotation for the corresponding position of rotation of the input shaft.

To permit this adjustment, there is a means provided to:

1. Rotate a lever relative to its shaft.
2. Shift the input relative to the input lever.

These three adjustments interact. Therefore, after any one adjustment, it is necessary to check for each of the other two. In general, the linearity adjustment can be made first and will not require further adjusting if the span and span location errors are minor.

Caution: Avoid using the micrometer screw on the pen for a span location adjustment. The micrometer is an adjustment for mechanical stops. Subsequent work on controllers and integrators will demonstrate the wisdom of avoiding the pen micrometer for a span location adjustment.

SPECIAL MECHANISMS

There are a number of special instrument mechanisms in addition to the "standard" link/lever mechanisms discussed. A major portion of the special mechanisms fall into four categories:

1. Linearity adjustment mechanism.
2. Motion multiplying and dividing mechanism.
3. Antiarcing mechanism.
4. Nonlinear "lever."

Mechanisms in the first three categories are used to overcome the limitation of the link/lever mechanism. These special mechanisms will be discussed in this chapter and examples will be given of each. It is important that one be able to recognize the special mechanisms as refinements of the basic link/lever mechanism.

Linearity (Angularity) Adjustment Mechanism

Nonlinear operation arises from the fact that the output of a link/lever mechanism exactly reproduces the input when, and only when, the "actual" lever coincides with the "effective" lever. The effective lever was shown to be the connection between the actual lever and the link so that it formed a 90-degree angle with the link. In all cases, the effect of an actual lever is equivalent to that of a lever of different length that is

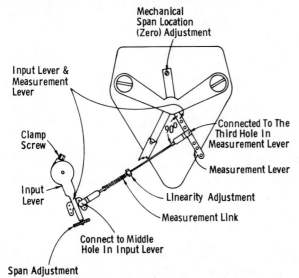

Fig. 1-8. Span, zero, and linearity adjustments in a link/lever system.

connected to the link so as to form a 90-degree angle. Of course, as the actual lever rotates, it forms a succession of angles with the link. In a mechanism in which the link always forms a 90-degree angle with the lever, no linearity problem exists. Such mechanisms do exist. For example, suppose the measurement causes a rack and segment of gear to move, where the axis of the gear is a shaft fixed to the gear. As the rack moves, the gear segment and shaft will rotate. In this case, the actual lever, which is a line from the shaft to the point of contact between the gear segment and the rack, always forms a 90-degree angle regardless of the position of the rack. Hence, there is no linearity error. Now, for each incremental movement of the rack there is an equal incremental rotation of the shaft. Foxboro uses essentially this idea except that instead of meshing gear teeth, the drive is coupled to the segment with flat flexible straps. Fig. 1-8 shows a number of adjustment points in the link/lever system of the Foxboro Model 9330 EMF Dynalog Recorder.

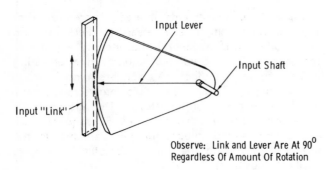

Observe: Link and Lever Are At 90°
Regardless Of Amount Of Rotation

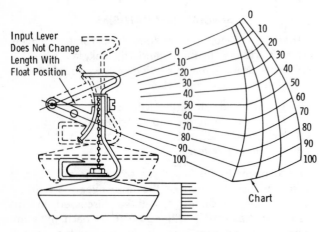

Fig. 1-9. Antiarcing mechanism.

Motion Multipliers

Suppose that instead of a gear segment and a rack, a gear segment and a gear are used. Such an arrangement will serve as an angularity compensating mechanism as the rack and gear did; but, now there is an additional possibility. Remember that the rotation of the output depends on the ratio of input to output lever length. If the gears are of different diameters, then the ratio of input travel to output travel will depend on the ratio of the diameter of the output gear to the input gear. This relation can be stated as follows:

$$\frac{\text{Angle of rotation of input}}{\text{Angle of rotation of output}} = \frac{\text{diameter of output gear}}{\text{diameter of input gear}}$$

The major advantage and use of a two-gear mechanism is that with it wide variations in the ratio of input to output can be obtained. For example, for an input of 10 degrees of rotation, it is possible to get an output

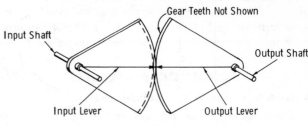

(A) Antiarcing mechanism.

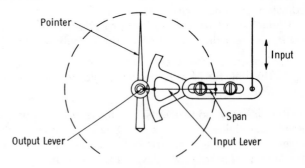

(B) Motion multiplier.

Fig. 1-10. Special mechanisms.

rotation of 300 degrees, or for an input of 300 degrees it is possible to get an output of (say) 25 degrees (see Fig. 1-10). In other words, an arrangement of two gears may act as motion multipliers or motion dividers. The common pressure gauge is an example of a motion multiplier; the pen drive mechanism of a Brown Electronic is a motion divider. (See Figs. 1-10 and 1-11.)

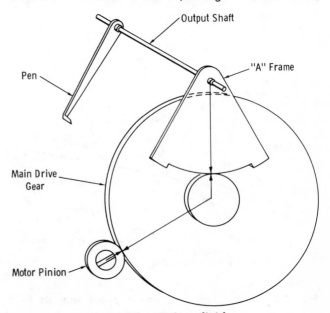

Fig. 1-11. Motion divider.

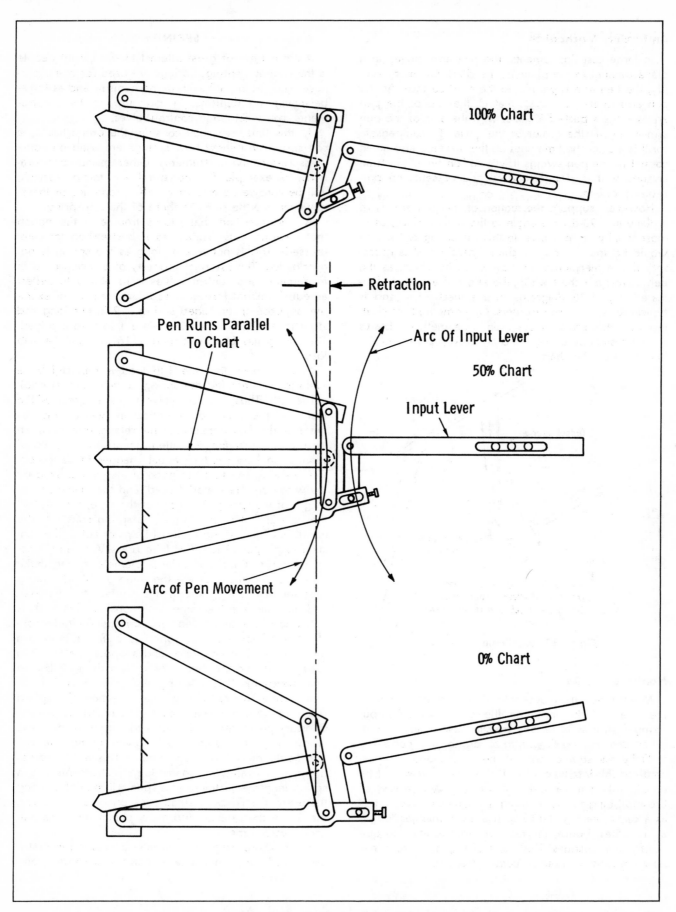

Fig. 1-12. Antiarcing pen linkage.

Antiarcing Mechanism

In large case instruments, the pen arm moves in a plane parallel to the plane of the chart. Or, more simply, the pen arm is parallel to the chart surface. As the pen arm rotates, it "arcs"; that is, the end of the pen arm swings a part of a circle, with the axis of the pen arm acting as the center of the circle. To compensate for this arcing, the time lines on the chart are also arced so that as the pen swings it will be "on time." Such an arrangement is straightforward and presents no particular problem.

However, suppose the motion of the pen arm is in a plane at a 90-degree angle to the chart surface, as in most small case recorders. In this use arcing of the pen would lift the pen off the chart. Therefore, it is necessary that a mechanism be developed in which, as the pen travels the chart width, the effect of arcing is eliminated. Fig. 1-12 diagrams such a mechanism and is typical for small case recorders. Other methods of dealing with this problem are used. One method obtains similar results by arcing the chart backup plate and the time lines on the chart.

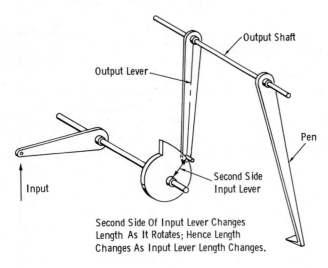

Second Side Of Input Lever Changes Length As It Rotates; Hence Length Changes As Input Lever Length Changes.

Fig. 1-13. Nonlinear linkage.

Nonlinear Links

Many times it is desirable to deliberately change the effect of the input on the output as the input changes. This is especially true in flow measurement. When determining flow with an orifice, it is necessary to "take the square root" of the input signal. For example if the input signal is 4, then the flow would be equal to the square root of 4, which is 2. One way of accomplishing this is by using a "nonlinear lever" such as a cam. (See Fig. 1-13.) Such a lever changes length as it rotates. Hence, the ratio of input rotation to output rotation changes. The shape of the cam determines how the ratio of input to output changes.

SPRINGS

A mechanism of great interest to instrument people is the common spring. Springs are used for many purposes such as in antibacklash mechanisms and as force-balancing mechanisms in pressure-sensitive instruments, controllers, and control valves.

At this time, we shall consider the properties of a coil spring and show how springs are used on some pressure-sensitive instruments. Other spring configurations, for example, flexure, spiral, and torsion springs, will be considered elsewhere. The properties of these, however, are the same as those of the coil spring.

A misconception that causes trouble is the notion that a spring gets "stiffer" as it is stretched (or compressed). This is not true as long as the spring is not overloaded. The essential property of a spring used in instruments and control valves is its ability to deflect an equal amount for equal additional loads. For example, suppose an unloaded spring is 2 inches long and stretches to 2-1/16 inches when a 1 lb load is added. The spring has been stretched 1/16 inch by the 1-lb load.

Now suppose that the 1-lb load is replaced by a 12-lb load, stretching the spring ¾ inch from its original length. Thus, a load twelve times as great as the first load has produced a deflection twelve times as great as the first deflection. This relationship between load and deflection is called linear; that is, equal changes in load produce equal changes in deflection.

The spring constant (stiffness) of a spring is fixed by the wire size, the material used, and the diameter and length of the spring. The heavier the wire, the "stiffer" the spring; that is, the larger the spring constant. The elasticity of the spring material helps establish the constant. Spring steel is stiffer than brass. A small diameter spring is stiffer than a large diameter spring if the wire size and material are the same. A "short" spring is stiffer than a long spring if the wire size, material, and diameter are the same. Let's consider this further.

Suppose we are given two springs similarly constructed except that one spring is 2 inches long and the other is 3 inches long, and suppose that a 12-lb load will stretch the 2-inch spring ¾ inch; a 12-lb load will stretch the 3-inch spring ¾ inch plus ⅜ inch. In other words, we can change the deflection of a spring resulting from a given load by changing its length. Consider this in terms of input and output. Using these words, we can say that for a given spring, we can change the output for a given input. This will be recognized as a change in span. Some instruments use a spring length adjustment as a span adjustment. Among these are the Foxboro small case pneumatic receiver, the Bailey draft gauge and many pneumatic force balance mechanisms.

The Foxboro usage is especially interesting in that it uses a coil spring and is a motion-balance instrument.

Chapter 2

Calibration

In chapter 1, we pointed out that recording instruments are mechanisms that record in visibile form the magnitude of the process variables being measured. The question then arises: How can we be sure that the recording of the instrument is accurate? We can be sure by calibrating the instrument.

Calibration is defined as the act of adjusting an instrument so that the record made by the recorder can be used directly to determine the magnitude of the measurement. A recorder is calibrated when the "output" (record) of the recorder expresses "input" (measurement), so that it is possible to say what the input is by examining the output. The preciseness with which the output reproduces the input is called accuracy.

Some instruments are uncalibrated, particularly those which perform a controlling function in addition to accepting and "displaying" a measurement. Such instruments are identical to the recorders except that they do not display the measurement in a visual form. The display is made in a way that the controller mechanism can "understand." These instruments are called "blind."

An important part of the servicing of industrial instruments consists of calibrating them and determining their accuracy. This chapter is devoted to the problems of calibration and accuracy.

CALIBRATION STANDARDS

Essentially, calibration consists of making it possible to determine the value of a measurement by examining the output of an instrument. For example, we can determine the temperature of a kettle of water by immersing into the water a closed glass tube with a small bore partially filled with mercury. The heat of the water causes the mercury to expand and, by ob-

serving the height of the column of mercury, we can tell the water temperature, provided that there are marks on the tube which "say," for example, that when the mercury is at the mark labelled 160, the temperature of the mercury (and the water in which the glass tube is immersed) is 160 degrees Fahrenheit. The glass tube will be recognized as a thermometer. The marks on the thermometer constitute the calibration that makes it possible to determine the temperature of the water. The input here is heat from water and the output is the rise of the column of mercury.

In order to calibrate an instrument, we must know the value of a given input to the instrument. Knowing this, we then adjust the instrument so that it indicates the appropriate value.

The methods, devices, and instruments that make it possible to know what the input is are called calibration standards. Some examples of these calibration standards are:

a. The height of a column of water.
b. The melting points of various materials.
c. A glass stem thermometer calibrated by the Bureau of Standards.
d. A potentiometer using a standard cell.
e. The weight of disks of metal (the dead weight tester).

Calibration standards furnish, or make it possible to determine, the magnitude of the signal that is applied to the instrument to be calibrated. Such signals shall be called "known inputs."

CALIBRATION PROCEDURES

To calibrate an instrument, inputs of known value are fed to the instrument, the response of the instrument to these known inputs is observed, and the instrument is adjusted so that it indicates the value of the input.

The inputs are usually set at 10, 50, and 90 percent of instrument range, and the instrument indication is observed for these values.

Linearity Adjustment

When the input is 50 percent or at the critical point, observe the relation of the levers and links. The levers should be parallel and the links should form 90-degree angles with the levers. If the levers and links are not properly related, adjust the length of the link and/or the center of rotation of the input lever, and/or rotate the lever relative to its shaft or pivot point.

Span Adjustment

Cause the input to vary from 10 to 90 percent of instrument range during which the pen (or indicator) should travel 80 percent of chart (or scale). If it travels more than 80 percent, decrease the length of the input lever, and/or increase the length of the output lever.

If it travels less than 80 percent, increase the length of the input lever, and/or decrease the length of the output lever.

Span Location (Zero) Adjustment

With a 50 percent input, observe the position of the pen on the chart (or the indicator on the scale). If the pen (or indicator) does not fall on 50 percent of chart (or scale) shift a lever relative to its shaft (or pivot point) until the pen position corresponds to the 50 percent input.

ACCURACY OF CALIBRATION

Accuracy defines how closely the pen (or indicator) agrees with the input. A recorder (or indicator) can never be any more accurate than the Calibration Standard because if the recorder (or indicator) were 100 percent accurate, it still would only be reproducing the measurement fixed by the Calibration Standard. If the Standard were off by 2 percent, then the recorder (or indicator) would also be off by 2 percent.

As a practical matter, the instrument being calibrated is always a bit less accurate than the "Standard" instrument. In general, it is unrealistic to attempt to get a better accuracy than that claimed by the manufacturer furnishing the instrument.

CAUSES OF INACCURACY

The basic accuracy is limited by the accuracy of the Standard and the accuracy claimed by the manufacturer. Most instruments have a claimed accuracy of 0.25-0.50 percent.

Causes of inaccuracy are:

1. Poor sensitivity.
2. Dead space.
3. Hysteresis.
4. Friction.

Sensitivity is defined as the minimum change in input that the instrument can detect. The sensitivities of instruments expressed as a percent of range are in the order of 0.01 to 0.1 percent. In general, little can be done to improve sensitivity of link/lever instruments.

Dead space is defined as the gap in pen (or indicator) travel when the input is reversed. To detect dead space, slowly increase the input to some convenient value on the Standard instrument and observe pen position. Increase the input to a higher value, then slowly decrease the input to its original value and observe the reading. The difference is dead space. This dead space is due to necessary clearance in the instrument mechanism and should be so small as to be invisible to the eye.

Hysteresis is a physical property of materials whereby when a material is subjected to a force that deforms it, the material remains deformed to some slight extent even after the force is removed. When the force is reversed and then removed, the material subjected to the force retains a slight permanent deformation opposite in direction to the original deformation.

An example of hysteresis might be a bellows acting against a spring. If air pressure is applied to the bellows, it expands and compresses the spring. However, the spring will not return exactly to its original position even though the air pressure is removed. Hysteresis is a major source of error in magnetic circuits and force balance mechanisms. In link/lever mechanisms, hysteresis errors can be neglected.

Friction is by far the most important cause of inaccuracies in link/lever instruments. Friction is the resistance to sliding motion between two bodies in contact with each other. Force is required to overcome this friction. Normally, the force available to move levers is fairly limited. Therefore, the mechanisms must be as free from friction as possible.

CALIBRATION OF A RECORDER

In the preceding text, link/lever mechanisms were discussed and the three basic adjustments (span, span location (zero), and linearity) were explained. The presence of, and possible interference by, mechanical stops was discussed and it was suggested that these stops be investigated first when working with an instrument.

Calibration was explained and it was shown that making a calibration consists of making the instrument agree with the Calibration Standard. To accomplish this may require changing the span, span location, and linearity adjustments on the instrument. The following paragraphs develop a calibration procedure that will apply to almost all link/lever mechanisms.

Equipment Required

To calibrate an instrument, the following equipment is required:

1. The Calibration Standard.
2. A means of feeding a signal to the Calibration Standard and the instrument being checked.
3. The materials (piping, wiring, etc.) to connect the Calibration Standard, the signal, and the instrument.
4. The tools needed to make the connections and to adjust the instrument.

One of the tests that help determine the causes of inaccuracy is the "dead space" test. Dead space is due to friction, slack in the linkage, clearance between holes and pivots, and sensitivity. Hysteresis can contribute to dead space but in linkage mechanisms it is negligible. When encountering dead space, eliminate friction as a contributing factor by slowly and smoothly changing the input and observing the pen or indicator movement. If friction is present, the pen will move in small steps as the input signal is changed.

The slack in linkage can be felt. Slowly and carefully move the pen (or indicator) to see if it can be moved without the input element moving. If it can, then the movement of the pen is due to slack in the linkage.

Preliminary Examination

1. **Mechanical Stops:** Are the mechanisms free to travel their range without hitting stops?
   a. Stroke mechanism by changing input signal. Pen (or indicator) should go slightly below zero and slightly above 100 percent. Adjust pen (or indicator) micrometer, zero adjustment on levers, slip levers on shaft, and shift input lever as required. Search for inadvertent stops which might be caused by misalignment or errors in instrument assembly.
2. **Accuracy:** Is the mechanism (a) free of friction; (b) free of dead space; (c) free of hysteresis; and (d) sufficiently sensitive? (Notice that this test· is the test for dead space. If friction and slack in the linkage are eliminated as per (a) and (b), following, the dead space remaining is due to the sensitivity of the instrument.)
   a. Examine for friction by slowing and steadily changing input and observing reaction of pen (or indicator). Pen should move smoothly, without any hesitation or jerkiness. Examine for friction by feeling resistance of mechanism to change. Feel clearances of shafts and at pivots. Feel link connections. All connections should be free-running.
   b. To examine for slack in the linkage, with pen (or indicator) mid-scale, gently attempt to move the pen upscale and down-scale without forcing the input. Feel for slack in mechanism which permits a slight pen movement without any input movement.
      If slack is found, check for worn shafts, pivots, or lever link connections and replace as required.
   c. Hysteresis does not apply to link/lever instruments.
   d. Examine for sensitivity. Slowly move input up-scale to a preselected point on Calibration Standard. Observe pen (or indicator). Then slowly move input down-scale to same point on Calibration Standard. Gap between final pen position should be less than 1/32 of an inch.
      If it is greater than 1/32 inch, recheck (a) and (b). There are no sensitivity adjustments on a link/lever instrument unless it is a "null balance" instrument.

Calibration

1. Does the instrument reproduce the input signal as measured by the Calibration Standard?
   a. Check linearity at midscale or at a critical point. Make levers parallel and cause link to connect levers at 90 degrees. Note: This adjustment is not critical and many times one must accept a compromise between levers which are nearly parallel and a 90-degree link/lever connection.
   b. Check span by feeding in a 10 percent signal, then a 90 percent signal. Pen (or indicator) should travel 80 percent of chart. If it does not, adjust length of levers.
   c. Check zero by feeding in a 50 percent or critical point signal. Put pen on 50 percent or critical point by shifting lever relative to shaft or by shifting input mechanism relative to input lever.
   d. Recheck (a) by putting a 10 percent, 50 percent and 90 percent signal into instrument. If pen does not fall on all three points, and if span and span location (zero) are correct, readjust linearity.
   e. Repeat (a) through (d) as required. Note: There is no requirement that the above sequence be followed, but in general, adjusting linearity first, then span, and finally span location (zero), gives the best results.

Linearity

Check linearity by plotting the output obtained for inputs of 10 percent increments from 0 to 100 percent. The difference between the input values and the actual values obtained is the error. The allowable error varies, depending on the instrument. The allowable errors in general are less than 1 percent and greater than 1/4 of 1 percent. The linkage instruments now being discussed can be calibrated so that no error exceeds ±1/2 of 1 percent. That is, the output (pen position) will be no farther away from the input than 1/2 of 1 percent.

The angle of the link relative to the lever determines the linearity of linkage instruments. To minimize linearity errors, the angles are adjusted. The specific adjustment depends on whether the linkage is "Z" or "U," the kinds of adjustment available, and whether the errors decrease or increase as the inputs are increased uniformly from 50 percent to 100 percent.

A good understanding of the difference between "actual" and effective levers, and of the way the effective lever has a maximum length at 90 degrees, decreasing on either side of 90 degrees, should tell whether angle should be increased or decreased.

Chapter 3

Pressure

Undoubtedly the major portion of all industrial measurements relates to pressure in its several varieties. This is so because in addition to measuring pressure itself, we also often measure flow by measuring pressure; we use pressure to determine the liquid level; we even measure temperature with the filled Bourdon system, which, mechanism-wise, is a pressure measurement. For these reasons, it is important to understand clearly the meaning of pressure and its variations.

WHAT IS PRESSURE?

Pressure implies a forcing of things or materials. For example, air is forced into an automobile tire by pumping with an air compressor. It is a basic law of nature that for every action there is a reaction. This law, applied to the filling of a tire, means that air in the tire attempts to force its way out with a force equal to that with which it was first put in. This air is said to exert a pressure; it is a force acting over some specific area. The most usual area selected is one square inch: the unit of force usually is pounds. We speak of pressure in pounds per square inch, which is abbreviated psi.

Any material under pressure exerts a counter pressure. The material may be solid, for example, a spring; or it may be a liquid or a gas.

GAS PRESSURE

A gas may be defined as a material in which there is no coherence or attraction between the particles (molecules) making it up. As a consequence, material in gaseous form will tend to fill any space in which it is placed. The application of heat "agitates" the molecules, causing them to move faster. This motion of the

molecules bombards the surfaces surrounding the gas. This bombardment constitutes gas pressure since the effect of all the individual molecules is a force against the retaining wall.

Pressure-Temperature Law

We have just said that heat causes the gas particles to move faster, and hence to bombard the container surfaces more frequently, and to exert more pressure. This relationship between pressure and temperature has been expressed mathematically:

$$\frac{P_1}{T_1} = \frac{P_2}{T_2}$$

This expression means that the original pressure divided by the original temperature will equal the new pressure divided by the new temperature. This relationship holds, provided the volume of the gas is kept constant.

We can conclude that the pressure exerted by a fixed volume of gas depends on the temperature of the gas. This principle is widely used in a class of temperature-measuring instruments.

FLUID PRESSURE

A fluid (or liquid) is a state of matter wherein there is a limited attraction between the molecules composing it. The attraction is such that if a liquid is poured into a container, it will fill the container to a uniform level. For comparison, remember a gas will completely fill the container, and a solid will retain its shape regardless of the container.

Fluids are fairly dense materials. That is, the effect of gravity on fluids is substantial. A 2 cu ft volume of water weighs 125 lbs. The density of the water is defined as its weight divided by the volume weighed. In our example, the density will equal 125 lbs. divided by 2, or 62.4 lbs per cu ft. Hence, the density of water is 62.4 lbs per cu ft. The density of mercury is 846 lbs per cu ft and the density of kerosene is 50.0 lbs per cu ft.

Head Pressure

If the 1 cubic foot of water has the form of a cube, then the area of each side of the cube is 1 sq ft or 144 sq in. In order to find the pressure exerted by this fluid, we must divide its weight (62.4) by 144 sq in, the area of the bottom surface. Hence, the pressure is 62.4 divided by 144. This equals 0.433 psi. Then it can be said that a column of water 1 ft high exerts a pressure of 0.433 psi.

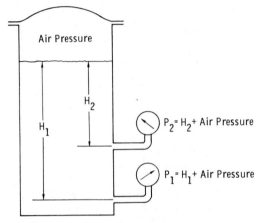

Differential Pressure = $P_1 - P_2$

= $(H_1 + $ Air Pressure$) - (H_2 + $ Air Pressure$) = H_1 - H_2$

(A) Differential pressure.

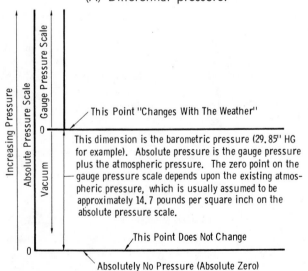

Absolute pressures are measured using absolutely no pressure as a starting point. Gauge pressures are measured using atmospheric pressure as a starting point and calling this pressure zero. The gauge zero shifts with atmospheric conditions, but absolute zero does not. Vacuums are gauge pressures less than gauge zero.

(B) Absolute and gauge pressures.

Fig. 3-1. Pressure and its variations.

It is common usage to express pressure in terms of a column of water. For example, one might hear that in a particular tank there is a pressure of 10 ft. of water, or that the head is 10 ft. This is shorthand for saying the pressure in the tank is equal to that pressure exerted by a column of water 10 ft high.

Differential Pressure is a term that refers to the difference between two related pressures. Suppose that one were measuring the pressure in a closed vessel partially full of water as shown in Fig. 3-1. The pressure at Point 1 on the side of the tank will depend on the height of water above that point PLUS the air pressure on top of the water. Suppose the pressure were measured again at Point 2. This pressure would equal the height of water above this second point PLUS the air pressure on top of the water. Or, the differential pressure would equal head pressure at Point 1 PLUS the air pressure MINUS the sum of the head pressure at Point 2 and the air pressure.

Or Differential Pressure $= (H_1 + P_{air}) - (H_2 + P_{air})$
Or Differential Pressure $= H_1 + P_{air} - H_2 - P_{air}$
Differential Pressure $= H_1 - H_2$

ATMOSPHERIC PRESSURE

Air, a mixture of gases, has weight. That is, the force of gravity attracts the air. The "standard" weight of the earth's atmosphere exerts a pressure of 14.7 psi. Or, the earth's atmosphere exerts a pressure equal to the pressure exerted by a column of mercury 29.9 inches high.

ABSOLUTE PRESSURE

Since we all are constantly subjected to the pressure of the earth's atmosphere, we may think of it as no pressure at all, and consider the pressure of the earth's atmosphere to be zero. Yet, it is a very real pressure, about equal to 14.7 psi. If we moved all the air out of a closed chamber, there would be no pressure within the chamber, or the pressure would be absolutely zero. To distinguish between the two different "zero" pressures, those pressures measured using earth's atmosphere as a reference are called gauge pressures. Those measured using a condition of no pressure at all are called absolute pressures.

Vacuum is a gauge pressure less than atmospheric pressure (see Fig. 3-1). It is common to refer to gauge pressures which are less than atmospheric in terms of inches of mercury (Hg.) For example, one might hear that the vacuum is "10 inches of mercury." This means that the pressure being measured has been reduced below atmospheric pressure by an amount equal to the pressure exerted by a column of mercury 10 inches high. Since atmospheric pressure is 29.9 inches of mercury, a vacuum of 10 inches of mercury would be equivalent to a pressure of 19.9 inches of mercury.

PRESSURE SENSITIVE DEVICES

In the first part of the chapter we discussed pressure of gases and liquids and defined such terms as atmospheric, absolute, and gauge pressures. When dealing with these pressures in a practical manner, we need to be able to measure them. In the remainder of the chapter we shall discuss several of the devices used to sense and measure pressures.

By far the most common pressure-sensitive device is the Bourdon element, which will be discussed later. In addition to the Bourdon element, several other important devices are the:

1. "Limp" diaphragm.
2. Bellows.
3. Diaphragm.
4. Manometer.
5. "Bell displacer manometer."

Which device to use in a given instance usually is determined by the pressure range and whether differential pressure is being measured. Pressure ranges, and the type of device recommended for each, are divided approximately as in Table 3-1.

Table 3-1. Pressure Measuring Devices

Pressure	Span	Device
Low	5 psi or less	Limp diaphragm Manometer Bell Manometer
Medium	5-25 psi	Bellows Manometer Diaphragm in conjunction with pneumatic circuit Bourdon element, if extreme sensitivity is not needed
High	25 psi and up	Bourdon element

For differential pressure measurements, the diaphragm and the manometer have their widest application. The diaphragm requires a pneumatic feedback circuit. The manometer can be arranged to record and/or indicate directly as an all-mechanical device, or it can be designed to transmit an electrical or pneumatic signal.

Construction of the Limp Diaphragm

As the name implies, the primary component of the limp diaphragm device is a limp diaphragm. A limp diaphragm is constructed of a non-resilient material such as a coated fabric and is attached to a linkage to the indicator. An example of a limp-diaphragm pressure indicator is shown in Fig. 3-2. Opposing the diaphragm is a flat flexure spring. The diaphragm is sealed within two compartments and the pressure is connected to the appropriate compartment so that it is possible to indicate hundredths of inches of water pressure (or vacuum).

The limp diaphragm device shown does not have sufficient power to drive a pen because of the friction of the pen moving over a chart. Consequently, most limp diaphragm devices are indicators or transmitters.

If the diaphragm is made sufficiently large, say about 12 inches in diameter, and if the sensitivity requirements are not too great, the diaphragm can be used to drive a pen.

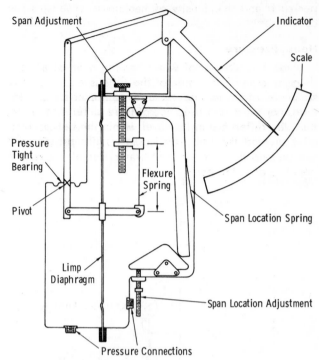

Fig. 3-2. Limp-diaphragm pressure indicator.

Construction of the Bell Displacer Manometer

The bell manometer (Fig. 3-3) employs an inverted bell-shaped unit that "floats", open end down, in a pool of mercury. The open end of the bell sinks in the mercury, forming two compartments. One is inside the bell and connects to the outside of the meter through a standpipe of sufficient length that its end is above

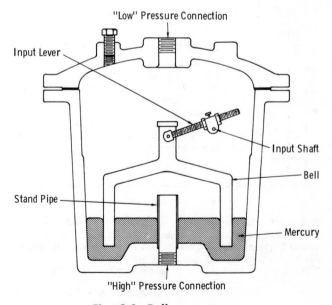

Fig. 3-3. Bell manometer.

the pool of mercury. The other compartment is that space outside the bell and inside the meter body. The mercury "seals off" these two compartments. If the bell meter is being used to measure differential pressure, the lower pressure connection is usually made to the compartment outside the bell and the higher pressure connection is made inside the bell. The pen (or indicator) driving lever is attached to the top of the bell. The input shaft runs through a pressure-tight bearing into the instrument case. The shaft rotates as the pressure within the bell tends to lift the bell. If the instrument is being used to measure differential pressure, the difference in the level within the bell and the level outside the bell balances the difference of the two pressures composing the differential pressures.

Construction of the Bellows Pressure Device

The essential component of the bellows pressure device is the bellows itself. The bellows (Fig. 3-4A) is a cylindrical thin-walled tube. This tube is "corrugated" so that it compresses or extends readily. The simplest arrangement is to have the bellows closed at one end and to admit pressure at the other end. The bellows expansion is opposed by a spring. As the pressure inside the bellows increases, the bellows extends, forcing the spring. The expansion stops when the force of the bellows is matched by the spring force. Bellows force is equal to the pressure times the effective end area of the bellows.

A second arrangement, and perhaps the most common, is to install the bellows and spring in a "can" as

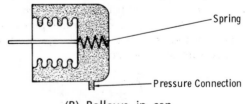

(A) Bellows.

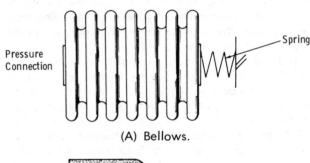

(B) Bellows in can.

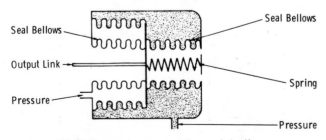

(C) Bellows in can with seal bellows.

Fig. 3-4. Pressure devices.

in Fig. 3-4B. In such devices, the pressure being measured is admitted between the outside of the bellows and the inside of the can. The pressure tends to compress the bellows and extend the spring. The system is balanced when the spring force equals the bellows force.

Regardless of the bellows arrangement, the output of the bellows must necessarily be taken from the closed end of the bellows. It is this movement which, through suitable linkage, drives the pen, indicator, or controller. It is important to remember that the deflection of the bellows for a given pressure is determined by the spring. For a given spring, the bellows deflection is fixed for each pressure. As a consequence, the linkage driving the pen is designed with a number of adjustments so that the bellows travel can be matched to the pen travel. These adjustments are angularity, multiplication, and zero.

Two bellows can be installed in one "can" as in Fig. 3-4C, so that the application of pressure to each of the bellows causes the bellows to force each other. The net movement is established by the difference in pressure. Such an arrangement then makes it possible to measure differential pressure and absolute pressure. For absolute pressure movement, one of the two bellows is evacuated.

Since, as before, the output of the bellows must be taken from the closed end of the bellows, use of the second bellows introduces the problem of how to get a linkage to the closed ends of the two bellows. The solution is the use of a flexible pressure-tight connection which almost always is a bellows, called a sealing bellows. It is important in the study of bellows systems to recognize which bellows are pressure sensitive and which serve a sealing function.

Diaphragm Pressure Device

An important pressure-sensitive device makes use of the flexure of a flat metal diaphragm clamped between two flanges. Pressure is applied to the diaphragm and this pressure causes the diaphragm to bow out. In principle, this device is the same as the bellows, but with this important difference: the amount that the diaphragm is free to move is only a few ten-thousandths of an inch. This extremely limited movement, as such, cannot be used to directly operate any mechanism. As a consequence, it is necessary to incorporate additional equipment. A common arrangement is to use a pneumatic circuit so arranged that the diaphragm motion is passed through a motion bar to a "flapper-nozzle," which causes an air pressure to build up in a bellows, forcing the motion bar back against the diaphragm. Thus the bellows force balances the force of the pressure against the diaphragm.

If pressure is applied to both sides of the diaphragm, the net force on the diaphragm is the difference between the two pressures times the effective area of the diaphragm. Thus, it is possible to use the diaphragm device to measure differential pressure. It is for differential pressure measurements that the diaphragm device finds its widest use.

Manometer

The manometer may be described as a liquid balance similar in operation to a mechanical laboratory balance. The laboratory balance is used to weigh an unknown mass by putting the unknown mass on a scale pan and balancing the scale by adding known weights. The action of the manometer is similar. An unknown pressure (which corresponds to the unknown weight) is applied to the manometer. This pressure forces the manometer fluid up in the tube, increasing the height of the column of fluid, and at the same time increasing its weight. When the weight of the column equals the force exerted by the applied pressure, the manometer is balanced and the column stabilizes. The height of the column multiplied by its density is equal to the pressure at the bottom of the column. This pressure equals the pressure being measured.

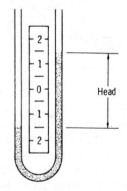

Fig. 3-5. "U"-Type manometer.

There are several important varieties of the manometer. Perhaps the simplest is the glass U-shaped manometer, shown in Fig. 3-5. A pressure is connected to one side. This pressure upsets the liquid level until the difference in level between the two legs balances the applied pressure.

A slightly modified version (Fig. 3-6) is called a "well" manometer. The pressure is applied to the well, forcing liquid up the column or tube until the head of liquid balances the applied pressure. The well is large compared to the tube. The fluid forced up the tube is a small portion of the total fluid in the well. Since it is a small part of the total fluid, the level in the well stays substantially constant so that the head balancing the

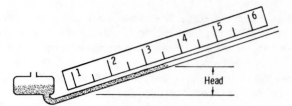

Fig. 3-7. Inclined manometer.

unknown pressure is substantially equal to the height of fluid in the glass. The advantage of the well manometer over the U-shape is that a single observation is sufficient to determine pressure, whereas the U-shape requires that both fluid levels be examined and the difference between the two determined.

A third manometer variety is a modified U-shape, in which one side of the U is sloped. As a result, relatively small pressure variations produce a noticeable movement of the fluid along the scale, without greatly increasing the head. Remember that head is always a vertical height. (See Fig. 3-7.)

Fig. 3-8 shows a fourth and perhaps the most important variety. The manometer is so arranged that the output is recorded mechanically rather than by observation of the height of a fluid, as was true in the first three varieties discussed. The output is obtained by placing a float on one of the liquid surfaces. The float rides up and down with this level. The level, in turn, is changed as the applied pressure changes. Attached to the float is a lever that rotates a shaft through a pressure-tight bearing. The pen, indicator and control levers are attached to this shaft. Thus, the change in level, which is determined by the pressure being measured, causes the shaft to rotate, thus positioning the pen and indicator levers.

In the discussion up to this point, we have considered the manometer as a device to measure pressure. Note: all manometers have two sides. If each of the two pressures composing a differential pressure is connected to each of the two sides of a manometer, then the difference in pressure forces the manometer fluid until the head of manometer fluid balances the difference in the two pressures. It is in this way that a manometer is used to measure differential pressure. The "mechanical" manometer is almost always used on differential pressure arrangements.

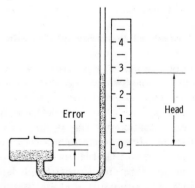

Fig. 3-6. Well-type manometer.

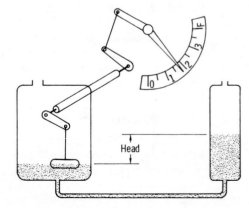

Fig. 3-8. Mechanical manometer.

Chapter 4

The Bourdon Element

Perhaps 98 percent of all industrial measurements involve the process variables, pressure, temperature, flow, and liquid level. Measurement of these process variables requires devices that react to the variable. For example, if the variable is pressure, then a device that is sensitive to pressure is required. Such a device is called pressure sensitive. If the device converts pressure to another medium such as an electrical or air-pressure signal, then it is called a pressure transducer. One of the most widely used pressure-sensitive devices is the Bourdon tube. The work of this chapter will be on the construction, operation, and application of various forms of the Bourdon.

CONSTRUCTION

A Bourdon tube is essentially an oval-shaped tube closed at one end and curved to form (1) a section of a circle; (2) several continuous circles having the appearance of a helical spring; or (3) a spiral that is a continuous tube of increasing diameter. The open end of the tube is attached to a base. The closed end is free to move.

The pressure to be measured is connected to the open end of the tube. The closed end of the tube is connected to a pen or indicator either directly or through a suitable mechanism.

OPERATION

The Bourdon tube is oval in cross section and bent to form a part of a circle or several complete circles. When pressure is applied to the tube, the oval shape tends to expand to a circle. Or, in other words, the cross sectional area increases, which means that the volume of the tube increases. This expansion acts to straighten out the tube. Actually, the movement is small, the total movement of the free end being perhaps ⅜ inch.

Consider the diagram in Fig. 4-1. The solid dark lines represent a segment of a Bourdon tube. When pressure is applied, the tube tends to round out. Let

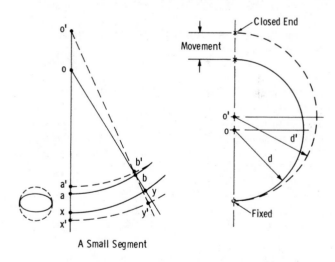

A Small Segment

Fig. 4-1. Theory of operation of Bourdon tube.

the rounded-out shape be represented by the dotted lines. Notice the arc lengths ab and a'b'. Since the metal will not compress, ab and a'b' must be the same length (in fact, they are the same physical portion of the tube). Since ab and a'b' are equal, arc a'b' must fall on a different radius circuit. What was said of arc ab is also true of arc xy. That is, xy and x'y' must also remain equal in length. The interception of x'o and y'b' extended is the center of a circle that represents the expanded Bourdon tube.

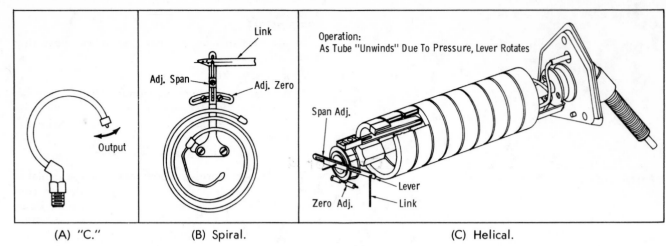

(A) "C." (B) Spiral. (C) Helical.

Fig. 4-2. Types of Bourdon tubes.

TYPES OF BOURDON ELEMENTS

The Bourdon tube may be fabricated in several shapes. The most common is the semicircular Bourdon tube shown in Fig. 4-2A and found in the widely used pressure gauge. The limited travel (that is, straightening) of this relatively short piece of tube makes it necessary to multiply the motion of the tube in order to obtain substantial pointer travel. The usual multiplication mechanism is a pinion and a gear segment.

Other forms of the Bourdon tube are made with built-in multiplication. In other words, the motion of the tube itself is adequate to drive a pen over a chart (or an indicator over a scale). To obtain this built-in multiplication, the tube is formed so that there are several complete circles of tube, as in the helical tube (Fig. 4-2C) and the spiral tube forms (Fig. 4-2B).

APPLICATION OF BOURDON TUBE

The Bourdon tube is a rugged, dependable piece of equipment if used properly. However, it must be protected from:

1. Excessive pressure.
2. Excessive temperature.
3. Excessive vibration.
4. Freezing.
5. Plugging of the tube opening.
6. Corrosion.

Excessive pressure will permanently deform the tube. Assuming that the range of the pressure instrument is adequate, the only way to protect against over-pressure or "overranging" is to install pressure relief valves on the vessels or pipe lines so that the pressure being measured does not exceed the instrument's capacity.

Although a Bourdon element will tolerate temperatures of the location where it is used, it will be damaged by the high temperatures of the fluid and gas pressures it may be measuring. To protect against excessive temperature, arrange the piping to the Bourdon instrument so that a pocket of fluid collects in the pipe line to the instrument. This pocket of fluid insulates the gauge against the high temperature of the fluid being measured. A convenient method of obtaining this pocket is the so-called "pig tail" or "syphon," which is a piece of pipe formed into a complete circle. Fig. 4-3 illustrates three possible mounting methods.

Vibration is a problem when the Bourdon tube pressure gauge is mounted directly on pipe lines and vessels. If this equipment vibrates, so will the gauge. To prevent gauge vibration, install the gauge away from vibrating equipment. In some installations, vibration is internal, caused by pulsation of the fluid being measured, as in the discharge of a reciprocal pump. To minimize this, pulsation snubbers may be used.

Freezing has the same effect as excessive pressure; it damages the tube and may even rupture it. Protection against freezing may require tracing or sealing the gauge with a fluid that does not freeze, or locating the gauge, if possible, at a spot where freezing will not occur.

Plugging is a serious problem if the gauge is used to measure fluids carrying solids (slurries). In such cases, the gauge may be "purged" with a suitable fluid. This means that a "clean" fluid is connected to the line near the gauge to prevent any of the slurry from getting to the gauge.

A second method is to seal the gauge with a diaphragm, as in Fig. 4-4. This diaphragm prevents the slurry from entering the gauge, but is flexible enough that the pressure forces the diaphragm against the sealing fluid. This fluid then is under the same pressure as the fluid being measured. Thus, the gauge will indicate the actual pressure.

Corrosion results from chemical attack on the Bourdon tube. The solution is to use a metal that will resist

Fig. 4-3. Methods for suppressing gauge vibration.

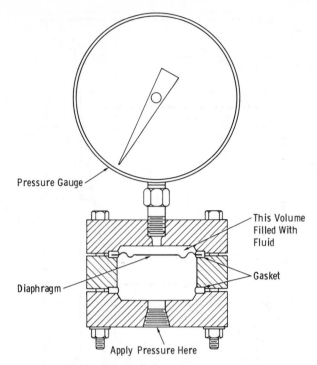

Fig. 4-4. Sealed pressure gauge.

the chemical action of the material being measured, or to protect the tube element from the material being measured by a diaphragm as was described for protection against plugging. Corrosion can be prevented by fabricating the tube from a metal that is not corroded by the material, or by keeping the tube from direct contact with the material. Gauges sealed by a diaphragm are called "chemical gauges."

MEASURING TEMPERATURE WITH THE BOURDON ELEMENT

The measurement of temperature is second only to pressure, the most important process measurement. In general, there are two methods of measuring temperature: electrical and mechanical. The electrical method uses a temperature-sensitive device that reacts to temperature by producing a change in resistance or voltage. The mechanical method uses a temperature-sensitive device that reacts to temperature by changing a mechanical property; for example, the force on a lever, or the deformation of a bellows, diaphragm, or Bourdon element.

In previous work, the Bourdon element was shown to be a pressure-sensitive device. Therefore, it is necessary that components be added to the Bourdon to convert the temperature being measured to an equivalent pressure. The possibility of doing this was indirectly referred to in the discussion of gas pressure when it was shown that there exists a definite relation between temperature and pressure, provided the volume remains constant. The components to convert temperature to pressure and the Bourdon element that converts pressure to mechanical movement compose the Filled System method of temperature measurement.

Components

The components for a filled system for measuring temperature are:

1. A bulb.
2. A pressure-sensitive component (usually a Bourdon tube, sometimes a bellows or a diaphragm).
3. A small-bore tube to connect the bulb with the pressure-sensitive component.
4. A material filling the closed system.

The pressure-sensitive component drives suitable mechanisms which position a pen, indicator or controller mechanism. In the following discussion, Bourdon elements will be described. The overall operation of the bellows and diaphragm is similar to the Bourdon.

TYPES OF FILLED SYSTEMS

The principle of operation of the filled system depends on the type of filling. There are three types of filling material: gas, liquid, and a mixture of gas and liquid. Each system will be described separately, though all are similar in operation.

Liquid-Filled System

The liquid-filled system is completely filled with a liquid, usually a hydrocarbon or mercury. A mercury-filled system is an important sub-classification of liquid-filled systems. A filled system with associated links and levers is shown in Fig. 4-5.

It will be remembered from the discussion on Bourdon elements that the Bourdon operation depends on the change with pressure of the cross-sectional area. As the pressure increases, the oval cross-sectional area tends to "round out" to a circle. This larger cross-sectional area, multiplied by the length of the tube, re-

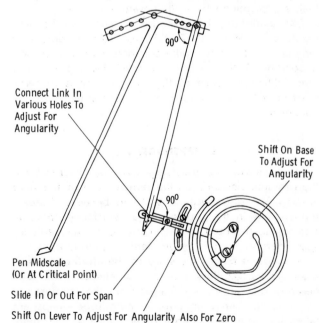

Fig. 4-5. Filled system.

sults in an increase in volume within the tube, causing the tube to straighten. This characteristic of the Bourdon is used for a temperature measurement in the following way.

A fluid will expand when heated. The amount of expansion depends on the temperature. As the expanded fluid will occupy a larger volume, the increase in volume must go somewhere. In the Bourdon, the only place available is in the filled system. The increase in volume of the fluid causes the Bourdon to change its volume. This necessarily results in the Bourdon straightening a small amount. Hence, the movement of the Bourdon depends on the volume of the fluid. This volume of fluid, in turn, depends on the temperature. Therefore, the Bourdon movement is a function of temperature. This movement drives a linkage identical to the linkage of a Bourdon pressure instrument.

Gas-Filled Systems

A review of Chapter 3 on pressure and pressure measurement will show that in the discussion of gas pressure a relationship between pressure and temperature was given. This relationship states that as the temperature of a given volume of gas changes, the pressure of the gas also changes. In a gas-filled system, therefore, as the temperature of the gas filling changes, the pressure with the Bourdon changes, and the end of the Bourdon moves an amount proportional to this pressure change.

Vapor Pressure System

A body of liquid, given enough time, will "vaporize" into gas. If the liquid is in a closed container and the gas cannot escape, a pressure, called vapor pressure, will build up. The amount of pressure that builds up depends on the particular fluid and the temperature of the fluid. If this vapor pressure is connected to a Bourdon element, it is possible to obtain a Bourdon output that is determined by a temperature.

The relationship between the pressure and the temperature is not linear. That is, for each increment of temperature there is a different increment of pressure, depending on the temperature level. See Fig. 4-6. The practical consequence of this nonlinearity is that the chart or scale of a vapor pressure instrument must be nonlinear.

COMPENSATION

In all the systems discussed, it will be observed that the pressure depends on the temperature of the fluid or gas. This introduces a problem because there is fluid or gas in the capillary and Bourdon element in addition to the fluid or gas in the bulb. This capillary and Bourdon fluid is at ambient temperature, which means it is at the temperature of the atmosphere surrounding the capillary and Bourdon element. This temperature, of course, is different from the temperature of the bulb, hence an error is introduced. Steps are taken to minimize this error or eliminate it. The methods are called temperature compensation.

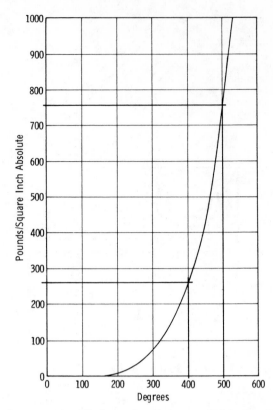

The above curve shows the temperature pressure curve for water. Other liquids have similar appearing curves. Note that the a change in temperature from 200 to 300°F results in a change of about 50 lbs., whereas a change in temperature from 400 to 500°F results in a change of pressure of 500 lbs.

Fig. 4-6. Pressure/temperature curve for filled system.

A second problem arises from the fact that if the bulb is located above or below the recorder, the head of fluid or gas exerts a pressure (positive or negative). This introduces a head error. The methods to eliminate the head errors are called head compensation.

A third possibility for error arises because of ambient pressure. However, with a Bourdon element, these errors are extremely minor. Where a diaphragm or bellows is used, variations in atmospheric pressure must be compensated for.

TEMPERATURE COMPENSATION

Liquid Systems

Temperature errors are minimized, first, by making the volume of fluid or gas within the bulb large relative to the volume of the capillary and Bourdon. However, there is a practical limit to how far the capillary volume can be reduced and the bulb volume increased, since doing this slows down the response of the instrument. The practical way of reducing capillary volume is to reduce capillary length. For liquid systems, some additional compensation is required if the capillary exceeds 10 or 12 ft.

There are methods for compensating for Bourdon errors only, which is called case compensation. To compensate for the Bourdon and capillary, a second

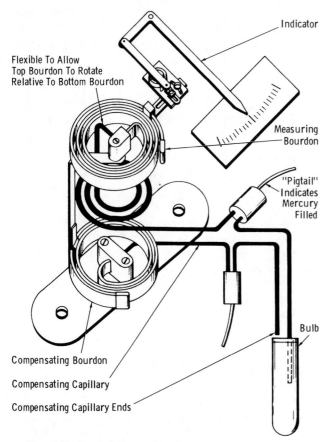

Flexible To Allow
Top Bourdon To Rotate
Relative To Bottom Bourdon

Indicator

Measuring
Bourdon

"Pigtail"
Indicates
Mercury
Filled

Bulb

Compensating Bourdon

Compensating Capillary

Compensating Capillary Ends

Fig. 4-7. Complete temperature compensation in filled system.

method is required. This method is referred to as complete compensation.

There are two methods for case compensation for temperature errors: bimetallic strip, and a second Bourdon.

The bimetallic strip is placed in the linkage so that as the temperature within the instrument case changes, the linkage is repositioned.

The second Bourdon element operates approximately in the same way as the bimetallic strip. In this case, the second Bourdon moves as the case temperature changes. This movement is added to or subtracted from the measuring Bourdon movement, thereby correcting for case temperature variations.

Complete compensation is obtained by introducing a second Bourdon and capillary, as shown in Fig. 4-7. The compensation capillary runs parallel with the measuring capillary. The compensation Bourdon is mounted with the measuring Bourdon so that the Bourdon output depends on the difference between the two capillary systems.

Gas Systems

Compensation in gas-filled systems is usually necessary if the bulb volume, relative to the capillary and Bourdon volume, is kept large. The ratio of bulb volume to Bourdon and capillary volume should not be less than 8 to 1.

Vapor Pressure Systems

No temperature compensation is required for vapor pressure-filled systems because the pressure within the system depends on the temperature of the surface of the liquid. However, this fact introduces a problem peculiar to vapor pressure systems called the cross ambient problem.

A simple vapor pressure system is not satisfactory for measuring temperatures which may go below or above ambient temperatures; or in other words, for measuring temperatures that cross the ambient temperature. If this is done, the liquid surface will drive to the coolest part of the system which may be in the Bourdon or the bulb, depending on which is cooler. This results in an erratic pen operation as the liquid moves from the bulb to the Bourdon or vice versa. A specially constructed vapor pressure system will eliminate this problem.

HEAD COMPENSATION

The need for head compensation arises out of the fact that gravity acts on the contents of the filled system. As a result, the fill exerts a pressure to which the Bourdon responds. Since the Bourdon should respond to pressure due only to temperature, the head pressure presents an error.

Head pressure is not a problem with gas-filled systems since gas has very little weight. The problem of head errors with vapor pressure systems depends on whether the capillary is filled with gas or fluid. The capillary will be filled with fluid if the capillary is cooler than the bulb, as is usually the case. Suppose that the temperature being measured is a temperature that also could occur around the capillary and case. If the temperature around the capillary becomes cooler than the bulb, the liquid will collect in the capillary, resulting in a fluid head pressure. If the temperature around the capillary becomes greater than the temperature at the bulb, the liquid in the capillary will boil out, thereby eliminating the liquid head. The pen will respond to these heads and will act erratically as the temperatures of the bulb and the capillary cross. This crossing of temperature is referred to as a "cross ambient" problem. If, however, the capillary is filled with fluid and remains filled, the zero of the pen or indicator is shifted back toward zero so as to "subtract" the pressure due to head.

For liquid systems, the head problem is most serious since liquids are relatively heavy; hence, the head pressure would be substantial. This problem is neatly solved by forcing the fluid into the system so that the system is under an initial pressure. That is, the Bourdon element exerts a force on the fluid equal to the force with which the fluid was put in the system. If the Bourdon force is greater than the force due to the head pressure, the Bourdon will not "expand." Hence, head pressures that do not exceed the initial pressure of the system have no effect. In general, 30- to 40-ft bulb elevation is about the maximum for liquid-filled systems. To understand this method of head compensation, one must realize that the liquid filled systems operate on the change in volume of the fluid due to temperature. Such volumetric changes exert tremendous pressure unless the increase in volume has some place to go. This place, of course, is in the Bourdon. Room for the increase in volume is obtained when the volume of the Bourdon increases. This increases as the Bourdon expands. The Bourdon as used on liquid systems is not primarily pressure-sensitive but is a volume-sensitive device.

CALIBRATION AND SERVICE

The linkage considerations for filled temperature instruments are identical with those for pressure instruments. Therefore, the adjustments are the same. The calibration standards for temperature instruments are atmospheres of known temperature. For example, the bulb may be immersed in boiling water for the high temperature and ice water for the low, depending of course on the range of the instrument. Other ranges may be handled by inserting the bulb into oil baths of known temperatures. The temperatures within a specially designed oven may be used. In any case, the bulb must be subjected to known low and high temperatures and the pen or indicator made to agree with those known temperatures.

Service problems are those of any link/lever mechanism plus the problems with the filled systems. Filled systems must be absolutely pressure-tight or else the temperature indication will fall off regardless of temperature.

SUMMARY

From a calibration and service point of view, filled temperature instruments may be considered as a special variety of pressure instruments. The introduction of the capillary and bulb constitutes a kind of transmitting system with special problems of temperature and head compensation depending to some extent on whether the system is a liquid, gas, or vapor pressure system.

Table 4-1 is a summary and comparison of various tube systems.

Table 4-1. Summary of Temperature Measuring Systems

Type of System	Capillary Length (Feet)	Temperature Limits °F	Bulb Size (Inches Diameter)	Compensation	Range Interval °F	Bulb Elevation Effect
Liquid-Filled (Mercury)	200	—80 to 1000	11/16 × 2-1/4 3/8 × 3-3/4 25/32 × 7-1/16	Yes	25 to 1000	35 ft above to 60 ft below. No correction
Liquid-Filled	150	—25 to 450	11/16 × 5-1/8 3/8 × 3	Yes	25 to 270	Approx. same as mercury-filled
Vapor Pressure	Depends on range 50 to 250	0 to 600	11/16 × 2-1/2	Not necessary	80 to 200	Depends on whether head is liquid or vapor
Gas	200	—100 to 1000	3/4 × 11 1 × 6-1/4	Not necessary	160 to 1000	None

Chapter 5

The Head Concept and Liquid Level Measurement

The term "head" is used to describe pressures, vacuums, friction, elevations, differential pressure, and velocity. The term continually shows up in discussions on liquid level and flow measurement in addition to pressure measurement. In this chapter we will show that head is a general term that makes it possible to compare and work with many different forms of energy. This approach will simplify the discussion on liquid level and flow measurements. It will also make less confusing the use of one term to describe many variables.

WHAT IS HEAD PRESSURE?

In previous work it was shown that a fluid exerts a pressure that depends on:

1. The height of the fluid above the point of interest.
2. The density of the material.

Then to determine the pressure of a column of fluid, the height of the column is multiplied by the density of the fluid. An example is shown in Fig. 5-1.

There are 12 × 12, or 144, columns of water with a base of 1 sq in and a height of 12 inches. Therefore, each column will weigh

$$\frac{62.4}{144} \text{ lbs} = .433 \text{ lb}$$

Thus, a column of water 12 inches high will exert a pressure of .433 lbs per square inch. A column of water 27.7 inches high will weigh $\frac{27.7}{12}$ or 2.31 times as much as the 12-inch column.

Since 2.31 × .433 = 1, a column of water 27.7 inches high will exert a pressure of 1 psi.

Suppose that we would like to know what pressure a column of fluid 30 inches high will exert. We first must know how much heavier the fluid is than water.

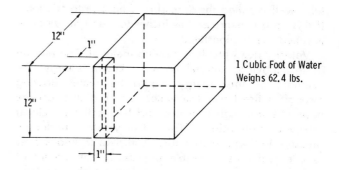

1 Cubic Foot of Water Weighs 62.4 lbs.

Fig. 5-1. Determining head pressure of column of fluid.

One of the common fluids used to measure pressure is a fluid that is 2.97 times as heavy as water. Therefore

$\frac{27.7}{2.97} = 9.35$ inches, which is the height of this fluid that will exert 1 lb pressure per square inch.

$\frac{30}{9.35} = 3.2$ lbs

Thus the pressure exerted by a column of fluid of any density can be determined if we know the weight of the fluid relative to the weight of an equivalent volume of water. This relationship is called the specific gravity of the fluid.

PRESSURE EXPRESSED AS HEAD

In the foregoing paragraphs heads of fluid were converted to pounds per square inch. The reverse procedure is often desirable. For example, it might be desirable to express the pressure exerted by a pump in terms of head, say, "30 ft of water." If this is done, one might hear such terms as "pump head," "head pressure," or the supply "head." In this case the pressure is converted to an equivalent column of water. Suppose the pump pressure is 30 lb, then—

$$30 \text{ lb} \times \frac{27.7}{12} \text{ in/lb} = 69.2 \text{ ft}$$

OTHER VARIABLES EXPRESSED AS HEAD

Some of the more common variables expressed as head are friction, velocity, and static pressure.

Static pressure is defined as the pressure of a dormant, or inactive, or always-present fluid or gas. For example, the air pressure or gas pressure on the surface of a liquid in a tank is referred to as a "static head." The pressure on a pump with the pump shut down is called a "static head." In general, static heads are static pressures converted to equivalent inches (or feet) of water.

Friction head describes the loss of pressure of a fluid flowing in a pipe line. For example, air may be flowing in a ¼-inch tube. At the inlet of the tube the pressure might be (say) 10 lbs and at the outlet the pressure might be (say) 9 lbs. Then the 1 lb pressure which is lost due to the friction of the fluid against the tube wall is called the "pressure drop due to friction." If this drop is expressed as inches (or feet) of water, it is called the friction head.

Velocity head involves moving material. The energy of this moving material is called kinetic energy. An example of this energy would be water flowing through a fire hose. The water is forced through the hose at fairly high pressure and leaves the nozzle at relatively high velocity. This jet of water is under no pressure but will exert a force sufficient to knock over people and other movable objects. If this stream of water were played into a pipe line which was bent to point up into the air, the water would run up the pipe to a level and hold there. This height (or head) is a measure of the velocity of the stream of water and is called the velocity head. A device to measure velocity head is the Pitot tube. The concepts of friction and velocity heads are illustrated in Fig. 5-2.

To briefly summarize the head concept, it is largely a conceptual or mathematical technique to put various physical properties on "equal footing." This is accomplished by converting the various physical properties into equivalent inches (or feet) of water. The advantage of this technique is that it enables us to add, subtract, and otherwise manipulate mathematically widely differing physical properties. The concept is of interest because various kinds of instruments are used to determine head. A second reason is that familiarity

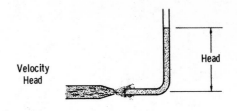
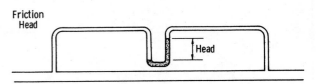

Fig. 5-2. Friction and velocity heads.

with the head concept makes it easier to discuss and understand how and why these instruments are used, and to service them.

PURGED PIPE FOR LIQUID LEVEL MEASUREMENT

Measurement of a liquid level is one of the "big four" in the processing industries, following measurement of temperature, pressure, and flow. There is a wide variety of level-measuring systems. One of the more widely used is the purged-pipe method, also known as the bubble-pipe or standpipe method.

The purged-pipe method is essentially a method of converting the head of fluid being measured to its equivalent pressure. It has been shown in previous work that "head" is an alternate way of speaking of pressure. Ways were shown for converting from one to the other. In the purged-pipe method, equipment is used that changes level (or head) to pressure automatically or converts one head (the level being measured) to an equivalent head (the height of a column of fluid in a gauge). The "link" connecting the head being measured to the level instrument is one (or more) pipe lines, through which air (or some inert gas) flows.

Components

The purged-pipe system (Fig. 5-3) consists of:
1. An indicator or recorder.
2. A purged pipe (or standpipe, or bubble pipe, etc.).
3. Two lines connecting 1 and 2.
   Note: One of the lines may not be used, in which case the atmosphere serves as the second line.
4. A source of air (or gas).
5. A "sight-flow" indicator.
6. A constant-flow regulator (optional).

Arrangement

The standpipe is immersed vertically in the vessel in which the fluid is being measured. A pipe line (usually ¼-inch copper or plastic tube) is connected to the top of the standpipe and to the indicator (or recorder). The indicator or recorder is a pressure-sensitive device and can be any of those mentioned in Chapter 3. A

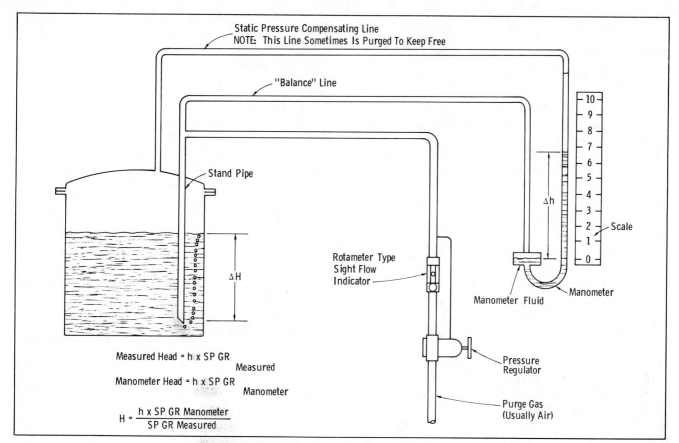

Measured Head = h x SP GR Measured

Manometer Head = h x SP GR Manometer

$$H = \frac{h \times SP\ GR\ Manometer}{SP\ GR\ Measured}$$

Fig. 5-3. Purged-pipe system.

source of air (or gas) pressure is connected to the line joining the standpipe and the indicator.

Thus the indicator and the standpipe are "linked" together by a common gas pressure. This gas flows through a sight-flow indicator that makes it possible to "see" how much gas is flowing.

Principle of Operation

Assume that the gas flow into the purged-pipe system is shut off. Then the level within the standpipe will be the same as the level within the vessel. Now allow a small amount of gas to flow into the system. As the gas flows into the system, the gas pressure builds up, forcing the fluid down the standpipe. This increase in pressure balances the pressure resulting from the difference in levels of the fluid in the standpipe and the vessel.

As the gas continues to flow into the system, pressure continues to build, balancing the increasing difference in levels. Finally a point is reached where the pressure equals that required to balance a difference in level that is equivalent to the length of standpipe covered by the fluid within the system. No further increase in pressure will be obtained even though the gas continues to flow into the system. This is because any "excess" gas bubbles out from the bottom of the standpipe and escapes through the fluid. The gas pressure that builds up is equal to the head of the fluid.

It should be remembered that the head of fluid depends on two factors: the density and the height. Or

head = height × density

Note: If head is in inches (or feet) of water, then density will be expressed as specific gravity.

As a consequence, if the level (height) of the fluid is to be determined from a measurement of the gas pressure, this gas pressure must be expressed as head. The usual conversion is to change pressure to equivalent inches (or feet) of water. Then this head must be divided by the specific gravity of the fluid being measured.

Usually the indicator on a purge system is a glass tube manometer. In this case, the gas pressure in the system is converted to an equal head at the indicator. That is, the column of fluid in the indicator balances the gas pressure. Thus the gas pressure will equal the head times the density of that fluid. Or, gas pressure equals height (manometer) times specific gravity (manometer fluid). And the gas pressure equals the height (tank) times the specific gravity of the fluid being measured. Or, equating these two expressions:

$$h_m \times G_{mf} = h_t \times G_{tf}$$

where,

h_m is height of the manometer fluid,
G_{mf} is the specific gravity of the manometer fluid,
h_t is the height of fluid in the tank,
G_{tf} is the specific gravity of the tank fluid.

In other words, the height of fluid in the manometer multiplied by the specific gravity of that fluid will balance the head of fluid being measured multiplied by its specific gravity. The link between the vessel and indicator is the gas pressure, and this link forms the equation sign in the mathematical equation.

COMPENSATION

It has been shown that the measurement of level using the purged-pipe method is essentially a pressure measurement and the indicator (or recorder) is a pressure-sensitive device. As a consequence, any factors that change the pressure will affect the pressure-sensitive device, causing error.

Two important sources of errors are:

1. Static head on the liquid being measured.
2. Friction head of the purging gas.

Compensating for Static Pressure

To compensate for static head, a second line is brought from the vessel to the indicator. This line is connected to the top of the vessel, thereby sensing the static pressure of the gas on the liquid. The other end of the line is connected to the second side of the manometer. The static pressure of the gas acts on the fluid, causing a false high head. This false head is connected to the manometer, forcing the manometer fluid down an amount equal to the amount it causes the fluid measurement to increase.

Compensating for Friction Head

The friction head depends on three factors; the amount of gas flowing, and the size and length of the connecting pipe. To minimize friction head, the length should be short, the size of the connecting pipe line should be large, and the gas flow should be kept to a minimum. Unfortunately, because of location of equipment, it is not always possible to keep the length short. An excessively slow rate of gas flow will result in the measurement not keeping up with rapidly increasing levels. This is especially so if the pipe line is large. So it can be seen that, at best, a short, large-diameter line with small air flows offers only a limited solution.

A better method of compensating for friction head is simply to subtract the friction head from the indicated reading. This would be satisfactory IF the friction head remained constant. The friction head would remain constant IF the gas flow remained constant. The gas flow would remain constant IF the level remained constant. This, of course, is not the case. However, constant-flow controllers are available that will control gas flow in an essentially constant manner regardless of level variations. Thus, one solution consists of feeding the purge gas through a constant-flow regulator.

A third method consists essentially of reducing the length of connecting pipe line to almost zero. This is accomplished by admitting the purge gas into the system at the top of the standpipe. This cuts out the connecting line friction since there is no flow of gas in this line (except temporarily when the level changes). This method results in two lines to the tank in addition to the static pressure line, and it therefore increases cost. Despite increased cost, the two lines are required if the sight-flow indicator is located at the instrument. To facilitate service, the sight-flow indicator should be located at the instrument.

Compensating for Standpipe Length

The end of the standpipe must, necessarily, clear the bottom of the tank—usually it is kept several inches off the bottom—in order to clear any accumulation of solids in the bottom. The usual way of compensating for standpipe clearance is to shift the zero of the indicator scale by an amount that the standpipe clears the bottom of the tank. A second way would be to add to the indicator reading the amount that the standpipe clears.

SERVICE PROBLEMS

Service problems are related to the kind of instruments used. Additional problems arise because:

1. The measurement is essentially a pressure measurement wherein the level is converted into an equivalent pressure.
2. Purge air must be continuously furnished to the standpipe.

To avoid problems from item 1 no pressure should be allowed to leak out of the system. As a consequence, the system should be leak-free. Equally important, no false pressures can be allowed to creep in. Such false pressures would result if the standpipe, or the pipe lines through which gas flows, clog or become pinched or partially plugged. Both leaks and partial plugs could result in substantial friction heads.

The second consideration is that air must continuously be furnished to the standpipe. If a leak is large enough, the purge gas may never get to the end of the standpipe. The supply pressure must be slightly greater than the greatest head to be measured. If it is not, then the gas will not flow into the system at the high heads. A sight-flow indicator should be furnished so that it is possible to "see" the gas flow.

Chapter 6

Level-Measuring Instruments

DISPLACER INSTRUMENTS

An important level-measuring device makes use of Archimedes' Principle, the fact that a body immersed in a fluid is buoyed up by a force equal to the weight of the fluid displaced. This method of measuring level makes possible measurements over wide changes. It does not require any compensation for static heads. If the level instrument is used with a pneumatic circuit, it is possible to "bring the level measurement out" through a solid pressure-tight connection.

Components

The components of a displacer level instrument are:

1. A displacer mechanism.
2. A mechanism for suspending the displacer in the fluid.
3. A spring to "weigh" the displacer.
4. A mechanism to detect the "weight" of the displacer.
5. A pressure-tight connection to bring out the weight of the displacer.

Arrangements

The displacer is suspended in the fluid and hangs on the spring. The change in the "spring" is passed through a pressure-tight bearing where it is detected by a pneumatic mechanism. The pneumatic mechanism "converts" the spring deformation to an equivalent air pressure. This air pressure is read from a pressure gauge that is calibrated in inches and feet.

Principle of Operation

The displacer must be heavy enough so that it would sink into the liquid if it were not supported by the spring. The operation is as follows:

Suppose that the displacer is weighed on an ordinary spring scale and is found to weigh (say) 10 lb. Now, suppose the displacer and scale are placed or hung in a vessel that is gradually filled with fluid. The fluid will rise until it reaches the displacer, at which point the device will "feel" the fluid rising about it. It will feel the fluid because the displacer will be buoyed up by a force equal to the weight of the fluid displaced. If the weight of the displacer fluid is 1 lb, then the scale will indicate 9 lb. As the fluid continues to increase in depth, more of the displacer will be submerged, which will reduce its effective weight until the displacer is completely submerged.

To calibrate this device it would be necessary to change the markings on the scale from pounds to inches and feet. This is readily accomplished if the following things are known:

1. The volume of the displacer.
2. The weight of the fluid (which depends on its density).

If these two quantities are known, then the "weight" of the displacer depends on how far it is submerged, which in turn depends on the level of the fluid. Thus, as shown in Fig. 6-1, weight is converted to level.

A DISPLACER INSTRUMENT

For purposes of describing the operation, a simplified system has been used. The actual instrument is somewhat more complicated, though in principle it is identical to the spring scale and displacer. The complication arises out of the fact that the actual instrument must be designed to measure fluid levels in vessels that are under pressure. To do this, provisions must be made for getting the weight of the displacer out.

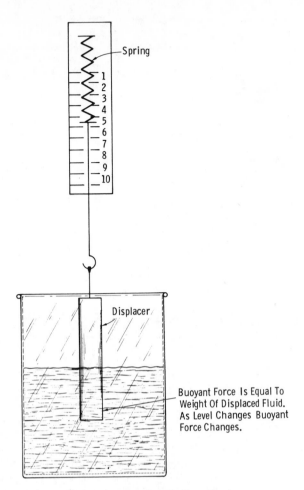

Fig. 6-1. Principle of the displacer.

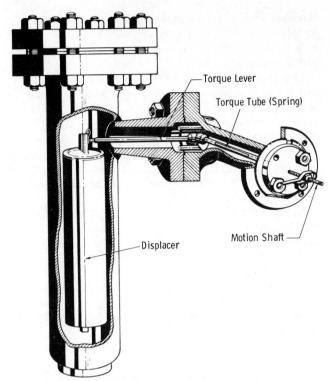

Fig. 6-2. Displacer level instrument.

of the high pressure atmospheres of the vessel. This necessitates a pressure-tight bearing.

The solution to this problem is to use a torsion spring. That is a spring that reacts to a twisting force. Such springs usually are thin-walled tubes called torque tubes. Attached to the movable end is a lever and fastened to the lever is the displacer. This causes the tube to twist a small amount, perhaps 5 degrees. As the effective weight of the displacer is reduced by a fluid submerging part of the float, the spring "unwinds." That is, its angular rotation changes from 5 degrees to (say) 3 degrees. This angular rotation is measured by placing a solid shaft inside the torque tube and fastening it to the lever end of the tube. Therefore as the torque tube rotates, the motion is passed down the solid shaft. This angular rotation is detected by a pneumatic mechanism that converts the rotation to equivalent pounds of air pressure. (See Figs. 6-2 and 6-3.)

OTHER LEVEL-MEASURING INSTRUMENTS

In addition to the purged-pipe system and the displacer method of level measurement, there are several other methods. These include devices that use a float, the differential pressure method, the pressure gauge method, the diaphragm box, and the pressure repeater.

The pressure repeater is essentially a force-balance pneumatic mechanism and will be discussed later. It is interesting to note that, with the exception of the displacer and float devices, all are essentially pressure-measuring devices.

We shall consider some of the varieties of the float devices, and discuss how pressure and differential-devices may be used. The diaphragm box will also be discussed.

Float Devices

There are numerous variations in the devices using the float as a sensing element, but all are based on the fact that the float will follow the surface of the liquid. The problem then becomes one of designing a mechanism to follow the float. In general, there are two methods; the first is to arrange to have the float position a lever. This lever motion then is used to drive

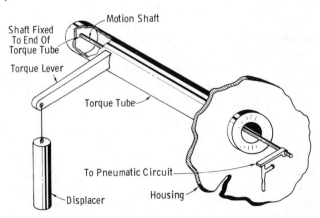

Fig. 6-3. Application of a torque tube.

linkages and/or pneumatic mechanisms. The second is to follow the float with a cable which is usually a wire or a flat metallic tape. The cable then serves as the input to pneumatic, electrical, or mechanical mechanisms.

The lever method has the advantage of simplicity, but it has the serious disadvantage that the range of lever measurement is sharply limited. This is necessarily so because the lever must be kept fairly short. The cable method does not have this disadvantage, the range being limited only by cable lengths. The cable method, however, requires a fairly formidable take-up mechanism if the measurement is to be displayed on recording devices.

Both methods share the problem of a pressure-tight bearing if the measurement is being made on a liquid within a pressure vessel. For the lever device, the pressure-tight bearing is usually a packing stuffing box through which the lever shaft rotates. Stuffing-box friction is not too much of a problem because the float may be made large to furnish the driving power required. A pressure-tight bearing for float and cable devices presents an extremely difficult problem. In general, the only practical solution is a gas-tight liquid seal through which the cable passes.

One acceptable method for avoiding a pressure-tight bearing is to follow the float with a magnet that drives the cable. The cable and magnet are inside a closed pipe immersed in the liquid. The float is guided by this pipe and rides up and down the pipe as the level changes. The magnet follows this float.

Differential–Pressure Devices

The differential-pressure devices that have been discussed can be used directly to measure liquid level. Which device to use depends on the nature of the fluid being measured, the static pressures involved, and the type of display desired. The fluid of the manometer differential-pressure devices must not combine with the fluid being measured. A large number of fluids that might require measuring do not combine with mercury. Therefore, mercury manometers are used fairly extensively. The second limitation is the static pressure of a level measurement within a pressure vessel. If these pressures are about 100 psi or greater, glass tube manometers may not be satisfactory. There are available some special manometers for high-pressure service. For high-pressure service the mechanical manometer, the bellows, and diaphragm devices may be used.

The third consideration is the type of display desired. The glass tube manometer is used where a visual display at the location is satisfactory. If a remote visual display, or recording and/or controlling is required, the mechanical manometer, the bellows, and the diaphragm devices must be used.

Fig. 6-4 shows how differential-pressure devices can be used. A connection is made to the lower part of the pressure vessel and a pipe line is run to the high-pressure side of the device. The second connection is made into the gas space of the vessel. This connection is run to the "low" side of the manometer. This second

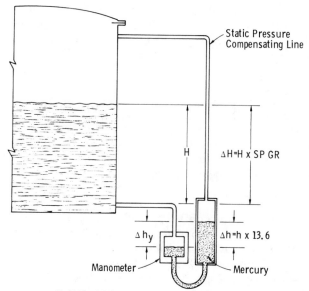

Fluid Head Being Measured=Fluid Head Of Instrument
Fluid Head Being Measured = H x SP GR Of Measured Fluid
Fluid Head of Instrument = h x 13.6 (The SP GR Of Hg Is 13.6)
H x SP GR Of Measured Fluid = h x 13.6

$$\text{Head} = \frac{h \times 13.6}{\text{SP GR Of Measured Fluid}}$$

NOTE: This Expression Does Not Take In Account The "False" Head Δh_y

Fig. 6-4. Manometer measurement of liquid level.

line compensates for the static pressure of the vessel. The head of fluid within the vessel upsets the fluid (or forces the bellows or diaphragm) until the head of the

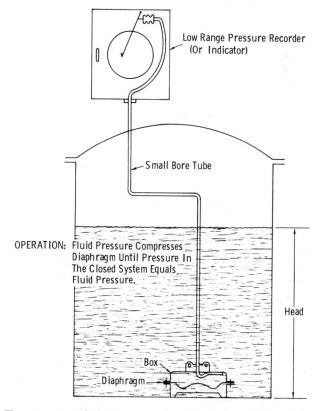

Fig. 6-5. Level measurement with a diaphragm box.

manometer fluid (or the counter force on the bellows or diaphragm) balances the fluid head being measured. The manometer head (or bellows or diaphragm force) then becomes an equivalent of the head being measured. The manometer fluid (or bellows or diaphragm force) then is the display.

If the level of liquid within a vessel containing steam or other condensable gas over it is to be measured, a special chamber must be used and the connection made to it. Otherwise the low-pressure line will fill with the liquid condensed from the steam or gas, resulting in a completely erroneous measurement.

Pressure Devices

If there is no problem of static pressure compensation, then the manometers, bellows, and diaphragm instruments may be used with only one connection; or, a simple pressure instrument may be used. In general, pressure gauges are not sensitive enough to be satisfactory for level measurements. Consequently, differential-pressure devices are used with one connection.

The other connection is a common atmosphere pressure.

The Diaphragm Box

The diaphragm box is a closed system composed of a flexible hat-shaped diaphragm mounted in a "box" forming a closed compartment. This compartment is connected to a low-range pressure recorder (or indicator) with a small-bore tube. The box is lowered into the liquid being measured. This liquid forces the diaphragm, "squeezing" the air in the closed system, thereby building up a pressure that is measured by the pressure recorder (or indicator). The pressure depends on the height of the fluid multiplied by its density. If the density is known, the pressure gauge can be calibrated in feet and inches of level. The system is shown in Fig. 6-5.

It is necessary that this system be absolutely pressure-tight. The slightest leak will soon bleed out all the air within the system. As a practical matter, it is almost impossible to keep the air in such a system.

Chapter 7

Differential-Pressure Instruments

MANOMETER/FLOAT TYPES

Up to this point we have discussed manometer/float differential-pressure instruments as if they were identical to the glass-tube manometers. In this chapter some important differences between the mechanical meter and the glass tube-manometer will be pointed out. The construction of such instruments will be more thoroughly discussed. In addition, various methods for "bringing out" the float-position level will be reviewed.

The instruments to be discussed are usually called flow-meters; however, it is well to remember that regardless of the ultimate instrument calibration, such instruments are differential-pressure sensitive. It has been shown that differential pressure-instruments may also be used to measure liquid levels as well as differential pressure. To be used to measure flow the proper primary device must be furnished.

Components

We shall define manometer/float differential-pressure instruments as instruments composed of the following parts:

1. A float chamber.
2. A range chamber.
3. A float.
4. A fluid (almost always mercury).
5. A mechanism for "taking out" the float position.
6. A display mechanism.

Arrangement

The two chambers are joined at the bottom, forming a "U"-type manometer. The fluid (usually mercury) is poured to a predetermined level into the ma-

nometer chambers. The float rides on this mercury level. The float movement is "felt" through a suitable mechanism. The signal that is brought out drives a display mechanism. One of the pressures composing the differential-pressure signal is connected to one chamber; the second pressure of the differential-pressure signal is connected to the second chamber.

Principle of Operation

A differential pressure signal consists of two components: the static pressure component, and the part remaining after the static pressure component is subtracted. The part remaining is the difference in pressure of the two pressures composing the differential-pressure signal. The part of the total signal that is of interest is the difference in pressure; hence, the term differential pressure.

One of the two pressures composing the differential-pressure signal is connected to one chamber, the other is connected to the second chamber. The static pressure component is cancelled out since, regardless of its magnitude, the same pressure is applied to both sides of the manometer; that is, equal pressures are applied to each of the two chambers forming the manometer. Since the pressures are the same, the mercury levels within the chamber will also remain the same. Thus, the static component has no effect. However, the differential pressure component causes the mercury level to change until the mercury head balances this pressure component. The change in mercury level causes the float riding on the mercury to change position. The change in position serves to drive a suitable display mechanism which displays the new mercury level. This mercury level in turn was established by the differential pressure applied to the instrument. Thus, the differential pressure is displayed. The magnitude of the differential pressure being measured can be determined if the display is calibrated.

THE DISPLAY

The several elements of the manometer/float differential-pressure instruments will now be discussed in detail. (See Fig. 7-1.) The one element that does most to determine the details of construction of the total instrument is the display required. For example, if the display is to be air signal, such that the pressure of the air signal is determined by the differential pressure, then, perhaps a diaphragm differential-pressure instrument is better suited than a mechanical-pressure instrument. If the display is to be an electrical signal, the construction of the instrument will be determined in part by this type display. If the display is to be a pen-on-chart, a different mechanism is called for.

In addition to the display, a second consideration that determines construction details is the problem of getting the differential pressure signal out of the high pressure areas of the meter body that come about due to the static pressure component. In other words, the measurement (float position) is under high pressure that has to be sealed up. Yet the float position must,

somehow, be transmitted out of the high pressure regions into a region of atmospheric pressure. To a large extent, this problem influences the type of display. For example, if a pneumatic or electrical display is used, this problem of high static pressure is almost no problem at all.

With the above comments in mind, we shall first consider the all-mechanical differential-pressure instruments; that is, an instrument with a mechanism designed to drive a pen over the chart through direct linkages. The problem of bringing out the level is solved by providing a lever which rotates a shaft through a bearing. The float drives the lever. The pen linkage is attached to the other end of the shaft. The problem of bringing out the float position is solved by using a pressure-tight bearing. It is important that this bearing be free of friction, otherwise, some of the float travel will be "lost" due to friction in the bearing. The second requirement is that the bearing hold the pressure, which may be several hundred pounds. As a consequence, the pressure-tight bearings are a fairly important component of mechanical differential-pressure instruments requiring some special handling. (See Fig. 7-2.)

The rotation of the shaft within the pressure-tight bearing is the input to a link/lever linkage that is identical with the link/lever mechanism previously discussed.

A second important variety of manometer/float differential-pressure instruments are those using magnetic circuits as a means of getting the float position out of the manometer body. Instruments using a magnetic coupling between the float and the pen do not require a pressure-tight bearing. In general, the magnetic coupling is used in conjunction with electric transmission. There are exceptions. Meters of this variety are called electric flowmeters. Remember, however, that regardless of the fact that such meters are called flowmeters, they are differential-pressure sensitive instruments. The operation of these instruments is similar to that of the all-mechanical. The difference in pressure upsets the mercury level until the mercury head pressure balances the differential pressure. The change in mercury level drives a float on which is mounted an armature that is a part of the magnetic circuit. The position of the armature is "felt" by the external electrical circuit. Due to the nature of magnetism, it is possible for the armature to be inside a completely closed

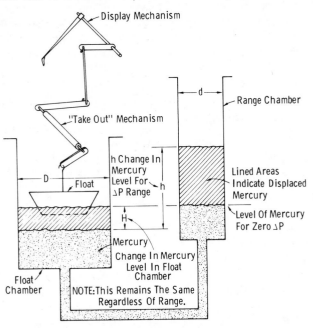

Fig. 7-1. Manometer/float D/P instrument.

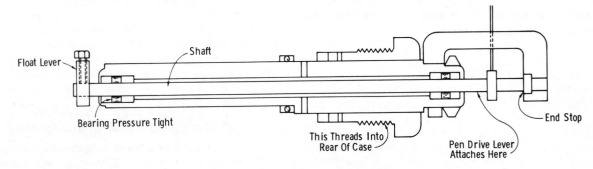

Fig. 7-2. Pressure-tight bearing.

tube, if the tube is nonmagnetic. Many stainless steels meet this requirement. Thus, the need for pressure-tight bearings is eliminated. Instruments using magnetic coupling will be discussed in more detail later.

Manometer/float devices, due to the way they operate, are relatively easy to "blow." This means that pressures may be applied to the instrument which are sufficiently large to force the mercury out of the instrument. This will happen if the instrument is overranged; that is, if a differential pressure is applied to the instrument that is greater than the maximum mercury head obtainable in the instrument. The instrument may also be blown if static pressure is applied to only one side of the instrument. This is a real possibility with manometer/float instruments when they are taken off or put on the line.

To protect against blowing due to overranging, check valves are furnished at the exits of the two chambers. These valves are usually float-operated. These valves close when the level of mercury is such that it might blow out the instrument, preventing a further transfer of mercury from one chamber to the other.

To protect against blowing an instrument when taking it off or putting it on the line, a bypass line is provided that connects the low-pressure line to the high-pressure line. A valve is placed in this line. In addition, a valve is placed in each of the two pressure lines to the manometer. These three valves must be opened and closed in the proper sequence. The important consideration is to operate the valves so that the total line pressure is not connected to a single side of the manometer at a given time. To prevent this, the valve in the bypass line is open when one of the pressure lines is opened. The bypass valve is then closed and the remaining valve opened. In general, only two valves are opened at any point of the operation of putting the meter on the line. To take the meter off the line the procedure is reversed. Shut one of the pressure lines, open the bypass, and close the second pressure line. In some cases, as with the Bailey Ledoux bell manometer for example, there is a requirement on whether the high-pressure or the low-pressure line be opened first.

To prevent the meter from "surging," (that is, fluctuating rapidly), a damping restriction is furnished. This restriction is usually a needle-type valve though cocks are also used. The valve is inserted in the connection between the range chamber and float chamber. The valve can be operated by hand, or by turning with a screwdriver or wrench. If damping is required, the needle is moved toward the seat.

RANGE CHANGES

The most significant difference between the manometer/float differential-pressure instrument and the glass-tube manometer is the requirement on the manometer/float instrument that the float move a fixed amount, regardless of the magnitude of the applied differential pressure. This requirement arises out of the

need for constructing instruments of standard parts so that a given instrument, with a limited number of component changes, can handle a wide range of applied signals. As this idea is applied to manometer/float devices, it means that it would be desirable to keep the display mechanism (recorder or indicator), the float, and the take-out mechanism identical for all ranges. As a consequence, the float travel must be the same for all ranges. This means that the amount of mercury displaced in the float chamber must be the same regardless of the range. The range, in turn, depends on the difference between the levels in each of the two chambers.

These two specifications can be accommodated by having different diameter range tubes for the several specific ranges desired. For example, suppose the specified float travel is 1 inch, the diameter of the float chamber is 4 inches, and the range desired is 100 inches of water.

1. Convert 100 inches of water to equivalent inches of mercury as follows:

$$\frac{100}{13.6} = 7.35 \text{ (specific gravity of mercury)}$$

This head of mercury is that required to balance 100 inches of water head.

2. The volume of mercury being transferred is taken from one chamber and put in the other chamber (Fig. 7-1). Hence,

$$V = v$$

Where,

　V is volume of mercury associated with float chamber,
　v is volume of mercury associated with range chamber:

$$\text{Volume} = \text{Area} \times \text{height}$$

$$= \frac{\pi}{4} \text{ dia.}^2 \times \text{height}$$

$$= .7854 \text{ dia}^2 \times \text{height}$$

$$V = .7854 \text{ } D^2 \text{ } H$$

$$v = .7854 \frac{d^2 \text{ } (h - H)}{4}$$

Where,

　D is the diameter of the float chamber,
　H is the amount of the float movement,
　d is the diameter of the range chamber,
　h is the total mercury head.

What this relationship says in nonmathematical terms is—the diameter of the range chamber is to the diameter of the float chamber as the mercury head desired, less the float movement, is to the float travel.

BELLOWS AND DIAPHRAGM DIFFERENTIAL-PRESSURE INSTRUMENTS

The mercury float differential-pressure instrument is an important instrument and perhaps will continue to be so for a long time. However, the mercury instruments have certain disadvantages. It is difficult to avoid mercury losses. Also, the mercury meter has fairly high inertia characteristics, with the result that mercury meters cannot follow a flow that changes rapidly. This rules out the mercury meter on many control problems. To overcome these two disadvantages, an increasingly larger percent of the flow measurements are being made with the diaphragm-bellows instrument.

In our discussion we will consider that diaphragm differential-pressure instruments are essentially equivalent to the bellows instrument, with the diaphragm being a "very flat bellows." Necessarily, this very flat bellows (diaphragm) imposes a restriction on the overall design of the instrument. This restriction arises out of the fact that the diaphragm is free to deflect only an extremely limited amount, in the order of 0.001 inch. As a consequence of this very limited travel, the take-out and display mechanisms are different from the counterpart mechanisms in a mercury or conventional bellows instrument.

BELLOWS DIFFERENTIAL-PRESSURE INSTRUMENTS

The bellows instrument is not limited by very small movements. In general, substantial movements are obtained for the full range of measured differential pressures. The bellows movements are in the order of several tenths of an inch.

Components

The components of a bellows instrument are:

1. A high-pressure compartment.
2. A low-pressure compartment.
3. A "movable wall" between these two compartments.
4. A take-out mechanism that is driven by the movable wall.
5. A display mechanism.
6. A balancing spring.

Arrangement

The two pressure compartments are arranged as in Fig. 7-3 so that one end of each of the two compartments is formed by the movable wall. The wall is movable because it is the closed end of a bellows. Attached to this movable wall is a lever that drives the display mechanism.

Principle of Operation

The two pressures of the differential-pressure signal are connected to the two pressure compartments. The difference in pressure exerts a force on the movable wall, causing the wall to move away from the greater pressure. This movement is opposed by a spring. The movement stops when the spring force balances the force arising out of the differential pressure acting on the movable wall.

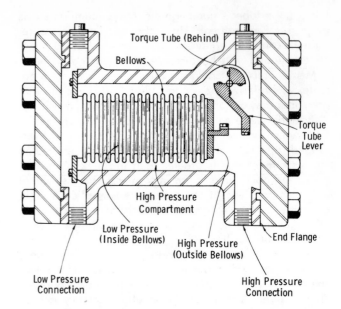

Fig. 7-3. Bellows differential-pressure instrument.

The movement is passed through a pressure-tight connection. This pressure-tight connection can have several forms such as a torque tube, one of the most common arrangements, or a sealing bellows. The torque tube is a widely-used component of many instruments in addition to the differential-pressure instruments. A good understanding of this component is valuable.

The movement which is "passed through" the torque tube or sealing bellows drives a display mechanism. This may be the usual link/lever pen (or indicator) mechanism, or it may be a transmitting mechanism.

Torque Tube

A torque tube combines two functions; first, it serves as the pressure-tight connection required to get a movement from a high-pressure area to a low-pressure area (atmospheric) and second, it serves as the spring force that opposes the measured signal.

Structurally, the torque tube (Fig. 7-4) consists of a thin-walled tube, one end of which is fixed to the meter body. The other end of the tube is closed. The complete tube is under the high static pressure of the measurement. Attached to the closed end of the tube is a lever that is caused to rotate by the bellows movements. The lever rotates, with the tube acting as its axis of rotation. The rotation of the lever twists the closed end of the tube through (say) 10 degrees of angular rotation. This angular rotation of the fixed end of the shaft is passed down a solid shaft, mounted inside the torque tube, one end of which is welded to the closed end of the torque tube. This shaft rotates as the closed end of the tube rotates. Attached to the other end of the solid shaft is the lever that drives the display mechanism (pen, indicator, etc.).

To change the range of a bellows instrument that uses a torque tube it is necessary to change the tube because it also serves as the spring that opposes the bellows travel.

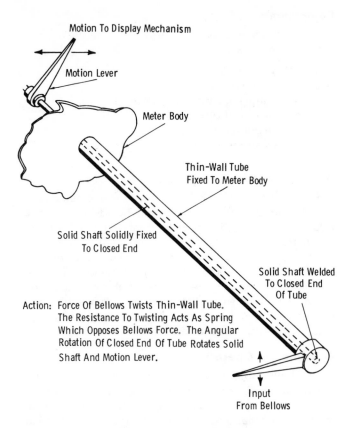

Motion To Display Mechanism

Motion Lever

Meter Body

Thin-Wall Tube
Fixed To Meter Body

Solid Shaft Solidly Fixed
To Closed End

Solid Shaft Welded
To Closed End
Of Tube

Action: Force Of Bellows Twists Thin-Wall Tube.
The Resistance To Twisting Acts As Spring
Which Opposes Bellows Force. The Angular
Rotation Of Closed End Of Tube Rotates Solid
Shaft And Motion Lever.

Input
From Bellows

Fig. 7-4. Torque tube.

Sealing Bellows

The second important method of "taking out" the bellows position is through a sealing bellows, or flexure. In some cases this flexure is referred to as a torque tube, perhaps because its construction may be similar to that of the real torque tube. It is well to remember, however, that devices which use the torque tube do not use range springs. Where the bellows seal or flexure seal is used, a spring is also used and the seal must be designed to offer as little resistance to the bellows movement as possible. When the sealing bellows is used, the motion (or force) of the bellows is opposed by a spring. In order to change the span of a bellows instrument using a seal, the spring must be changed for one having a different spring constant.

Damping

The bellows instrument just considered was a single-bellows device where the high-pressure compartment was formed of the volume outside of the single bellows and the low pressure compartment was formed of the volume inside the bellows. Such an arrangement has the advantage of simplicity. However, this arrangement cannot be "damped down" and, hence, is subject to a great deal of pulsation and flutter.

To solve this problem, instruments are supplied with two bellows. The inside volume of each is connected through an adjustable restriction. This volume is filled with a suitable fluid (such as glycerine or water). The differential pressure is applied to the outside of the

bellows, exerting a force on the bellows, tending to compress them. The fluid inside the bellows is also compressed, restraining the bellows from contracting. The fluid is "squeezed" out of one of the bellows through the restriction into the second bellows. Thus, the rate at which the bellows will contract or expand is regulated by the amount of restriction. This is a damping action. The bellows drive a shaft connecting both bellows. This shaft in turn drives a lever through a sealing tube. The spring loading on the bellows system establishes the range of the instrument.

Compensation

Use of the filling fluid introduces a temperature compensation problem since the fluid volume changes with changes in temperature. A variable-volume compartment is provided at one end of the bellows system. The increase in fluid volume due to temperature expands into this variable-volume compartment. In the strict sense, this is not a temperature compensation since the compensation is for changes in the volume of the filling fluid to prevent damage to the bellows system.

DIAPHRAGM DIFFERENTIAL-PRESSURE INSTRUMENTS

The diaphragm differential-pressure instruments will now be considered. Our discussion will be limited to the diaphragm mechanism and the take-out mechanism. The display mechanism will not be considered in any detail, because the display on this type instrument is a pneumatic or electrical signal.

One of the important characteristics of the diaphragm instrument is the very limited diaphragm deflection available before the diaphragm becomes taut. This deflection is in the order of a very few thousandths of an inch. As a consequence, the instrument must be designed so that, essentially, the diaphragm does not move when the differential pressure is applied to the instrument. This is accomplished by using the force exerted by the diaphragm due to the differential pressure on the diaphragm. (In the bellows instrument the motion of the bellows was used). The force is then counter-balanced by an outside force, usually an air pressure. The details of how this is accomplished will be discussed under the pneumatics section of this course.

Components

The components of a diaphragm instrument are:

1. A high-pressure compartment.
2. A low-pressure compartment.
3. A movable wall between the two compartments (the diaphragm).
4. A force beam.
5. A pressure-tight connection.
6. A display mechanism (pneumatic).
7. A balancing force (an air pressure in a feedback bellows).

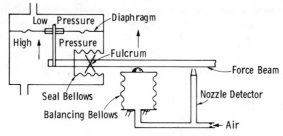

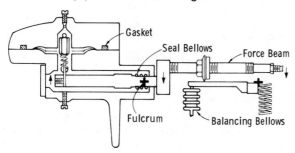

(A) Fundamental diagram.

(B) Simplified schematic.

Fig. 7-5. Diaphragm differential-pressure instrument.

Arrangements

The diaphragm is bolted between hollowed-out flanges, thus forming the high- and low-pressure compartments. The diaphragm is fastened to one end of the force beam, the other end of which is loaded with the force of a pneumatic bellows. This is the balancing force. The position of the beam is detected by a flapper-nozzle assembly as shown in Fig. 7-5.

Operation

The differential pressure across the diaphragm exerts a force on the diaphragm. This force is applied to the force beam, causing it to rotate a very small amount. The axis of rotation is at the seal (bellows or flexure). This extremely small movement is detected by a flapper/nozzle mechanism, causing an air pressure to build up in the feedback bellows. The bellows expands, exerting a balancing force on the force beam. When the differential-pressure force is balanced by the bellows force, the force beam comes to rest. The air pressure, which builds in the bellows, is then a measure of the differential pressure being applied to the instrument. This air pressure is connected to a pressure-sensitive instrument that can be calibrated in flow, liquid level, etc., depending on the specific instrument application.

BELL DISPLACER MANOMETERS

A fourth type of differential-pressure instrument, called the displacer type, uses the buoyancy principle to measure a differential pressure. Instruments based on this principle are widely used to measure low differential pressure (say 4 inches of water or less) and to measure flow.

Operation and construction of the displacer differential-pressure instrument is the subject of this chapter.

Components

The components of the displacer differential-pressure instrument are:

1. A high-pressure compartment.
2. A low-pressure compartment.
3. A sealing fluid (usually mercury).
4. A bell-shaped displacer.
5. A take-out mechanism.
6. A display mechanism.

Arrangements

Refer back to Fig. 3-3 for a bell manometer. The bell-shaped displacer is immersed upside down in a pool of mercury. The open end of the bell sinks in the mercury, forming two compartments. One compartment is inside the bell and is connected to the outside of the meter through a standpipe long enough that its end is above the surface of the mercury. The second compartment is the space outside the bell and inside the meter body. The mercury seals (separates) these two compartments.

Principle of Operation

The bell displacer will sink into the mercury until the weight of the displaced mercury equals the weight of the displacer. This action will be recognized as Archimedes' principle. The differential pressure is applied across the displacer and will either lift the displacer out of the mercury or push it farther into the mercury, depending on whether the high pressure connection is to the compartment inside the bell or the compartment outside the bell. In any case the force of the differential pressure will displace the bell until the change in the buoyant force balances the differential pressure force.

The bell movement is taken out of the meter body in the same way that the float position in float manometers is taken out.

Suppose the range of the displacer manometer is 10 inches of water, and suppose the displacer travel required to stroke a pen over a chart is 1 inch. Also, the high-pressure connection is made under the bell. Now suppose the 10 inches of pressure is applied to the instrument. This pressure will tend to lift the ball out of the mercury. The force tending to lift the bell will be equal to the 10 inches of water pressure multiplied by the area of the bell. As the bell rises, it displaces a smaller amount of mercury; hence, the buoyant force of the mercury is diminished, because part of the bell has been lifted out of the mercury pool and less mercury is being displaced. The buoyant force is reduced an amount equal to the weight of a volume of mercury equal to the volume of bell that was lifted out of the mercury. For the low-range differential-pressure instrument, equal volumes of bell are raised out of the mercury for equal increments of applied differential pressures because the wall thickness of the bell is the same throughout. This gives a linear relationship between pressure input and bell movement.

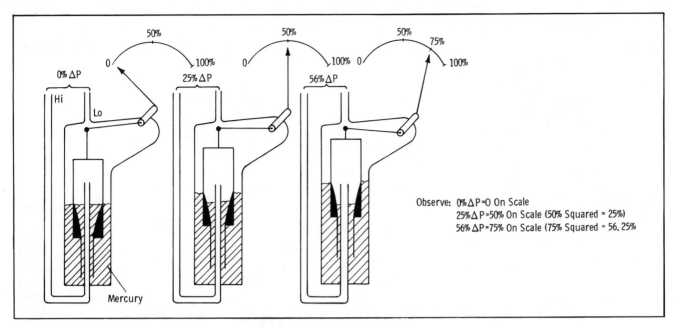

Fig. 7-6. Characterized displacer.

THE CHARACTERIZED DISPLACER

Suppose the wall of the bell, rather than being the same thickness at all points, were tapered so that a section through the wall would be (say) triangular, as in Fig. 7-6. If this were done, different increments of differential pressure would be required to raise the bell equal incremental amounts. If the thick part of the displacer were down, then relatively small differential pressure would raise it at the low end of the range.

In our discussion, a tapered displacer was suggested, but it can be seen that a specifically-shaped displacer could be designed to obtain different incremental lifts for the same increments of applied differential pressure. For example, it would be possible to design the shape of a displacer so that for 50 percent of the head range the displacer would move 70.7 percent of its travel. The square root of .50 is .707. Thus, the displacer can be characterized so that it causes a display equal to the square root of the applied differential pressure.

The value of the characterized displacer will be better appreciated when flow measurements using an orifice are studied in the chapter dealing with square root problems.

Chapter 8

Calibrating
Differential-Pressure Instruments

The calibration of differential-pressure instruments represents a substantial portion of the work of an instrument service group. When these devices are used with an orifice, the problem of the square root relationship arises. A second problem arises out of the false heads on mercury instruments when these instruments are "run wet." A third problem arises out of the terminology used to describe types of meters and how they are applied. The fact that differential-pressure instruments are expected to respond to fractions of inches of water further compounds all these problems. This chapter will be devoted to these problems. In addition, calibration procedures will be developed which will apply to all differential-pressure instruments.

WHAT DOES CALIBRATE MEAN?

An instrument is calibrated when by examining the display the magnitude of the measured variable can be determined.

For example, if the pen indicates that the flow is 75 gallons/min and the flow is 75 gallons/min, the instrument is calibrated. Suppose that the flow is 70 gallons/min and the instrument reads 75 gallons/min, we cannot say the instrument is calibrated. All that can be said is the installation is out of calibration. The flow meter may or may not be calibrated. In addition to the flowmeter, the installation may be out of calibration because of the orifice, or the connecting pipe. It is important that this be remembered because, all too frequently, flow installations are assumed correct because the instrument is in calibration.

In general, the best approach to checking out an orifice flow installation is, first, to check out the piping; second, check out the flowmeter; and third, check out the orifice installation. The checking of the calibration of the instrument is only one, though the most comprehensive, of the several meter checks commonly used.

The general calibrating procedures outlined in Chapter 2 apply equally well to differential-pressure instruments and perhaps would be sufficient, if it were not for the problems mentioned in the introduction. Also, some comment on specific calibration standards would be helpful. It is suggested that Chapter 2 be reviewed at this time.

TERMINOLOGY

The problem of terminology essentially is one of the specific meaning of "wet and dry," and the various ways an instrument may be used. For example, a dry meter may be run wet and calibrated wet; or a wet meter may be run dry and calibrated wet. The terms needing definition are:

wet meter	dry meter
run wet	run dry
wet calibration	dry calibration

A wet meter is a mercury meter. A dry meter is a non-mercury instrument, that is, a bellows or diaphragm instrument. Run wet means that the instrument has a fluid in the meter body, usually water; but, also it may be a transfer fluid, or gasoline, oil, or alcohol. Run dry means that the instrument has air, carbon dioxide, or other gas in the meter body.

The terms wet and dry calibration are not so straightforward. The most common definition of a wet calibration is a calibration made with water in the meter body. A dry calibration is one made with air in the meter body. The confusion of wet versus dry calibration arises out of the fact that there is no real difference between the two. The only difference is the magnitude of the input signal. The question is simply one of technique and convenience. Yet, there is a fairly well established idea that a meter that is run wet must be calibrated wet. This is not the case. The section on wet versus dry calibration should clear up this point.

THE "FALSE HEAD" PROBLEM

The "false head" problem arises whenever a wet meter (that is, a mercury meter) is being used or calibrated with a liquid, usually water, within the meter body. When a differential pressure is applied to the meter, the mercury level is upset to balance this applied differential pressure; but observe that the water head on the meter is upset also, because the space vacated by the mercury is replaced with water. This addition of a water head contributes to the differential pressure being applied, with the result that the total head is composed of the applied differential pressure plus the differential water head occurring because the mercury level in the float chamber is different from the mercury level in the range chamber. As a consequence, if a meter is to be calibrated with water in the meter body, the applied differential pressure must be less than it would be if there were no water in the meter body. If the fluid is water, the applied differential pressure is reduced by a factor of .93. Fluids of other densities require a different factor. When the transfer fluids are used, the density of the transfer fluid establishes the factor. (See Fig. 8-1.)

WET VERSUS DRY CALIBRATION

A meter can be calibrated with no water in the body (such a calibration is called a dry calibration) or the meter can be calibrated with water in the body (which is called a wet calibration). In either case, the total differential pressure applied to the meter is the same. However, in the case of the wet calibration, it is necessary only to apply part of the total head because automatically the remaining part is made up by the water filling the space vacated by the mercury. Specifically, the part to be applied is 93 percent (if the fluid is water) of the range values.

For example: Calibrate with water in the meter body, a mercury meter of the range 0 to 50 inches. Get calibrating values from column B, Table 8-1. Values in column B are 93 percent of values in column A.

Observe that the calibrating of a meter either wet or dry results in exactly the same calibration, and as a consequence, the end use of the meter is not an essential consideration when a calibration is to be made.

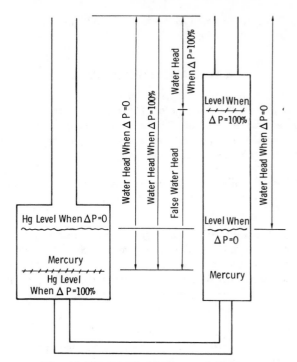

When △P=100%, Total Head On Mercury Is Equal To Applied Head Plus "False" Head

Fig. 8-1. False head problem.

The determination of whether to calibrate wet or dry, is one of convenience only. If a field check is to be made and the meter has water in the body, it is more convenient to calibrate wet than to dismantle the meter and remove the water.

Table 8-1. Values for Wet Calibration

Percent of Scale	(A) Range Values	(B) Calibrating Values
90	45 inches	41.85 inches
50	25 inches	23.25 inches
10	5 inches	4.65 inches

It should be further realized that in the calibration of meters that do not use mercury, the problem of a water head being automatically added, as a differential pressure is being applied, is no longer a consideration. Since there is no displacement of mercury in a dry meter (one without mercury), the applied differential pressure always equals the total differential pressure and no correction factor need be used when making a wet calibration.

The replacement of a wet meter (mercury) with a dry meter of the same range will result in an error in the flow calculation, however, the instrument calibrations remain the same and are correct. The error lies in assuming that for a 100 percent chart reading for a meter running wet that a differential pressure of 100 percent is being applied. It is not. The applied differential pressure is the differential pressure being delivered by the orifice. To drive the pen to 100 percent of chart only

93 inches of water (93 percent of 100) need be delivered by the orifice.

CALIBRATION EQUIPMENT

The usual calibration standard is a column of fluid in a glass tube manometer. The fluid may be water or some of the "red oils" of known specific gravity. A common heavy red oil has a specific gravity of 2.94. The use of this oil cuts the length of the manometer by a factor of 1/2.94.

For all calibration, except the wet calibration (water in the meter body), the following equipment is required:

1. The calibration standard (a precision gauge).
2. An input signal (a pressure source).
3. A visual display.
4. Tube and fittings to assemble the standard, the signal, the meter to be calibrated, and the display.

Item 1 is a precision gauge of sufficient accuracy.

Item 2 is usually compressed air furnished through a pressure regulating device.

Item 3 is the meter itself if it is a recorder. If the instrument is a transmitter, the display is a calibrated instrument that is sensitive to the transmitter output.

For example: If the transmitter display is an air pressure that varies from 3 to 15 lbs, the display would be a calibrated pressure gauge or a manometer of a suitable range. A four-foot manometer using mercury, and calibrated in terms of inches of water forms an excellent display.

Item 4 is the necessary fittings and piping to assemble the equipment as shown in Fig. 8-2.

WET CALIBRATION RIG

The wet calibration rig consists essentially of the same components as the gear just described. There are a few differences, which can be seen in Fig. 8-3. The

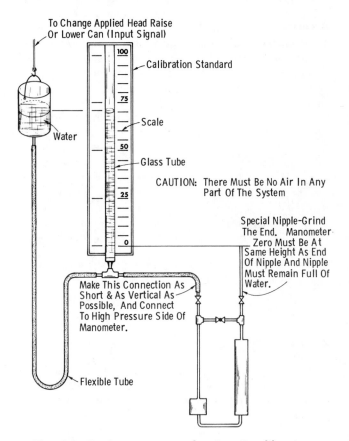

Fig. 8-3. Equipment setup for "wet" calibration.

signal is obtained by raising and lowering a can of water, thus changing the head on the meter. The bottom of the can is connected to the high pressure side of the instrument being calibrated. The calibration standard is a water filled manometer. In order to reduce meniscus errors, the glass tube of the manometer should be no smaller than ½ inch in diameter. All connections should be ½-inch pipe or larger. In determining pipe sizes, the general consideration is the need to get all the air out of the connections, tubing, and instrument. Large sizes make it easier to eliminate the air.

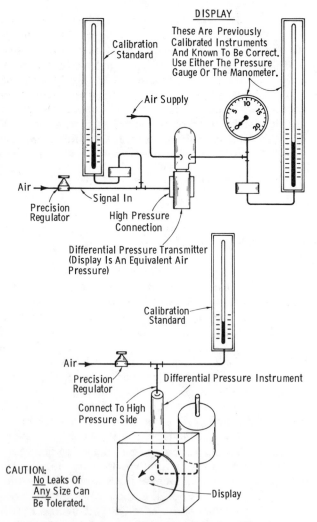

Fig. 8-2. Equipment setup for "dry" calibration.

48

CALIBRATION PROCEDURE

Mechanical Stops

1. Are the mechanisms free to travel their range without hitting stops?
   a. With no mercury in body, pen should go slightly below zero or above 100 percent, depending on the specific meter. If it doesn't, bring the pen to slightly above 100 percent, (or below zero) by adjusting the pen micrometer in the required direction.
   b. Add mercury until pen goes slightly below zero (or slightly above 100 percent). [Note: Above procedure can be used for wet calibration. Caution: Sharply tap meter body and very slowly add the mercury. Some fairly appreciable times are required for mercury levels to equalize, and both check valves must be unseated.]

Accuracy

1. Is the mechanism free of friction and dead-space hysteresis and sufficiently sensitive? [Note: In addition to all checks of a link/lever mechanism (see Chapter 2) the pressure-tight connection can be a serious friction problem.]

   a. Feel for end play. There should be some end play and the bearing should freely move in and out.
   b. Observe pen position.
   c. Gently push the float a slight amount into the mercury. Use a stick through vent connection, causing the pen to move (say) ⅜ inch.
   d. Very slowly lift stick, allowing float to return to its starting position.
   e. Observe pen position. It should return to within a 1/32 inch of original pen position. If it does not, recheck link/lever mechanism as suggested in Chapter 2. If this does not correct the condition, overhaul the pressure-tight bearing.

2. Check the pressure-tight connection as in a through d.

Calibrate

1. Does the instrument reproduce the input signal as indicated by the calibration standard? [Note: The methods for adjusting span angularity and zero are those of the general calibration procedure for link/lever mechanisms. See Chapter 2.]
   a. Apply approximately a 50-percent-of-range head to instrument, or apply head equivalent to critical point. [Note: On flowmeter, 75 percent of chart is usually the critical point.] Adjust to minimize angularity errors.
   b. Check span by feeding in a 10-percent head, then a 90-percent head. Adjust as for any link/lever instrument.
   c. Check zero by feeding in a head (any value between 10 and 90 percent). Adjust as for any link/lever mechanism.
   d. Recheck as in Step "a" by putting in a 10-percent, 50-percent and 90-percent head. If pen does not fall on all three points, readjust angularity as you would for any link/lever mechanism.
   e. Repeat "a" through "d" as required.

Wet Calibration Procedure

The procedure just discussed is applicable to a wet calibration. There are two precautions; first, the instrument must be free of all air bubbles. Vent connections are provided in the meter for freeing the meter of air pockets. Notwithstanding, a fair amount of rapping is required to shake the instrument free of air bubbles. It is equally important that the tubing of the test rig also be freed of air. Some juggling of the tubing is required to do this. To facilitate freeing the tubing of air, locate the manometer relative to the instrument so that the connections between them are as short and as vertical as possible.

The second precaution is that the special nipple on the low-pressure compartment must be filled with water at all times. The manometer zero should be level with the top of this nipple.

Chapter 9

The Orifice and Flow Installations

In previous chapters, it was stated that differential-pressure sensitive instruments may be used to measure flow if a suitable primary device is used. The primary device is needed to convert flow into an equivalent differential-pressure signal.

The most common flow-to-differential-pressure converter is an orifice in a thin plate. This chapter will explain the principle of operation of the orifice to furnish insight into the problems and limitations of the orifice differential-pressure method of flow measurement.

WHAT IS AN ORIFICE?

When we speak of an orifice it is generally an abbreviation for an orifice plate. An orifice plate is a disc of metal about 1/16- to ¼-inch thick. Usually, a circular hole, or orifice, is cut from the center of the disc. The size of the disc, outside diameter (abbreviated O.D.), is such that it will fit within the bolts on standard pipe flanges. The orifice diameter is usually between .5 and .8 of the inside diameter (abbreviated I.D.) of the pipe on which the orifice is being used.

The orifice is a closely defined piece of equipment. Its construction and dimensions are shown in Fig. 9-1. The complete name for this piece of equipment is the orifice in a thin plate. A thin plate is defined as not greater than 1/16 inch. In most cases, the orifice plate is thicker than 1/16 inch and may be ¼ inch thick. In order to meet the 1/16-inch requirement, the plate is "thinned down" or beveled to 1/16 inch around the orifice opening itself. A second requirement is that the leading edge of the orifice (the side that faces the flow) be a square edge. Square here means that the

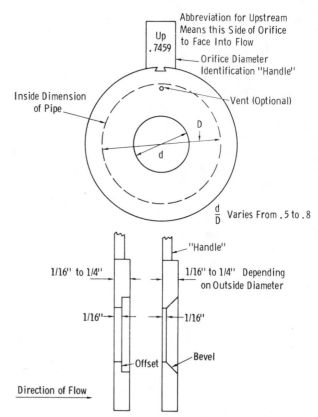

Fig. 9-1. Construction of orifice.

edge be sufficiently sharp to cut. It also must be free of "wire edges" or burrs.

These relatively stringent requirements are necessary because, essentially, the performance of an orifice is determined empirically—that is, by actual testing. These tests are made with orifices meeting the above requirements. In general, the bulk of experimental information is on pipe sizes less than twelve inches using air, water, and steam as a fluid. The significance of these observations is that the calculation of flow differential-pressure relationship can be fairly involved (and questionable) for uncommon fluids; for example, sulphur, sodium nitrate, or phthalic anhydride, whose physical properties are not thoroughly known. For our purposes it is sufficient to remember that the kind of fluid and the larger pipe sizes may make it difficult to predict flows. In general, however, the major source of problems with orifice differential-pressure installations is in the connecting piping between the orifice and the differential-pressure instruments.

PRINCIPLE OF OPERATION

One of the basic physical laws is that energy can neither be created nor destroyed. The orifice obeys this law. Suppose we study the following pipe line (Fig. 9-2), specifically points A and B. Assume that a flow of Q gallons per minute enters at the "A" end of the pipe.

The first conclusion we may make is that if Q gallons per minute enter the pipe then Q gallons per minute must also leave the pipe. Observe, however, that the pipe diameter at B is less than the diameter at A. If the same amount of fluid is to pass by B, as passed by A, the speed (velocity) of the fluid flow must be greater at B than at A.

Examine point A:

1. At this point the fluid has internal pressure which will be called P_A and is the pressure head at A.
2. The fluid has kinetic energy which will be called V_A and is the velocity head at A.
3. The fluid has elevation above some reference height. This elevation will be called H_A.

At point B we have the same three kinds of heads as observed at point A, namely P_B, V_B, and H_B. The law of conservation of energy states that the local energy at A must equal the total energy at B, or (if friction is neglected) stating this mathematically:

$$P_A + V_A + H_A = P_B + V_B + H_B$$

To simplify this relationship suppose points A and B are at the same height, that is, $H_A = H_B$. The relationship is:

$$P_A + V_A = P_B + V_B$$

Remember that due to the difference in diameter at points A and B, the velocity of the fluid at B is greater than at A. Examine the last equation. If V_B is greater than V_A, then P_B must be less than P_A if the equality is to hold.

In other words, the restriction of the smaller-diameter pipe at B causes the velocity to increase at B. To balance this increase in velocity, the pressure must drop. Hence, there is a difference in pressure between

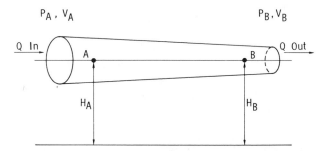

Fig. 9-2. Illustration for basic flow laws.

P_B and P_A. This is a differential pressure whose magnitude depends on the velocity. The velocity for a given system is a measure of the quantity of fluid flowing through the pipe. It is in this way that flow is converted to differential pressure. Suppose this pipe is "squeezed" together so that it is about 3 inches long. This is the equivalent of an orifice plate in a short section of pipe so that discussion applies equally well to the orifice.

Basic Flow Law

The actual relationship between flow and differential pressure depends primarily on the ratio of the diameter of the orifice to the inside diameter of the pipe, and the physical properties of the fluid. The actual relationship is stated as so many inches of water pressure (differential pressure) per unit of flow. The basic expression is:

$$Q = cA \sqrt{2gh}$$

Where,

Q is the flowing quantity,
c is a coefficient (a number) which takes into account the physical properties of the fluid being measured,
2g is due to the force of gravity and equals 64.8,
h is the differential pressure,
A is the area of the orifice.

The important thing to remember is that flow is related to the square root of the differential pressure. It is this fact that introduces the square root problem that will be discussed in a later chapter.

Orifice Variation

Our discussion to this point has been largely on the orifice in a thin plate. In addition, several variations of the orifice should be mentioned. The theory of the orifice in a thin plate applies equally well to these other devices.

The Venturi (see Fig. 9-3) is the most accurate and the most efficient primary device. Efficiency of an orifice is a measure of the recovery of the pressure drop due to the orifice. For example, a common differential pressure for the orifice at maximum flow is 100 inches of water pressure. On most thin-plate orifice installations, perhaps 30 to 50 percent of this head is recovered, depending on the ratio of the orifice diameter to the pipe diameter. The Venturi pressure recovery may be as high as 85 to 90 percent.

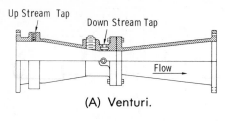

(A) Venturi.

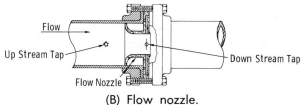

(B) Flow nozzle.

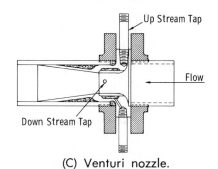

(C) Venturi nozzle.

Fig. 9-3. Orifice variations.

The Flow Nozzle is a flanged nozzle usually designed to be installed between flanges. Nozzles have a higher throughput capacity. (See Fig. 9-3.)

The Venturi Nozzle is a combination of a nozzle with a tapered downstream recovery section.

The Dall Flow Tube is a special variation of the Venturi designed to give appreciable pressure differentials with a high recovery factor, around 95 percent.

The orifice itself has several variations as follows:

1. Concentric.
2. Eccentric.
3. Segmental.

These variations are shown in Fig. 9-4.

These orifices may be provided with a small vent hole which falls just inside the pipe diameter. The vent hole allows gases in a liquid stream to flow by the orifice, or, it allows condensed liquids in a gas stream to flow by the orifice. If the vent is for gases in a liquid stream, the vent is "up." If the vent is for liquids in a gas stream, the vent is "down."

In this discussion, we have touched only the highlights of the orifice. The study of orifices and the calculation of flows and orifice diameters is an engineering function. It is sufficient for our purpose to understand some of the limitations and the operation of the orifice in order to understand the total flow installation. It is helpful to think of an orifice as a device that converts flow to differential pressure. The flow varies as the square root of the differential pressure.

FLOW INSTALLATIONS

The manner of connecting the orifice to the meter is extremely important. The specific arrangement is determined by three factors: the variations of piping required for the kinds of flow being measured, the physical location of the orifice in the pipe line and relative to the meter body, and the type of meter, orifice and orifice connections. The overriding consideration in all judgments on piping arrangements is the necessary requirement that the differential pressure generated by the orifice be accurately and quickly transferred to the meter body.

Our viewpoint will be to emphasize the need to understand the physical considerations so that when working on an actual flow installation, the instrument man can judge the adequacy and potential trouble spots of the total installation. This necessarily involves the orifice, the meter, and all connecting piping. We shall group the fluids being measured into categories according to the specific piping arrangements they require. The meters will be grouped in a similar fashion. We will study the effect that the physical location of the orifice in the line relative to the meter body has on the piping connecting the orifice and the meter. Some typical installations will be shown. As the variations even in typical installations are almost without limit, the best method of attack is to understand the fundamental considerations. This is unquestionably the case for the field service man because, first, he is the fellow who "gets the meter going" regardless of how proper the installation may appear to be, and second, he doesn't have the time or wherewithal to research the literature on flow installations to find a specific recommendation for a particular problem. Even if he did, often there just aren't specific recommendations on the unusual streams of many chemical processes.

ORIFICE TAPS

A specific orifice installation may have the actual pressure connection located in several distinct positions relative to the orifice. Three examples are shown in Fig. 9-5.

The flange taps are made through the flange body itself. The orifice flanges are the same as standard flanges except that the flange itself is thicker, making it possible to drill through the flange into the pipe line. These openings are tapped for a ½-inch nominal pipe size. Orifice flanges may be screwed onto the pipe or welded. Two types of welded orifice flanges are shown in Fig. 9-6—weld-neck and slip-on.

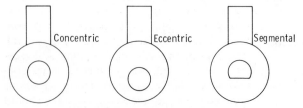

Fig. 9-4. Types of orifices.

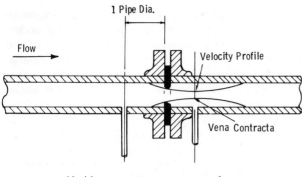

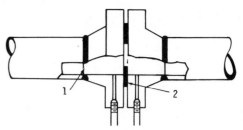

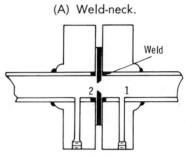

At 1 Observe Following:
       Inside Of Weld Must Be Clean.
       Flanges Must Be Concentric On Pipe.

At 2 Observe Following:
       Orifice Concentric With Flange.
       Gasket I.D. Must Be No Smaller Than Pipe I.D.

(A) Weld-neck.

1 Hole Thru Pipe Wall Must Be
   Free Of Burrs Or Wire Edges
2 Burn In Weld And File Smooth

(B) Slip-on.

Fig. 9-6. Weld-neck and slip-on orifice flanges.

(A Vena contracta connections.

(B) Flange taps.

(C) Pipe taps.

Fig. 9-5. Tap locations.

Pipe Taps

These taps are made into the pipe line itself at some fixed distance from the orifice, usually 2½ pipe diameters upstream and 8 diameters downstream. Pipe taps are far enough from the orifice that the differential pressure measured at the taps is, essentially, the permanent pressure drop due to the orifice.

Vena Contracta Taps

One connection is made about one pipe diameter upstream from the orifice. The second is located at the vena contracta. The vena contracta is the point downstream from the orifice where the velocity is maximum and the pressure minimum. The maximum velocity is not at the orifice since the kinetic properties of the fluid result in the stream "pinching down" for a short distance after passing through the orifice. The actual location of the vena contracta depends largely on the ratio of the orifice diameter to the pipe inside diameter. This type of orifice connection results in measuring the maximum pressure drop.

Flange Taps

Perhaps a major portion of the new orifice installations use flange tap connections. The reason is largely one of convenience. The installation of a connection in a pipe wall is a fairly critical job in that the entrance into the pipe must be at right angles to the pipe wall and at the proper distance from the orifice. The inside of the pipe must be smooth and the hole itself free from burrs and wire edges. Under field construction conditions, it is difficult to consistently get good field

fabricated connections. The welding neck orifice flange eliminates all of the problems of making an entrance into the pipe since the connections are "pre-machined" in the flange. However, there is the problem of the butt weld upstream from the orifice. The flange must be absolutely concentric with the pipe, no welding ring should be used, and the inside of the pipe must be cleared of weld buildups.

The slip-on and screwed flanges do not eliminate the problem of entering the pipe. After the flanges are put on the pipe, it is necessary to drill through the pipe wall itself. The hole through the pipe wall must be free of burrs and wire edges and the pipe wall must be smooth. However, since these connections are near the flange, they are accessible. This is not the case with pipe tap connections. The slip-on flange should be located so that the face of the flange and the end of the pipe are almost flush. The usual practice of setting the conventional slip-on flange forward one pipe wall thickness is not satisfactory. The welder must "burn in" the back weld bead, and a lot of filing is necessary to smooth the face of the flange.

The vena contracta, flange tap, and pipe tap connections are the three standard connections. In addition, there are several special arrangements. On pipe sizes less than 2 inches and over 12 inches, these special arrangements are fairly common. These variations do not present any service problem, but one should be alert to these variations and check to see whether the connections agree with the flow data for which the orifice was designed.

METER TYPES

Three types of differential pressure instruments have been discussed: the float/manometer, the bellows, and the diaphragm. The significant difference that influences piping connections is the internal volume of the kind of instrument. The float/manometer and bellows instruments, when stroked their range, displace a relatively large quantity of measured fluid. For example, to stroke a manometer/float instrument, where the float moves 1 inch and the diameter of the float chamber is 4 inches, 12½ cubic inches $(1 \times \pi 2^2)$ of measured fluid must move into the float chamber and the same amount must move out of the range chamber. The diaphragm instrument requires negligible quantities of measured fluid to stroke the instrument, perhaps on the order of hundredths of cubic inches. If the diaphragm instrument is used, there will be very little inflow and outflow of measured fluid. If the float/manometer or bellows instruments are used, substantial quantities of measured fluid move into and out of the connecting piping and meter body.

MEASURED FLUID PROPERTIES

The properties of fluids that determine piping arrangements are:

1. The state of the measured material at flowing temperatures and at the ambient temperature of the differential pressure instrument.
2. Chemical properties, chiefly the material's corrosiveness.
3. Mechanical properties such as viscosity and solids content.

Each of these properties will be considered in some detail.

The State of the Material

State refers to whether the fluid is a gas, a liquid, or a solid. The state of a material is almost wholly determined by the temperature. Pressure is also a determining factor, but since all parts in the installation are at the same pressure, pressure is important only in determining the pressure rating of meters, flanges, piping valves, etc.

In actual flow installations, it is common to have a material at elevated temperatures as it flows through the pipe and at reduced (ambient) temperatures as it flows through the instrument. This difference in temperature may, depending on the material being measured, result in the material changing state. For example, consider steam; in the pipe line it is gaseous. However the steam condenses to water at the ambient temperature of the meter, so the state at the meter is liquid. This is an example of a gas changing to liquid. Suppose the material carbon dioxide, for example, was at a reduced temperature. At reduced tem-

perature, the carbon dioxide is a liquid, but at the ambient temperature of the meter, carbon dioxide may be a gas. This is an example of a liquid-to-gas change of state.

A fair number of chemical streams are liquids at their elevated flowing temperatures, but would be solid if the temperature dropped to ambient. In other words, a fair number of chemicals freeze at ambient temperatures and would be a solid in the meter body. The solutions to change-of-state problems are:

1. Prevent the change by raising (or lowering) the temperature of the meter body.
2. Allow the change in state.
3. Introduce a second fluid as a "transfer" liquid.

A discussion of these alternates follows:

It is necessary to prevent change in state from liquid to solid by methods 1 or 3. The limitation of method 1 is that it is possible to raise the temperature of the meter only limited amounts. As a practical matter, the diaphragm instrument can be raised to (perhaps) 150 degrees centigrade. The bellows instrument, using an air pressure as the display, may be raised to approximately 100 degrees centigrade provided it is not a double-bellows instrument with a damping fluid. Non-mercury differential-pressure instruments with an electrical display are limited to less than the temperature which will break down the electrical insulation, and as a practical matter, electrical transmitters do not allow any significant temperature increase in the meter body temperatures.

The second alternate, allowing the change of state, is acceptable for many fluids if the change is from a gas to a liquid. An example of this would be to allow steam to condense to water, but to prevent the water from freezing. In no case can the material change its state to a solid.

The third alternate, introduction of a transfer fluid, can solve some change-in-state problems. This method is to introduce a second fluid into the system so that the meter body is filled with this fluid. The differential pressure of the orifice is transferred through this fluid to the instrument.

This method is limited by the small number of transfer fluids available. A fluid, to be suitable, must:

1. Be liquid at the meter body temperature. It is possible to raise the temperature of the meter body to some limited extent.
2. Remain liquid at the elevated temperatures of the material being measured.
3. Not "mix" with the material being measured. This includes absorbing and subsequently giving off the measured fluid when the fluid is a gas.
4. Have a density greater than the material being measured.
5. Have chemical stability over long periods of time.
6. Not react with the material being measured.

Availability of materials meet.ng these requirements is sharply limited.

Chemical Properties

The chemical properties of the measured fluid determine piping arrangements in the following way. If the material is corrosive, the meter body and piping must be made of materials which will not be attacked by the fluid. Many corrosive liquids can be metered successfully using nonmercury meters fabricated of special alloys. If there are not alloys available which will resist the chemical attack of the fluid being measured, a solution would be to introduce a transfer fluid. The properties of the transfer fluid used for chemical protection are the same as for the change of state except that in most cases there is no upper temperature requirement.

Mechanical Properties

The mechanical properties of interest are viscosity, the percent of solids in the liquid stream being measured, and the percent of liquids and/or solids in the gas stream being measured. Viscosity is important because fluids may be sufficiently viscous that the inflow and outflow will be restrained to the point where the sensitivity of the instrument is seriously affected.

The percent of solids in a liquid stream is a substantial consideration. Regardless of how limited the amount of solids in a stream, the solids tend to separate out in the meter due to the inflow-outflow. These solids plug the connecting pipe lines and collect in the meter body. Solids also are likely to collect in front of the orifice, introducing errors in flow measurement.

As the solids increase, the stream becomes more difficult to measure. If there is appreciable solid content, special steps are required to obtain a satisfactory primary flow element. A special primary device, for example a flow nozzle or a venturi, must be used. The solution to the solids problem may be:

1. The introduction of a transfer fluid either continuously or intermittently.
2. Sealed orifice connections.

The cost of the purge fluid may be important. The possibility of contaminating the measured stream must also be considered. The cost factors permit the use of only very cheap transfer fluids such as air, water, carbon dioxide (perhaps) or product streams. For example, perhaps a liquid from a separator might be fed back into the system. The dilution effect of the purging stream must be considered since the purge materials enter the process. In general, all possible effects of the purge stream on the process stream must be considered.

Sealed orifice connections are similar in construction to the seals used to keep process fluids out of pressure gauges. If these seals are made to the pipe line directly without the use of pipe, a very satisfactory installation can be obtained. Frequently such seals are used together with purging, with the purge fluids entering just under the seal.

A few comments on liquids and/or solids in a gas stream might be helpful. In general, liquids or solids in gas streams result from gases condensing into liquid droplets, or product dusts which have not been separated out of the gas stream. In some instances, powdered products are deliberately mixed with air to facilitate transporting the product.

Liquids, if they are a very small portion of the total stream, can be collected in catch pots strategically located in the connecting piping as was the case with small amounts of solids in a liquid stream.

If the liquid content is high, drip pots may not be sufficient. Depending on the kind of liquid, it is possible to let the connecting lines fill with the liquid. This is similar to the alternate of permitting the change in state from a gas to a liquid. Purging, sealing, and introduction of a transfer fluid are also possible solutions, depending on the particular gas and the liquid entrained.

SUMMARY

It has been shown that the total accuracy of a flow installation is determined by the individual accuracies of all the parts. The total system is designed for the type orifice, orifice taps, fluid properties, instrument type, instrument and orifice location. These have been discussed to provide understanding of the total installation and the interdependence of the parts.

Chapter 10

The Rotameter and Other Flow Measuring Instruments

THE ROTAMETER

Consider the basic flow equation:

$$Q = cA \sqrt{2gh}$$

This equation says the flowing quantity varies as the area times the square root of the head. Up to this point, the only comments on the area were to the effect that the numerical value depended on the ratio of the orifice diameter and the inside diameter of the pipe and for a given orifice this value was a "constant"; that is, its value does not change. Notice that the basic flow equation allows two flow devices in that this equation says flow varies as the square root of the head IF the area is constant; or, it says flow varies as the area IF the square root of the head is constant. If the head is constant, then the square root of this head is also a constant. This second possibility is the basis for a large group of flow-measuring instruments called area-type meters. The rotameter, the subject of this chapter, is one of the more important area-type meters.

Components

The essential rotameter components are:

1. A tapered tube.
2. A plummet (Common terminology describes the component as a "float." This is a misnomer since in no sense does the "float" float.)
3. A take-out mechanism.
4. A display.

NOTE: One rotameter uses a tube made of glass. The display of this rotameter is the position of the plummet (float) within the glass tube.

As a consequence, there is no take-out mechanism, as such, unless one adopts the view that the design of the tube of glass constitutes a take-out mechanism.

Arrangements

The ends of the tube are arranged so that the tube can be installed vertically in a pipe line. End fittings are furnished. The tube is inserted into the end fittings and packing is squeezed down around the tube, making a pressure-tight connection. The end fittings are joined, forming a rigid member. If hazardous fluids are being measured, a housing of safety glass is put around the glass tube, thereby preventing the hazardous fluid from showering the area if the glass tube breaks. (See Fig. 10-1.)

If the tube is made of metal, end fittings are welded on the tube and the connecting pipe is screwed (or flanged) to the end fittings.

The plummet, or float, is put into the tube and is free to run up and down. Usually the tube walls guide the plummet, but some plummets run up and down on a rod. The plummet is shaped so that the flow tends to center it within the tube. The tube end fittings are equipped with stops so that the plummet will remain within the tube.

The plummet itself may be made of various materials such as stainless steel or ceramic carbon; however, in the majority of cases it is made of one of the steels. The other materials are used for flows that would corrode the various steels. The shape of the plummet varies from a ball, used on the simple rotameters, to fairly elaborate cylinders with cone ends, flares, and guides. (See Fig. 10-2.) For our purposes, its

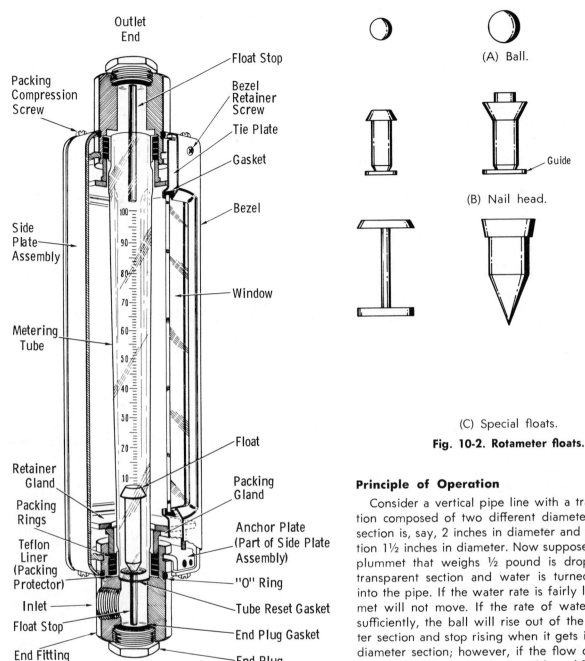

Fig. 10-1. Glass tube rotameter.

(A) Ball.

(B) Nail head.

(C) Special floats.

Fig. 10-2. Rotameter floats.

Principle of Operation

Consider a vertical pipe line with a transparent section composed of two different diameters. The upper section is, say, 2 inches in diameter and the lower section 1½ inches in diameter. Now suppose a top-shaped plummet that weighs ½ pound is dropped into the transparent section and water is turned on, flowing into the pipe. If the water rate is fairly low, the plummet will not move. If the rate of water is increased sufficiently, the ball will rise out of the 1½-in diameter section and stop rising when it gets into the 2-inch diameter section; however, if the flow of water is increased further, it may be possible to lift the plummet out of the transparent section altogether. The reason for this is that two things, the stream of water and the top, cannot occupy the same space within the pipe. As long as the flow rate is small, there is "room" for both the water and the top. When the water stream increases to a certain size, there is not enough room for both the water and the top and, since the top is held down only by its weight, the water is able to lift the plummet. When the plummet is lifted into the 2-inch section, it rises no further because there is sufficient room for both the water and the top until the water flow is increased further. In other words, the position of the top within the pipe is determined by the relation between the cross-sectional area occupied by the water and cross-sectional area occupied by the plummet.

shape is not of any serious consequence except for the case of the glass tube rotameter. For these instruments, it is important that the "top" of the plummet be recognized so that the plummet is inserted in the tube top side up. A second point is that the proper part of the plummet is compared to the scale, whereas others Some plummets are designed so that the bottom of the plummet is compared to the scale, whereas others use the top, and still others use a flare somewhere between the top and the bottom. The plummets used on nonglass rotameters have extensions so that there is little likelihood of installing the plummet upside down.

The area available to the water is that annular space between the pipe wall and the cylinder wall that is equal to:

$$\frac{D^2}{4} - \frac{d^2}{4} = \text{Annular Area}$$

Where:

D is the inside diameter of pipe
d is the outside diameter of the plummet (top)

Suppose the transparent pipe just described is tapered continuously so that the outlet is a larger diameter than the inlet, and the plummet is designed so that it occupies almost all the total tube area when it is at the small end of the tube. As fluid is allowed into the tube, the plummet will be pushed up, permitting the water to pass between the outside of the float and the tube wall. It will be pushed up until the differential pressure across the plummet results in a force under it that is just equal to the effective weight of the plummet. The effective weight is equal to the weight of the plummet minus the buoyant force of the fluid being measured. For a given fluid and a particular plummet, the effective weight is constant. Since the effective weight is constant, the differential pressure across the plummet is constant. As the flow rate changes, the annular area must change to accommodate the various flow rates.

Since the variable is area, the position of the plummet within the length of the tube can be used as a measure of the area for a given tube. Hence, the plummet position can be used to determine flow. Observe that there is a direct relation between flow and position. Hence, there is no square-root problem when measuring flow with a rotameter.

TAKE-OUT AND DISPLAY MECHANISMS

Tube and plummet arrangements have been discussed under "Principle of Operation." Items 3 and 4 of the components—take-out mechanism and display—have not been discussed except for the glass tube rotameter where the take-out mechanism is the glass tube and the display is the position of the plummet within the tube. For cases of metal tube rotameters or where a visual display alone is not adequate, more elaborate mechanisms are required.

For recording and/or transmitting instruments, the take-out mechanism is almost always a magnetic coupling. The magnetic couplings as applied to rotameters are very similar to the magnetic couplings discussed under differential-pressure take-out mechanisms. There is one important difference. The plummet position for rotameters may vary several inches (10 to 12 inches is not uncommon), whereas the plummet or displacer in a differential pressure instrument travels something less than 1½ inches.

For an electrical display, that is, an electrical output that is a function of the plummet position, the impedance bridge principle is used.

For a recorded display or for a pneumatic display, a magnetic following mechanism is used. This method

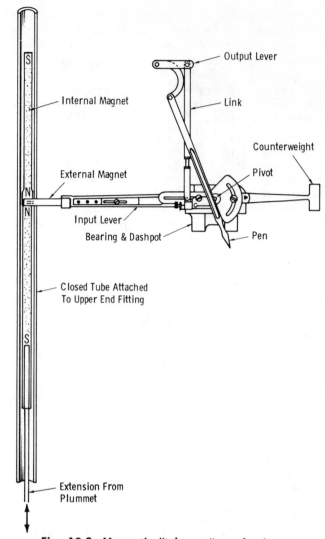

Fig. 10-3. Magnetic "take-out" mechanism.

for taking out the plummet position is accomplished by putting an extension on the displacer. A permanent magnet is placed inside the extension at its extreme upper end. The extension runs inside a closed tube mounted on the upper end fitting. This extension is nonmagnetic. A second permanent magnet is located outside the tube. This second magnet is mounted on a lever and is free to follow the movement of the magnet in the plummet extension. The second magnet may be replaced by an armature mounted on a lever. A link is connected to this lever and to a pen (or indicator) lever. If the display is pneumatic, a second link is taken from the lever to drive a pneumatic mechanism. (See Fig. 10-3.)

OTHER FLOW-MEASURING INSTRUMENTS

The measurement of flow with the orifice-differential method, and the rotameter, perhaps, accounts for as much as 90 percent of all the chemical plant flow measurements. These two methods, however, are but two of many. Other methods will be discussed in some detail; some will be only mentioned. The viewpoint and emphasis will be directed toward classifying flow-measuring devices. In so doing, the flow devices so far discussed will be used as examples of an important classification. Other devices will be introduced, explained, and classified as we progress.

It is not too important in our work to rigorously categorize flow instruments. The important consideration is that some workable basis be developed for keeping the various devices straight in one's mind. The object of doing this is to furnish a basis for understanding how the devices do accomplish the job of measuring flow. Once this is done, the mechanisms themselves fall into a pattern. This is a fairly important consideration because, from a mechanism point of view, the only things these mechanisms have in common is that they are used to measure flow. To simply categorize these mechanisms as flow-measuring devices is a rather unsatisfactory arrangement for the purposes of this course.

In order to accomplish the purpose of this chapter, some time will be spent discussing terminology. To facilitate that discussion and to summarize the work, a flowmeter "family tree" has been prepared. (See Fig. 10-4.)

BASIC MEASUREMENT

It will appear rather strange at this point to ask the question, "Just what are we doing when we are measuring flow?" The answer, perhaps, is not as obvious as it might appear. Our answer will be: a measurement of flow is a measurement of a quantity of moving material (solids, liquids, gases or mixtures). This definition raises, in turn, two further points: the significance of "moving material" and just how a quantity is measured. On the question of a moving quantity there are two possibilities for making a measurement: to make the measurement "on the fly" as the material moves, or to interrupt its movement so that the flow is a continuous series of uniform batches.

Just how is a measure of a quantity of material made? There are two possibilities:

1. Weigh it.
2. Measure its volume.

In order to weigh a material, we measure the force of gravity on the material, using a scale. In order to measure a volume we must determine its dimensions. For example, if the material is a fluid, we might fill a number of quart bottles and then count the number of quarts of the material. Either of these methods is a direct measurement of the material.

In addition to the direct method of weighing or measuring its volume, another possibility exists. We might attempt to infer what the quantity is by subjecting the flowing quantity to some disturbance and then measuring the effect of this disturbance. These two methods are the basis of the two major classifications of flow measurement types. The first method is direct; the second is inferential.

Using the above definitions, it will be possible to classify most of the flow measurements under the two classifications of direct and inferential, but, as is usually the case, there is a gray area between these two major groupings where one is hard put to precisely state whether the device uses direct or inferential measurement. Meters which measure velocity fall into this gray area. One valid viewpoint on velocity measuring devices is that they are direct. The reasoning is that they measure the volume of the material, since they measure the length of the material and the diameter is known. That is, a measurement is made of the number of feet of material that flow by a point in a pipe line. An analogy might be made using a tube of tooth paste. The quantity of tooth paste used might be determined by squeezing the paste out in a straight line and measuring its length. Its length times the area of the opening in the tube equals the volume of the paste used. The second viewpoint on whether a measurement of velocity is a direct or inferential flow measurement would class the velocity measurement as inferential, since flow is determined by measuring a velocity that is not a direct property of a material in the same sense that volume and mass (weight) are.

Our viewpoint will be "down the middle" in that a velocity measurement, which is obtained by subjecting the flowing material to a disturbance, shall be classified under inferential; whereas the velocity measurement made directly (without an outside disturbance) shall be considered as direct.

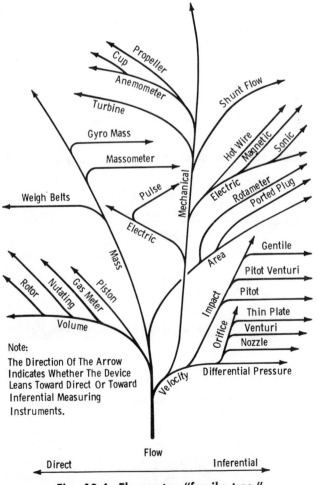

Fig. 10-4. Flowmeter "family tree."

FLOW MEASUREMENTS—INFERENTIAL TYPE

The most important inferential flow-measuring devices are those that are based on the formula:

$$\text{Flow} = cA \sqrt{2gh}$$

The rotameter and the orifice differential-pressure instruments clearly fall under the general heading of inferential. The rotameter is a variable-area device and is one of several variable-area instruments. The area meters are a branch of inferential meters. The differential-pressure instruments are a second branch. The differential-pressure branch includes measurements made with the orifice and its variations.

Velocity Inferential Instruments

The basis for this grouping is the elementary relationship that Quantity = Area × Velocity. The differential-pressure method converts the velocity of the flowing stream to a corresponding head and this head is measured; however, there is a group of instruments that measure the velocity more directly.

Velocity-Measuring Inferential Type—The Pitot tube is a device that balances the velocity head of a flowing stream with a liquid head, usually mercury or water. An open-end tube is placed in a stream, with the open end facing directly into the stream. The stream fluid pushes up into the tube. The height the fluid drives up the tube is the velocity head. The measurement of the velocity head is a differential-pressure measurement and may be made with an appropriate differential-pressure instrument. The bent tube is the Pitot.

The Pitot and associated devices are referred to as impact devices. These are primary devices in the same sense that orifices (and their variations) are primary. Both groups require a differential-pressure sensitive instrument in the total installation. Some other devices similar in operation to the Pitot are the Pitot-Venturi and the Gentile flow nozzle, shown in the family tree of Fig. 10-4. Methods of using the Pitot tube and the Pitot-Venturi are shown in Fig. 10-5.

Velocity-Measuring Inferential Type, Electrical Signal—Some interesting devices for flow measurements are the hot wire anemometer, the magnetic flowmeter, and ultrasonic devices. All these devices depend on disturbing the stream and measuring the effect of the disturbance. The hot wire anemometer is arranged to feed a known quantity of heat into the stream. The increase in temperature of the flowing stream depends on the flow rate. The increase in temperature is measured and calibrated in terms of flow. The ultrasonic instrument subjects the stream to two high-speed vibrations, which enter the stream at an angle and are reflected. The time relationship between the reflected vibration and the input vibration is a measure of velocity.

The magnetic meter disturbs the flowing stream by subjecting the stream to an alternating magnetic field. The stream cuts the lines of magnetic force composing the magnetic field. A voltage is generated that is proportional to the rate at which the lines of force are

cut. The rate (velocity) is then measured by measuring the generated voltage.

A review of the devices mentioned will show that all measure velocity by disturbing the stream, hence the reason for classifying these devices as velocity-measuring, which lean toward an inferential type.

Velocity Measurements, Propeller Type—It is possible to measure the velocity of a stream by placing a propeller in the stream. Since speed of rotation of the propeller depends on the velocity of the flowing stream, a measure of the speed of rotation is also a measure of the velocity. This measurement is accomplished by electrical and mechanical means. All these devices fall in the no-man's land between direct and inferential devices. In general, they lean toward the direct category since the stream is not disturbed by some outside impulse.

Velocity-Measuring-Direct Type, Electrical Output—An example of a device falling under the above heading is a pulse-generating turbine. The turbine rotor contains a magnet. As the rotor rotates, the magnetic field produced by the magnet "cuts" through a coil of wire. Each time it cuts the coil a pulse of current is caused to flow through the coil. These pulses are counted by electronic counters. The output of the counters can be displayed as a series of digits (num-

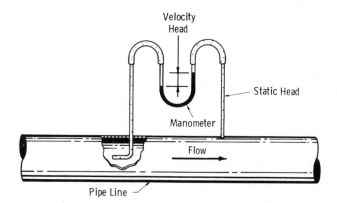

(A) Pitot tube.

(B) Pitot-venturi.

Fig. 10-5. Flow measurement with Pitot tube.

bers) or converted to a signal acceptable to conventional electronic recording instruments.

Velocity-Measuring-Direct Type, Mechanical Output— There are several propeller velocity instruments arranged so that the propeller drives a counter through a series of gears.

The shunt flowmeter is a common flowmeter and an interesting one in that it is a cross between an orifice and a propeller velocity instrument. The segmental orifice causes a fixed portion of the total stream to be directed through a shunt (bypass) around the orifice. The propeller is located in this shunt and rotates proportionally to the velocity of the shunted flow. The propeller drives a magnet through a reducing gear train. The reduction is such that the rotation of the magnet is about 1 rpm at rated flow. Attached to the shaft between the propeller and the gear train is a blade that provides damping action for the propeller. This blade and the gear train run in a fluid. Water, if the meter is used on steam service, causes a drag on the propeller.

The rotation of the magnet driven by the propeller is followed by the rotation of a second magnet that drives a counting mechanism. Between these two magnets is a diaphragm. The diaphragm forms a pressure-tight connection, eliminating packed bearing problems. (See Fig. 10-6.)

Anemometers— Anemometers generally imply a velocity measurement of a gas. These can be propellor-operated or an equivalent. The cup anemometer used to measure wind velocities is an example. The hot wire anemometer has already been discussed; however, to describe that device as an anemometer is, perhaps, confusing in that the hot wire anemometer is a totally different kind of mechanism than the more common rotary device.

DIRECT FLOW MEASUREMENT

The direct flow measuring devices measure either volume or weight (mass). Those measuring volume are described as being volumetric meters. Those measuring weight will be called mass meters.

Repeating what has been said earlier, it is difficult to clearly categorize flow instruments under the specific heading of direct or inferential. For our purposes the important consideration is to develop a scheme which makes it easier to remember what devices use what principles. We shall adopt the same viewpoint on direct flowmeters as we did on inferential, namely, some devices will be classed as direct, yet inclining toward inferential. They will be so classified because the stream in these cases is disturbed by an outside force. The effect of this disturbance is measured. The magnitude depends on the mass (weight) of the flowing material.

Volumetric Meters

The volumetric meters are designed to take specific and known values of the streams being measured. These volumes are counted. In previous work these vol-

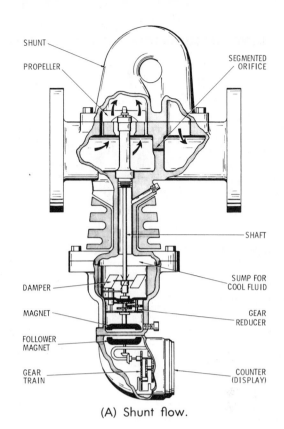

(A) Shunt flow.

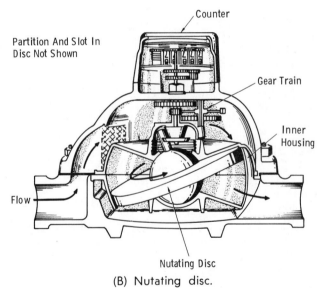

(B) Nutating disc.

Fig. 10-6. Flowmeters.

umes were described as "cup-size batches." Since the size of each of these cup-size batches is known, the number of cupfuls multiplied by the volume of each cup is a measure of the quantity of fluid passing through the meter.

Following is a list of some of the more important volumetric meter types:

Piston
Rotor
Nutating Disc
Liquid Seal Gas Meter

61

Meters of this kind are frequently described as being positive displacement meters. Of the four types mentioned, the piston and the nutating disc are perhaps the most common in the chemical plant. Each of these two will be discussed in more detail.

Nutating Disc—The nutating disc meter, Fig. 10-6, is used to measure domestic water flow. The action of this meter defies an adequate description. Paradoxically, the operation is extremely simple. Perhaps it will be sufficient to say that the moving part of the meter is a flat, thin, circular plate. Through the center of this plate, and at right angles to it, is a vertical axis projecting through the plate. The bottom of the axis rests in a socket. The upper end is unrestrained and tends to "fall over" in such a fashion that the plate forms an angle of about 15 degrees with the vertical axis of the meter housing.

The flat plate is slotted from the outside of the disc to the axis. The disc is installed in the meter housing so that a fixed vertical partition lies within the slot. The effect of this arrangement is to restrain the motion of the disc so that any diameter of disc may only "see-saw," one end of the diameter lifting while the other drops.

Inside the meter body is a section formed such that when the disc is in place two compartments are obtained. One compartment lies under the disc, the second is above the disc.

The water enters the meter body, causing the disc to nutate (wobble). With each nutation a known volume of water is passed through the meter. The free end of the axis of the nutating disc moves in a circular path as the disc nutates. The circular motion of the axis drives a gear train and counter (usually).

Piston Meter—The piston meter is a piston water pump operating in reverse. The water entering the meter enters through a valve, forcing the piston up. At the upper end of the travel a second port opens, allowing the fluid to leave the cylinder. In order to get a self-starting meter a gang of pistons is used (usually 5). These cylinders and pistons are arranged in a circle. While one piston is filling, the opposite piston is discharging. The pistons are attached by piston rods to a circular crankshaft that is a nutating circular gear. The action of the pistons causes the crankshaft to nutate. The counting mechanism is similar to that of a nutating disc meter.

Mass Meters

Conveyor Weigh Meters—The simplest mass meter consists of a conveyor section on a scale. As the material passes onto the conveyor, it is weighed by the scale, as shown in Fig. 10-7. The conveyor is driven at a known and constant speed. The length of the belt is also known. This information then is sufficient to determine the amount flowing. A meter of this type is suitable for dry materials. Such a conveyor weigh meter is one of the very few ways to measure the flow of a solid material.

Centrifugal and Gyro Mass Flowmeters—These meters are based on the law that a force is required to

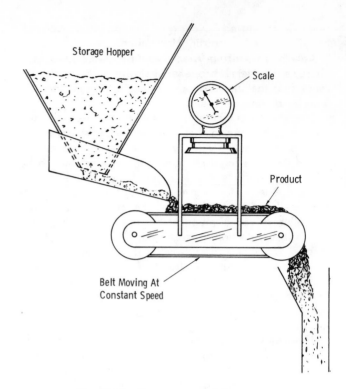

Fig. 10-7. Conveyor weigh meter.

accelerate a material. The force required to accelerate the material, or the effect of the acceleration, is measured, Since the fluid is disturbed, mass meters of the centrifugal or gyro type are classified as direct, leaning toward inferential.

SUMMARY

One aspect of the problem that has not been discussed is the "cross breed" flow-measuring device. "Cross breed" means that the flow-measuring principles of two devices are combined. For example, an area meter (not rotameter) may be used in series with a turbine meter; or, a rotameter may be used across an orifice. The shunt flowmeter already discussed is a "cross" of an orifice and a turbine meter and in certain important respects is quite similar to the orifice-rotameter cross.

Volumetric meters are different from all other types mentioned in that they are essentially batching devices. That is, the stream is cut into discrete batches, and each of these is successively counted. Such an action is an integrating action. The display of these meters is a count of the total number of batches that have passed through the meter in a specified period of time. In a very real sense these flowmeters are not so much flowmeters as they are integrators. In order to obtain a display that is other than a count, a mechanism that will react to the angular velocity of the disc, turbine, or rotor must be used. A fairly common arrangement is to attach an emf tachometer to the disc or turbine. The tachometer converts the angular velocity to a proportional voltage. This voltage is measured by a voltage-sensitive instrument that is calibrated in flow terms.

CONCLUSION

An effort has been made to classify the numerous kinds of flow devices, with the object of furnishing some kind of mental framework for organizing the flow measuring problem.

An understanding of the basic methods and mechanisms, regardless of their configuration and variations, should be of value when the student of flow measuring instruments is confronted with an unfamiliar or novel flow measuring device. He can then analyze its action, part by part.

Chapter 11

Square-Root and Integration Problems

THE SQUARE-ROOT PROBLEM

In the chapter on orifice theory, it was shown that a flow varies as the square root of the differential pressure across the orifice. This differential pressure is measured by a differential-pressure sensitive device such as the float-manometer, diaphragm, or bellows instruments just discussed. The differential-pressure device converts the signal to an equivalent display. Since the instrument senses the differential pressure, the display necessarily will also be differential pressure. Yet, if the flow is to be determined, the differential pressure should be displayed as the square root of the differential pressure. The problem of converting a differential-pressure measurement into a display of flow will be called the square-root problem. It is helpful to remember that the problem exists whenever flow through an orifice is to be displayed, and the differential-pressure sensitive instrument remains differential-pressure sensitive whether it is tied to an orifice or not. The instrument becomes part of the square-root problem only when its response is "doctored up" so that it displays the square root of the differential pressure it senses. The "doctored up" differential-pressure instrument is one solution to the square-root problem and will be studied in some detail. Also, several other methods of solving the square-root problem will be considered.

COMPENSATING FOR SQUARE ROOT

The several methods for compensating for square root are:

1. Paper and pencil.
2. Square-root charts.
3. Square-root displacers.
4. Square-root mechanisms.

Paper and Pencil Compensation

This method is very rarely used, as such, on industrial recorders or indicators. Yet, the persons who service instruments should be quite conversant with this method of compensating for square root. In principle, the square-root problem is rather simple. However, under field conditions with the various combinations of data presentation, calibrations, and special square root mechanisms, the question of what device should be doing what at a particular time can get rather involved.

Remember the basic flow equation is Flow $= cA \sqrt{2gh}$. This equation says flow varies as the square root of the differential head h.

When a differential-pressure instrument is calibrated, the pen movement (or indicator movement or output signal) is matched to the differential pressure being applied to the instrument. Since flow varies as the square root of the differential pressure, the pen does not directly indicate flow. The flow can be determined by taking the square root of the pen (or indicator or output) reading as in this example:

Say the pen reading equals 50 percent of chart. Find the flow that causes the pen to go to 50 percent of the chart. To determine the flow, find the square root of 50 percent. This equals 70.7 percent. This means that 70.7 percent of the total is flowing when the pen is on 50 percent of chart.

The above calculation can be repeated for all pen (or indicator) positions between 0 and 100 percent, thus making it possible to determine the actual flow for every pen reading. The above procedure is tedious and impractical for a continuously operating flow measurement. For calibration and servicing of an instrument, however, this paper and pencil method is most

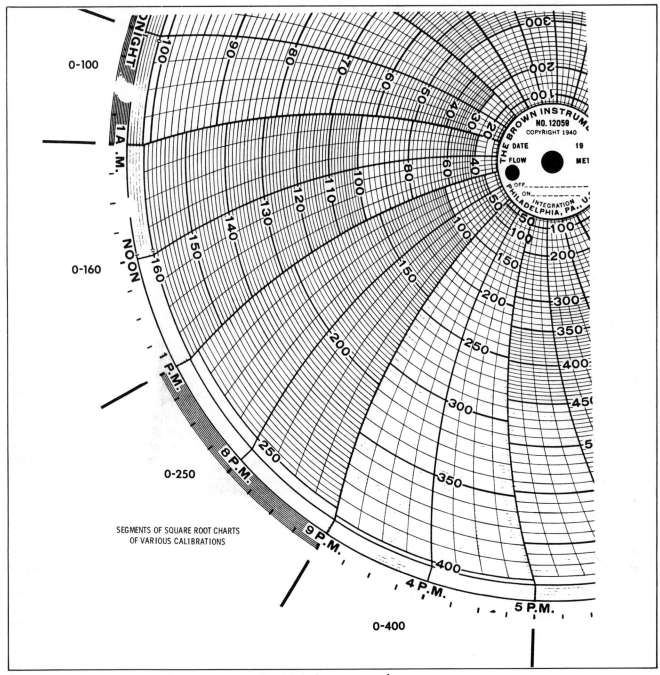

Fig. 11-1. Square-root chart.

practical and in many cases the only way. For these reasons, it is important to learn how to convert from head to flow or, alternately, from flow to head.

Square-Root Chart

Perhaps the most straightforward way to handle the square-root problem on a continuous basis is to use a square-root chart.

If the square-root chart (or scale) is used, the instrument remains a differential-pressure sensitive instrument and must be calibrated by applying the proper inches of water of differential pressure. In a way of speaking, all the chart or scale does is "fudge up" the reading. The way this is done is to so design the chart

that when 50 percent of the water range is applied to the instrument, the pen will go to 50 percent (actual) of the chart. Yet, for this 50 percent pen position, the chart will be marked 70.7 percent of flow. Or, if 81 percent of the range is applied to the meter, the pen will go to 81 percent of the chart. Yet, the chart will be marked 90 percent of flow. (The square root of 50 percent is 70.7 percent and the square root of 81 percent is 90 percent.) Such a chart is nonlinear and is similar to the charts used for measuring temperature with the vapor-tension filled system. (See Fig. 11-1.) The square-root chart appears crowded at the lower values. This is necessary since 70.7 percent of the divisions have to be put on the lower 50 percent of the chart and only 29.3 percent of the divisions go on the upper 50 percent of the chart.

An interesting problem arises when one is asked what is the head on the instrument when the pen indicates on a square-root chart (say) 70.7 percent flow? Which is another way of asking—given the flow on a square root chart, what is the corresponding head? Assume the instrument range is 100 inches of water. In this case, the flow value would be squared as follows:

$$.707^2 = 50 \text{ percent}$$

and since the range in the original problem is 100 inches of water, the corresponding inches of water is 50 percent of 100 inches, or 50 inches.

Square-Root Displacer

The square root, also called characterized, displacer was introduced in Chapter 7. It is mentioned here since the square-root displacer is a "solution" to the square-root problem. The use of this special displacer makes it possible to record, indicate, and transmit flow in units that are equal throughout the total range. The charts used on these recording instruments have equal divisions. Instruments that employ the square-root displacer or other square-root mechanisms are called "square-root compensated."

Square-Root Mechanism

The square-root mechanism will be considered to be any mechanism which relates the square root of an input signal to a linear output (equally divided). Such mechanisms are used rather frequently in flow measurement, either in the measuring section of the instrument or in the display. One display, as yet not considered, is the display of the accumulated total units that have passed through the orifice. The devices that accomplish this are integrators. Integrators, used on noncompensated instruments, require a square-root mechanism somewhere in their design. Integrators will be discussed in a following chapter.

The square root mechanism is usually a cam so designed that the radius at a particular point on the cam varies as the square root of the number of degrees to that point. For example:

When the cam is rotated to (say) 50 degrees, the radius will be $0.1 \sqrt{50}$ or approximately 0.7 inch where 0.1 is a "cam constant."

When the cam rotates 80 degrees, the radius will be $0.1 \times \sqrt{80}$ or approximately 0.9 inches. When the cam rotates to 21 degrees, the radius will equal $0.1 \times \sqrt{21} = 0.45$ inches approximately. Notice that the radius changes 0.2 inch for a 30-degree angular rotation in the region from 50 degrees to 80 degrees. But, for the same 30-degree angular rotation in the region from 20 degrees to 50 degrees, the radius changes 0.25 inch.

Fig. 11-2 shows the idea of the square-root cam as applied to a slider, with a follower being the output and the movement of the slider being the input. The

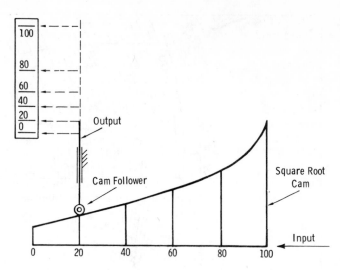

Fig. 11-2. Principle of square-root cam.

cam is similar in principle and is more practical for rotary movements. The ideas as shown in Fig. 11-2 are directly used on many integrator mechanisms. The cam is also used on integrator mechanisms.

In summary, different instruments solve the square-root problem in different ways. Usually the solution is one of the several just discussed. There are other methods that have not been discussed, that are peculiar to specific instruments; yet, if the square-root problem is well understood, it should be possible to analyze these special solutions. In general, the solutions of this chapter cover almost all the flow measurements currently being made.

THE NEED FOR INTEGRATORS

It is frequently desirable to know the total quantities used over a specified period of time. For example: The water company furnishing water to your home must know how much water you used for a period of time, usually a month. The water company is not interested in the day by day amounts, but only in total amounts. Nevertheless, in order to determine total amounts, it is necessary to know how much water is flowing at all times. If this rate of flow is multiplied by the time that such an amount were flowing, the product would be the total flow for the time period of interest.

For example:

Assume the rate of flow (g/m, cubic ft/hr, etc.) is 21 gallons/min and this rate of flow was maintained for 5 minutes. Find the total flow at the end of the 5 minutes.

Ans. $21 \times 5 = 105$ gallons

Suppose for the next five minutes the rate of flow were 23 gpm. Find the total flow at the end of 10 min.

Flow for first five minutes	= 105 gallons
Flow for second five minutes 5×23	= 115 gallons
Total flow	220 gallons

In industry there are many applications for determining total quantities at the end of specific periods of time, each day, hour, week, and month. Usually this information is used for cost control.

In addition there is need for knowing total quantities without time being specified. For example: It may be required that 365 cubic feet of a material be added to the contents of a reactor. The length of time required to add this amount is of no interest as long as it can be added within a reasonable period. In order to accomplish the operation just described, it would be possible to batch out a quantity of 365 cubic feet in a "batch" tank by a volume measurement and then add this quantity to the reactor.

A more common method in a modern industrial plant is by use of instrumentation. The instrumentation can be flowmeters of either the "inferential" or "direct" types (see Chapter 10).

If the direct types are used, the principle is analogous to the "batch" tank operation just described. The direct instruments are essentially "batch" operations in that the instrument takes a known "cup-size batch" from the supply and dumps it into the reactor through appropriate piping. The instrument counts each "cup-size batch" as it dumps it and the total passed is indicated on a counter that registers the number of cupfuls that have passed through the meter.

INTEGRATORS

The problem of determining the total flow when using an inferential instrument is somewhat more complicated in that both time and the rate of flow have to be taken into consideration. The usual solution is to measure the flow using the conventional measuring meters and add to the measuring instrument an integrator that couples the pen (or indicator) position with a time measurement. There are four things that the integrator must do:

1. Mark off units of time.
2. Know where the pen is—that is, the integrator must be arranged to sense the flow rate.
3. Multiply this rate by each unit of time.
4. Add and display each of the answers obtained in the third step.

Components

As a consequence of the preceding considerations, an integrator as used on inferential meters is composed of three parts:

1. A mechanism that couples the pen and the integrator.
2. A timing mechanism (usually a small synchronous motor of the telechron type) that performs the timing function. It may also serve to power the mechanisms that "feel" the pen position (that is, sense the flow rate).
3. The adding and counting mechanism that indicates the total flow.

Arrangements

The most general arrangement for integrators is as follows: A continuously running driver rotates at a predetermined and known speed. A "follower" engages this drive for a portion of a fixed cycle. That portion is a function of the pen position. That is, if the pen were 80 percent (say) of the chart, then the follower engages the driver for 80 percent of the fixed cycle. The follower, in turn, drives a counting mechanism that registers the turns of the follower. Since the number of turns that the follower goes through is determined by the period the follower engages the driver, and since the period and the pen position engagement are, in turn, established by the pen position, a count is registered on the counter that is a function of the flow rate. This counter displays the total units counted. These units were obtained by multiplying the flow rate by a period of time (the time of the fixed cycle).

ALIGNMENT AND ADJUSTING

Alignment and adjustment procedures necessarily involve three things that an integrator must do.

The coupling mechanism, which "feels" the pen position, must be such that it does not restrain the pen. If it were to do so, it becomes obvious that not only is the integrator in error, but also the measurement is made erroneous by the integrator action on the pen. It should be noted that an instrument must be calibrated before any adjustments are made to the integrator since the integrator reflects the pen position.

The adjustments consist of making the follower engage the driver for the proper portion of the fixed cycle. That is, for each pen position there is a specific count to be registered for a unit of time. The procedure is to disconnect the input link, thus making the pen free. Then, fixing the pen at various places over the chart, check to see that the counter is registering the proper count. If it does not register, make an adjustment to change the duration that the follower engages the driver. This will be recognized as being comparable to the zero and multiplication adjustments of a link/lever mechanism.

Since the timing mechanism is usually a gear train and a small synchronous motor, very little adjustment is required. The gears might require replacement and the motor might fail or slow down. A visual or aural inspection will usually locate faults in the gear train and motor. In some cases, it may be advisable to check the driver cam with a stop watch.

If the flow meter is not compensated for square root then it is necessary to incorporate a square-root mechanism in the integrator. This is usually accomplished in the coupling mechanism by using a square-root cam or helix. (See Fig. 11-2.)

In the case of flow transmitters it is not uncommon to arrange the integrator so that it is coupled to the flow through the transmitted signal. For example: If the transmitted signal is 3-15 psig air, the integrator will be coupled to this air pressure.

Chapter 12

Self-Balancing Instruments

SELF-BALANCING INSTRUMENTS

We will now consider a class of instruments wherein the output is directly compared to the input, and the result is the indication of the magnitude of the input. This kind of instrument has a self-balancing aspect in that it is arranged so that the output always balances the input (within the range of the detector). Such an instrument is a feedback, a self-balancing, or a null-balanced type of instrument. These terms all refer to the same basic type. In our work, we shall describe such instruments as self balancing. Later, we will break the category of self-balancing instruments into motion-balance and force-balance devices.

Components

The essential components of a self-balancing instrument are:

1. An input mechanism.
2. An error detector mechanism.
3. An output or balance mechanism.

Arrangements

These three mechanisms are arranged on a linkage or beam mechanism so that any difference between the input and output mechanisms is "felt" by the error detector. Any difference is an error. The error detector mechanism operates in such a fashion as to change the output mechanism, hence the output, so that it will balance the input.

Principle of Operation

The operation of a self-balancing instrument can be likened to an "automatic scale." (See Fig. 12-1.)

Suppose that we have an unknown quantity of weight in the left-hand tray of the scale, and we wish to determine its magnitude. We determine this by adding weights of known quantity to the right-hand tray, until the indicator is lined up with the zero mark. We then would conclude that the unknown quantity in the left-hand tray is equal to the total of the weights in the right-hand tray. To determine the unknown, we simply add up the known weights.

Notice that, after balancing, the indicator returns to the same position regardless of the magnitude of the unknown weight. The purpose of the indicator is to tell us when the output weight equals the input weight. The way we determine the magnitude of the input (unknown weight) is by balancing the input with known weights (output). This makes it possible to determine the input by an examination of the output.

So far, the scale is a conventional laboratory balance, and there is nothing automatic about it. Suppose that we arrange the scale so that when the indicator is

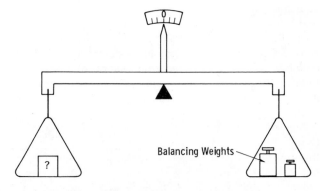

Fig. 12-1. Balancing principle shown by a weighing scale.

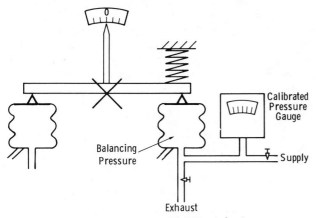

Fig. 12-2. Balancing principle in pneumatic instrument.

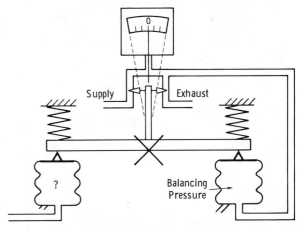

Fig. 12-3. Self-balance principle.

away from the zero mark, weights will be automatically added to the right-hand pan until the indicator is brought back to zero. We now have a self-balancing scale.

Let us apply the ideas just discussed to an instrument. Suppose that we have the same beam mechanism, but instead of the input scale pan, we install a bellows. (See Fig. 12-2.) Let's suppose the purpose of this instrument is to determine what pressure is being applied to the input bellows. We then would connect the unknown pressure to the input bellows. Let us hook up a bellows identical to the input bellows and mounted the same distance from the fulcrum point as the input bellows. Now let us connect to the output bellows an air supply and in that line provide the valves shown in Fig. 12-2. By manipulating these two valves, it will be possible to obtain all pressures between zero and supply pressure. It will be possible for us to position the valves to obtain a pressure that just balances, or is equal to, the unknown pressure. We know when the pressures are balanced by the position of the indicator. If the indicator is at the right of the zero, we must increase the balancing pressure. If it is at the left of zero, we must decrease the balancing pressure. When the indicator is at zero, the pressures are equal.

What have we accomplished so far? Not really much, because we still do not know what the pressure is in the balancing bellows. Let us then connect a pressure gauge as shown in Fig. 12-2. This pressure gauge will tell us what the balancing pressure is, and hence what the unknown pressure is if the indicator is at zero. So you see, it is possible to determine what the unknown pressure is by an examination of the magnitude of the balancing pressure. So far, our instrument is not self-balancing. It does not automatically balance itself.

Suppose we arrange the valves, which are used to change the balancing pressure, in such a fashion that the indicator directly positions the valves so that when the indicator is at right of the zero mark, the exhaust valve is closed a small amount, and the supply valve is opened a small amount. We now have an instrument that is self-balancing. (See Fig. 12-3.)

When we had the indicator drive the two valves, we introduced what we have previously called an error detector mechanism. The error detector mechanism is available in several forms, electrical as well as pneumatic. Our discussion will be limited to pneumatic mechanisms.

ERROR DETECTORS

Having explained the need for and the operation of the error detector, we will now consider it in detail. The error detector mechanism can be considered as the heart of the self-balancing instrument. It is the error detector mechanism that makes possible self-balancing (or feedback) instrumentation. An error detector mechanism will be found in every self-balancing instrument whether it is a controller, transmitter, recorder, or valve positioner. In all these applications, its function is identical. It is important that this mechanism be fully understood; it is important to recognize that the function of an error detector is the same regardless of the variations of pneumatic error detectors that will be discussed. There are two basic types of pneumatic error detector mechanisms, and there is a combination of the two.

1. The baffle/nozzle mechanism.
2. The pilot.

A combination of the two types is the most common error detector mechanism. Pilots driven by baffle/nozzles are called relays.

Components

The elements of the baffle/nozzle error-detector mechanism are:

1. The baffle.
2. The nozzle.
3. Restriction.
4. The nozzle backpressure compartment.

It is important to recognize that the nozzle backpressure compartment is an integral part of the error detector mechanism.

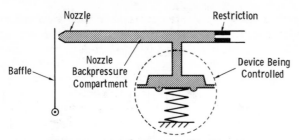

Fig. 12-4. Typical baffle/nozzle mechanism.

Arrangements

The baffle is mounted independently of the nozzle and just in front of it, in series with the nozzle and the restriction. The supply of air is connected to the mechanism ahead of the restriction. A backpressure compartment consists of that volume between the nozzle and the restriction, and includes all tubing control devices and any other volumes connected between the nozzle and the restriction. The most typical arrangement of the baffle/nozzle mechanism is shown in Fig. 12-4. However, the baffle/nozzle mechanism is used in a wide variety of forms. Regardless of the physical appearances that can be shown in mechanisms of this type, they are essentially the same and consist of the four elements previously mentioned.

The function of an error-detector mechanism is to convert a small mechanical movement to a proportional backpressure. The movement is the variation in clearance between the nozzle and the baffle. The proportional backpressure is the pressure built up in the backpressure compartment. Later in this chapter we will consider some of the properties of the baffle/nozzle error-detector mechanism.

Principle of Operation

If we position a baffle some distance from the front of the nozzle, the air flowing through the nozzle is essentially unrestricted, provided the nozzle diameter is considerably larger than the restriction diameter. In this case, the pressure in the nozzle backpressure compartment will be nearly atmospheric. On the other hand, if the baffle is brought into contact with the nozzle, the flow through the nozzle will be shut off except for the slight leakage occurring between the baffle and the nozzle. In this case, the backpressure will build up almost to the supply pressure. If the supply pressure is 20 psig, we can expect to see the nozzle backpressure approach 20 psig. If the supply pressure were 40 psig, then the nozzle backpressure would approach 40 psig. If we were to move the nozzle a very small distance away from the baffle, or if we were to move the baffle a very small distance away from the nozzle, more air would flow through the nozzle, with a resulting decrease in the nozzle backpressure. If we were to move the nozzle a small distance farther away, the backpressure would drop a proportional amount (Fig. 12-5). The baffle/nozzle is a variable restriction. Notice that the pressure between the two restrictions is the output. This is always true.

The baffle/nozzle clearance required to change the nozzle backpressure from zero to almost the supply pressure varies according to the manufacturers of such mechanisms. Typically, the clearance is two thousandths of an inch. There are numerous cases where the clearance is less, and many cases where it is greater. In our discussion, we shall use the two thousandths of an inch clearance. Bear in mind, however, that this number is indicative and that there are numerous instances when different baffle/nozzle clearances are used. If we were to plot nozzle backpressure versus clearance between the baffle and nozzle, we would find that pressure is not strictly proportional to the distance between baffle and nozzle.

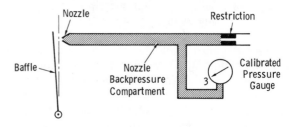

(A) Nozzle uncovered.

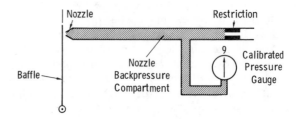

(B) Mid-position of baffle/nozzle.

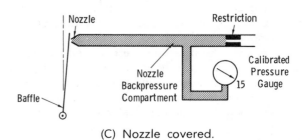

(C) Nozzle covered.

Fig. 12-5. Effect of various baffle/nozzle positions.

Examine Fig. 12-6 and notice that the portion of the curve between 3 and 15 pounds is fairly linear; that is, it is almost a straight line. It is this portion of the curve that is most widely used, and most final elements are designed to operate at signals between 3 and 15 psig. We have been describing the operation of the baffle/nozzle detector as a movement of the baffle towards the nozzle. The important consideration is not whether the baffle moves to the nozzle, but whether or not the clearance between the baffle and the nozzle changes. We will find examples where the baffle is stationary and the nozzle moves, where the nozzle is stationary and the baffle moves, or where they both move. In all cases, however, it is the clearance that is changed.

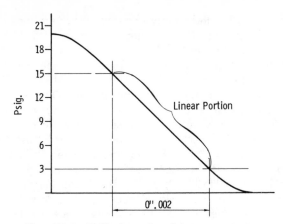

Fig. 12-6. Baffle/nozzle clearance versus nozzle backpressure.

SOME PROPERTIES OF THE BAFFLE/NOZZLE DETECTOR

The baffle/nozzle detector is a rather remarkable device. Signal level gains of 10,000 are typically obtained and much higher gains are possible. If a bellows element is used with the baffle-nozzle detector, power gains of 10,000 are typically obtained. Interestingly enough, one of the problems of the baffle/nozzle detector mechanism arises out of its high gain properties and we will find in later work that much attention is given to the problem of reducing this inherent gain of the detector.

A second limitation of the baffle-nozzle arises out of the forcing effect of the air blast on the baffle. Power, which must be furnished by the input element, is required to force the baffle towards the nozzle. Even though the required power is measured in thousandths of ounces, unless the instrument is carefully designed the baffle/nozzle can introduce an error in measurement. The method used to minimize this error is to reduce the force required to position the baffle in front of the nozzle. The force can be reduced either by reducing the size of the nozzle or by decreasing the air pressure, or both. If the air consumption of the baffle/nozzle is kept small, (and it can be kept small if the nozzle is kept small), the forcing effect is lessened. This is frequently done. However, decreasing the nozzle size can be self-defeating because, if the nozzle size is reduced, the ability of the nozzle detector to rapidly change its backpressure is reduced, hence, the time it takes to change the nozzle backpressure is increased. In many applications this longer time is excessive.

Consider further this problem of the time it takes to change the pressure. The nozzle backpressure compartment typically consists not only of the volumes within the instrument, but also the volume of the connecting tubing and of the device being operated. If that device is a control valve, a large volume is added to the baffle/nozzle system. If the distance between the instrument and the valve is large, the volume of the connecting tubing necessarily becomes large. Yet, by the nature of the baffle/nozzle mechanism, all the air that

is required to change the pressure in that large volume must pass through the restriction. If the nozzle is small, the restriction must also be small, though in all cases the nozzle is bigger than the restriction. The full supply pressure, usually about 20 psi, must be reduced to 0 psig by the two restrictions in the baffle/nozzle detector. One is the baffle/nozzle clearance, and is variable; the other is the fixed restriction. That portion of the 20 psig that is dropped across the baffle/restriction is, in fact, the output of the baffle/nozzle detector.

If it is our intention to rapidly change the valve position, we should provide a large restriction so that large amounts of air can flow into the nozzle backpressure system. On the other hand, if the restriction is large, the forcing effect on the baffle is large.

Happily enough, ways have been developed to make it possible to have both a small nozzle, hence a small forcing effect, and the ability to rapidly change the pressure in the closed system. These contradictory objectives are solved by the introduction of a relay to be used in conjunction with the baffle/nozzle detector.

The forcing effect on the baffle is not necessarily a liability. In fact, there are instances where this forcing effect is used to good advantage. For example, in the electric-to-air transducers manufactured by the Taylor Company, it is the force on the baffle arising from the nozzle blast that is used to balance the electrical signal. As a second example, the Foxboro 41A Controller uses the blast effect of a nozzle to balance the input.

ALTERNATE ARRANGEMENTS

There are a variety of baffle/nozzle configurations, some of which are shown in Fig. 12-7. Also of interest

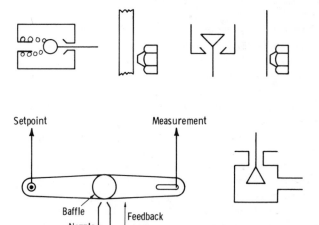

Fig. 12-7. Various baffle/nozzle configurations.

are some variations in the baffle-nozzle detector mechanism such that, unless one is quite careful, the physical appearances of the elements will be confusing in developing an understanding of the mechanism.

Examine Fig. 12-8. This mechanism is the baffle/nozzle detector mechanism for use with the 200T differential pressure transmitter. It is labeled with the standard baffle/nozzle detector elements. Notice that there is a restriction, a nozzle, a baffle, and a nozzle backpressure compartment. Note, however, that the air flow through the nozzle appears to be backwards. Let us scrutinize this by asking the same questions about this mechanism, as we asked about the mechanism shown in Fig. 12-4.

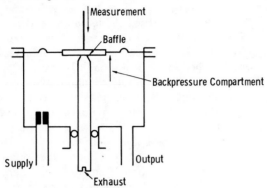

Fig. 12-8. Baffle/nozzle used in Taylor 200T differential-pressure transmitter.

In Fig. 12-4, the supply of air is connected ahead of the restriction and flows through the restriction first. This is also true in the Taylor mechanism. Notice that the flow of air out of the pressure compartment is through the nozzle and out to the atmosphere. This is also the case in the Taylor mechanism. Observe that the backpressure compartment in the illustration is made up of the volumes between the restriction and the nozzle. The backpressure compartment of the Taylor mechanism is also that volume between the nozzle and the restriction. Consider the baffle in Fig. 12-4. The baffle in Fig. 12-4, and in the Taylor mechanism, moves as the input signal causes it to move. As it moves, it varies the baffle-to-nozzle clearance, hence, the nozzle backpressure changes. This is also the case in the Taylor device. Also notice again that the output is that pressure between the two restrictions. So it can be seen that an examination of each element, in these two dissimilar-looking mechanisms, will show that in fact they are functionally identical.

Chapter 13

Pilots and Relays

THE PILOT VALVE

In the previous chapter, we discussed the nozzle/baffle detector and found that its function was to convert a small displacement to a proportional backpressure. You will recall that essentially the detector consisted of a fixed restriction, a variable restriction (a nozzle/baffle) and a backpressure compartment. The pilot valve, which is the subject of this chapter, is somewhat different in that it consists essentially of two variable restrictions. Functionally, however, the two devices are identical.

The terms pilot, pilot valve, relay, and relay valve are used by various people to mean the same or different things. We shall use the word pilot meaning those devices which convert a small mechanical displacement to a proportional backpressure by simultaneously varying two restrictions.

Components

The elements of a pilot are:

1. Two variable restrictions.
2. A mechanism for simultaneously varying these restrictions.
3. A backpressure compartment.

Arrangements

The pilot valve can be likened to a three-way valve. (See Fig. 13-1.) Notice a supply connection, an output connection, and an exhaust port. Mounted between these ports is a two-seated valve plug. Positioning the valve plug is a valve stem. The output is taken off between the supply and the exhaust port. This is a common arrangement. However, as it was in the case of the nozzle/baffle, it is important that one not become

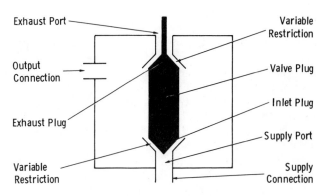

Fig. 13-1. Pilot valve construction, diamond-shaped plug.

confused by the physical appearance, since pilot valves can be found in a wide variety of forms. In all cases, however, the function is identical; and, in all cases, the pilot valve is characterized by the fact that two restrictions are being varied simultaneously by an input displacement.

Principle of Operation

Assume that the valve plug is in its uppermost position. (See Fig. 13-1.) The exhaust is closed and the supply is fully open. For this valve plug position, the output pressure equals the supply pressure. Let us move the valve plug against the supply port. In this position, the exhaust port is fully open and the supply port fully closed. As a consequence, all of the backpressure is exhausted to atmosphere; hence, the backpressure is zero. As we lift the plug away from the supply port, we permit the backpressure or output pressure to increase. If we continue to lift it further, the output pressure increases further. We find that the backpressure is proportional to the valve plug position.

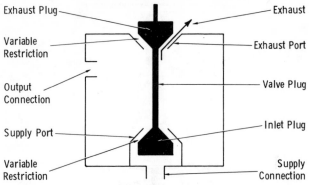

Fig. 13-2. Pilot valve construction, dumbbell-shaped plug.

Hence, the backpressure is proportional to the displacement of the valve stem. It is in this way that a small displacement is converted to a proportional pressure. In other words, as the valve plug moves up, the backpressure increases.

Suppose that we have a pilot arranged as shown in Fig. 13-2. As before, raise the plug to its extreme position. If we do that, the supply will be closed. The exhaust will be fully opened; hence, the backpressure will drop to zero. On the other hand, if we move it to its lowermost position, the exhaust will be closed. The supply will be open, and the backpressure will equal the supply pressure. For an intermediate position, we will get a pressure that is proportional to the valve stem displacement.

Notice that in the case of Fig. 13-2, the plug is shaped like a dumbbell. In the case of Fig. 13-1, the plug is diamond-shaped or, putting it another way, in the case of Fig. 13-2, the seating surfaces on the valve plug "look" at each other, whereas in Fig. 13-1, the seating surfaces on the plug look away from each other. These two plug forms are characteristic pilot-valve forms. In our discussions of relays, we shall encounter a third form wherein these seating surfaces look in the same direction.

Alternate Arrangements

Fig. 13-3 is a diagram of the detector mechanism used in Foxboro's Model 59 controller. If a superficial examination is made of the detector mechanism, it would be difficult to classify this detector as being either a baffle/nozzle detector or a pilot-valve detector. One might be tempted to conclude that this detector is neither, but is special because it appears to have two nozzles and one baffle.

Let us study the mechanism further and see what kind of a detector is used. Examination of the diagram shows, first of all, that there is no fixed restriction. Yet, we concluded in our work on baffle/nozzle detectors that a fixed restriction is an essential element of the baffle/nozzle detector. Therefore, the Foxboro mechanism cannot be classified as a baffle/nozzle detector.

As you know, then, if it isn't a baffle/nozzle detector, it must be a pilot detector. Recall that a pilot detector is characterized by two variable restrictions. Superficially, the Foxboro mechanism consists of two nozzles with a baffle between them. Let us examine this further.

Move the baffle to the right. In that position, the supply nozzle is closed and the exhaust nozzle is fully open. Therefore, the backpressure is atmospheric. Move the baffle to the left against the exhaust nozzle; the inlet nozzle is fully open for this baffle position. The backpressure will equal the supply pressure. Notice further that the backpressure is taken off between the supply and exhaust nozzles. Therefore, we must conclude that, as the so-called baffle is moved, we simultaneously vary two restrictions. This is the essential characteristic of a pilot. Therefore, we must conclude that the detector mechanism shown is a pilot, and that which appears to be a baffle is in fact a very flat valve plug. The so-called nozzles are, in fact, simply supply and exhaust ports, and not nozzles at all.

Let us consider this as a second example of how appearances can be confusing. The functional definition of an element is the key to the analyzing and classifying of elements and mechanisms.

It is not uncommon to find compound pilots; that is, pilot valves with two sets of seating surfaces. Pilots of this kind are frequently found on double acting piston operators. We mention pilots of this kind at this time so that the presence of more than two seating surfaces won't confuse you when you attempt to classify detector mechanisms.

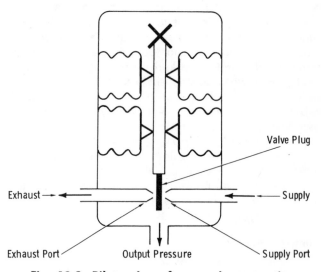

Fig. 13-3. Pilot valve of unusual construction.

RELAYS

By far the most widely used detector consists of a baffle/nozzle detector mechanism combined with a pilot. A pilot so arranged is called a relay. You will recall that the baffle/nozzle mechanism had some serious limitations. First was the fact that if the restrictions were made large enough to make it possible to rapidly change backpressure, excessive amounts of air would be required. If, on the other hand, the restrictions were kept small to reduce the air consumption, the time it would take to change the backpressure would become excessively long. The second limitation with the baffle/nozzle is its blast effect. That is, the air blast from the nozzle forces the baffle, making it necessary for the input mechanism to drive against this blast force. If the restriction is large, the forcing effect is large. If the restriction can be made small, the forcing effect will remain small. If we can lower the supply pressure to the baffle/nozzle mechanism, we lower the blast effect for a given restriction. The relay makes it possible to do these things.

A word of caution: What we shall call a relay is also called a pilot valve, relay pilot, and relay valve by some people.

Components

The essential components of the relay are:

1. A pilot.
2. A pressure-to-displacement converter (bellows, diaphragm, etc.).
3. A nozzle backpressure compartment.

Arrangements

The pressure-to-displacement converter is arranged to drive the pilot stem. The nozzle backpressure is connected to the pressure-to-dlisplacement converter. The pressure-to-displacement converter appears in various forms; it may be a bellows, a diaphragm capsule, or a relay diaphragm. The relay valve plug may be one of three types. The seats on the plug either "look" at each other as in Fig. 13-4, away from each other as in Fig. 13-5, or in the same direction as in Fig. 13-6. Also, relays are said to be bleed type or non-bleed type. The non-bleed relay will be discussed in detail later. The baffle/nozzle back pressure is connected to the nozzle backpressure compartment of the relay valve. (See Fig. 13-4.)

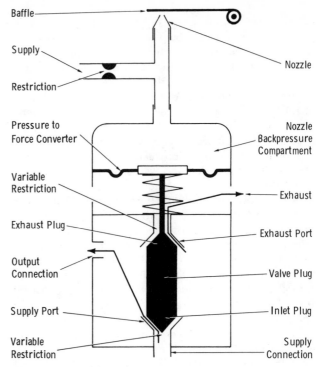

Fig. 13-5. Reverse-acting relay.

Principle of Operation

If the baffle covers the nozzle, the nozzle backpressure will build up almost to the supply pressure. This backpressure applied to the pressure-to-displacement converter results in a displacement proportional to the backpressure. This displacement, acting through the stem of the relay, positions the valve plug so that the exhaust port is closed and the supply port is fully opened. Consequently, the relay backpressure will be

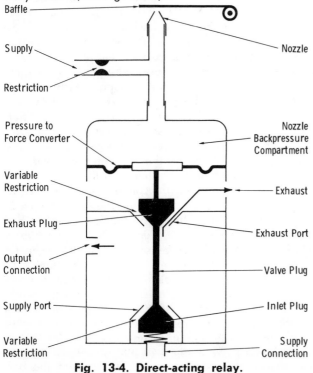

Fig. 13-4. Direct-acting relay.

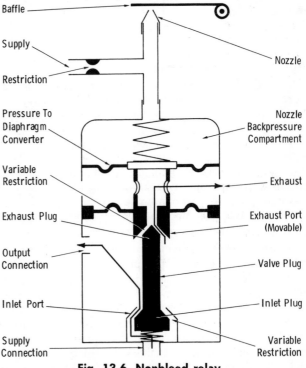

Fig. 13-6. Nonbleed relay.

equal to the supply pressure. You will recall that the pilot backpressure is proportional to the stem displacement. Since the stem displacement is proportional to the nozzle backpressure, the relay backpressure is proportional to the baffle/nozzle displacement.

Does this then meet our definition of an error detector? In other words, does this mechanism convert a small baffle/nozzle displacement to a proportional pressure? The answer is clearly yes. But notice in this mechanism the conversion takes place in two stages. The baffle/nozzle clearance is converted to a proportional pressure. This proportional pressure is converted to a displacement, and this proportional displacement is reconverted back to a proportional pressure. We have two stages of amplification. Notice, too, that the output of each stage is that pressure between the two restrictions. The output of the baffle/nozzle detector is the pressure between the baffle/nozzle and the fixed restriction. It is the input to the relay. The output of the relay is the pressure between the two restrictions again.

This arrangement makes it possible to use a baffle/nozzle with small restrictions. Further, it makes it possible to reduce the blast effect by reducing the nozzle backpressure. Typically, the nozzle backpressure will vary from 2 to 3 psig, which will cause a full stroking of the relay valve plug. This is made possible by making the range of the pressure-to-displacement converter 2 to 3 psig rather than 3 to 15 psig. It is in this way that the relay makes it possible to obtain fast response using a small restriction.

The device just described is direct acting in that as the nozzle backpressure increases, the output air pressure increases. If we use a diamond-shaped valve plug (one with the valve plug faces looking away from each other) rather than a dumbbell-shaped plug, the output pressure will decrease as the nozzle backpressure increases, giving us a reverse acting detector. (See Fig. 13-5.)

Alternate Arrangements

Although the relay valve makes it possible to reduce the size of the restriction, thereby reducing the blast effect, it does not, in the example just cited, reduce air consumption inasmuch as the supply port of the pilot needs to be large if the relay backpressure is to be changed rapidly. Notice, that when the nozzle backpressure is in its midposition, the valve plug is positioned so that the exhaust port and the supply port are half open. This, of course, results in large amounts of air bleeding through the valve, even though the relay backpressure is held constant.

There is a valve arrangement that makes it possible to maintain a fixed relay backpressure without simultaneously exhausting large amounts of air to atmosphere. Examine Fig. 13-6. Notice that the exhaust port is mounted so that it can move as the nozzle backpressure changes. As the nozzle backpressure increases, the exhaust port moves down. If it continues to move down, it will seat against the valve plug, closing off the exhaust port. Notice that at the point where the

exhaust port is just closed off, the supply port is also closed. If both of the ports are closed, the relay backpressure will stay constant. Hence, for a balanced condition, there is no air consumption. Let the nozzle backpressure continue to increase, then the exhaust port will continue to move downward, but now it also moves the valve plug downward, opening the supply port. The exhaust port is still closed, but the supply port is opened. Consequently, the relay backpressure will increase. If the nozzle backpressure continues to build up, the supply port will fully open, and the relay backpressure will equal the supply pressure.

Let us follow the operation of this relay as the nozzle backpressure decreases. As it decreases, the diaphragm will move upward, permitting the exhaust port to move upward, which in turn lets the valve plug move upward, starting to close the supply port. As the nozzle backpressure continues to decrease, the valve plug continues to rise until it closes the supply port. If the nozzle backpressure drops off further, the exhaust port will start to open because the valve plug, seated against the inlet, cannot rise any further. The opened exhaust port will permit the relay backpressure to reduce to atmospheric pressure.

To summarize, notice that the only time the relay uses air is when the supply port is open. The only time the supply port is open is when the exhaust port is closed; hence, no air exhausts from the relay when it is balanced. When the relay is balanced, the nozzle backpressure and the relay backpressure are constant.

A relay so constructed is called non-bleed. The key idea in the non-bleed relay is the movable exhaust seat. In a valve plug wherein the two seating surfaces "look" in the same direction the movable exhaust seat makes it necessary to use two pressure-to-force converters. One of these converts the nozzle backpressure to a proportional force. The second has a double function: to convert the relay backpressure to a proportional force, and to seal the exhaust port in a way that makes it possible for the exhaust seat to move.

Notice that these two pressure-to-force converters are arranged so that the forces oppose each other. If these two forces are equal, the exhaust seat takes a fixed position. If, on the other hand, there is a difference in force, the exhaust seat will move up or down, depending on which force is greater. If the upper diaphragm has six times the area of the lower, the upper, for a given pressure change, will cause a downward force six times as great as the upward force of the lower diaphragm for the same pressure change. In other words, a 6-psi change on the lower would balance a 1-psi change on the upper. A 1-psi change in nozzle backpressure has caused a 6-psi change in relay output. So it can be seen that changing the ratio of the areas makes it possible for a small nozzle backpressure to require a much larger relay backpressure. It is in this way that it is possible to operate with a reduced nozzle backpressure and still obtain a standard 3 to 15 psig output air pressure. The mechanism just described is our first example of a force balance mechanism.

RELAY VARIATIONS

There are several common relay variations as far as appearances are concerned, but functionally they are identical. The variations in appearance are due to the fact that there is a variety of pressure-to-force converter elements. In Fig. 13-4, the pressure-to-force elements are diaphragms. You will recall that in addition to diaphragms, there are several other pressure-to-force elements, including:

1. The diaphragm.
2. The bellows.
3. The "O" ring piston.

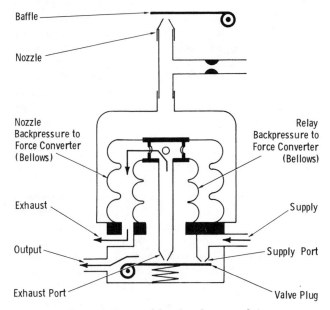

Fig. 13-7. Nonbleed relay used in Air-O-Line controllers.

The diaphragm can be found in two forms: flat and rolling. The trade term for the rolling diaphragm is bellophragm. The bellows can be a stacked capsule, a single capsule, or one with corrugated convolutions. There are several manufacturers who use different combinations of pressure-to-force converters. For example, consider the relay shown in Fig. 13-7. This is a nonbleed relay used by Minneapolis-Honeywell in their Air-O-Line series controllers. Notice that they use two bellows elements instead of two diaphragm elements as shown on Fig. 13-4. The inner bellows permits the exhaust port to move. The outer bellows converts the nozzle backpressure to force. The relay backpressure, acting on the inner bellows, creates a force that is balanced by the nozzle backpressure acting on the outer bellows. Functionally, the two bellows in Fig. 13-7 are equivalent to the two diaphragms in Fig. 13-6.

Fig. 13-8 shows a detector mechanism used by Fisher Governor. Notice in this relay a flat diaphragm and "O" ring and piston converters are used. The diaphragm forms the nozzle backpressure compartment and converts the nozzle backpressure to force. The "O" ring and piston form the relay backpressure-to-

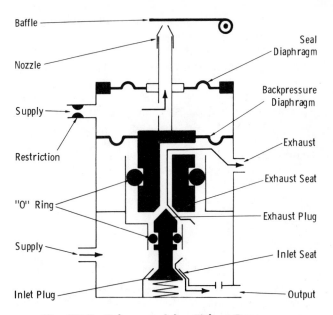

Fig. 13-8 . Relay used by Fisher Governor.

force converter. These two forces balance each other. Fig. 13-9 is a diagram of a Foxboro relay.

Fig. 13-10 is a diagram of the detector mechanism used by the Taylor Instrument Company in their 210 series transmitter. In this detector, a rolling diaphragm and bellows are used. A rolling diaphragm converts the nozzle backpressure to a proportional force. The bellows converts the relay backpressure to a proportional force. These two forces balance each other. Notice, that in the three devices just discussed, the relay backpressure-to-force converter is smaller in diameter than the nozzle backpressure-to-force converter. Therefore, we can conclude that the ratio of the nozzle backpressure to the relay backpressure is not one-to-one. Further, the nozzle backpressure is less than the relay backpressure when the relay is balanced. We will find that in all cases the nozzle backpressure times the area

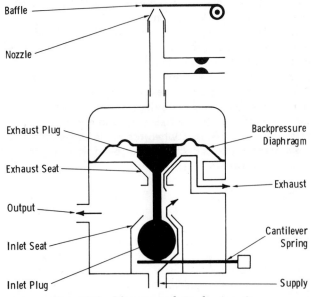

Fig. 13-9. Diagram of Foxboro relay.

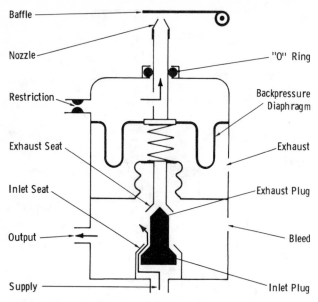

Baffle

Nozzle

Restriction

Exhaust Seat

Inlet Seat

Output

Supply

"O" Ring

Backpressure Diaphragm

Exhaust

Exhaust Plug

Bleed

Inlet Plug

Fig. 13-10. Relay used by Taylor Instrument Co.

of the pressure-to-force converter equals the relay backpressure times the area of the relay backpressure-to-force converter. Therefore, we can conclude that the output relay backpressure is always greater than the nozzle backpressure. It is in this way that we get an amplification of pressure level.

SUMMARY

A pilot and a baffle/nozzle mechanism combined form a relay-type detector. To combine these two mechanisms, a pressure-to-force converter is used to drive the pilot. This combination mechanism is a relay. A relay, in addition to the direct and reverse acting forms, can be a bleed or a non-bleed type. The relay is, in fact, a pilot wherein the pilot valve plug is operated by a baffle/nozzle backpressure. This necessitates the introduction of a pressure-to-force converter. This pressure-to-force converter can be a diaphragm, bellows, capsule, bellophragm, or any of the other pressure-to-force converters available. Frequently, the relay is found in the so-called non-bleed form. The essential difference between the non-bleed and the bleed relay is that the non-bleed uses air only when it is in an unbalanced condition, whereas a bleed type uses air during the balanced condition. The non-bleed is our first example of a force balance mechanism in that the relay comes to balance when the force due to the nozzle backpressure is balanced by the force due to the relay backpressure.

These two forces, which act against each other and must be equal during balance, are directly proportional to the pressures that create them. The ratio of these two pressures is governed by the ratio of the effective area of the feedback diaphragm (output pressure-to-force-converter) to the effective area of the input diaphragm (nozzle backpressure-to-force converter). Typically, this ratio is 4 to 1.

The non-bleed relay has the advantage of being economical in air consumption and the disadvantage of having a flat spot in its operation. See Fig. 13-11, which shows nozzle backpressure versus relay backpressure. As the nozzle backpressure increases, the relay backpressure increases proportionally, except at the point where the exhaust port and the inlet port are closed. At that point, there is a flat spot where the nozzle backpressure increases. Though slight, this flat spot can be objectionable on certain control applications. To eliminate this flat spot, many non-bleed relays have a slight air bleed from the relay backpressure compartment. In other words, we have a "bleeding" non-bleed valve. The presence of this bleed eliminates the flat spot by making it necessary that the supply port be opened slightly to furnish this bleed without the relay backpressure falling off.

The non-bleed valve can be identified by the fact that the exhaust seat moves. This requires pressure-to-force elements. It is frequently possible by an examination of the outside of the relay to see two diaphragms, thus identifying non-bleed relays without disassembling them. In any case, examination of the valve plug will show that, in the case of non-bleed valves, the two seating surfaces "look" in the same direction.

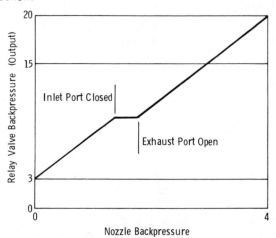

Inlet Port Closed

Exhaust Port Open

Relay Valve Backpressure (Output)

Nozzle Backpressure

Fig. 13-11. Nozzle backpressure versus relay backpressure.

Chapter 14

Moment-Balance Transmitters

THE MOMENT-BALANCE PRINCIPLE

We have indicated that the heart of the self-balancing instrument is the detector mechanism. In previous chapters, we have discussed in some detail the variety of detector mechanisms available. We will now show how these mechanisms are used in a variety of instruments. The instruments we shall choose will be force-balance types, as differentiated from motion-balance types which will be discussed later.

Unfortunately, the term force balance refers to two distinct mechanism types. The mechanisms commonly described as force balance are more accurately termed moment balance. An example of a "true" force-balance mechanism is the non-bleed relay we have discussed. We shall, in our work, consider a limited number of true force-balance mechanisms. Among these mechanisms are the Taylor 200T differential pressure transmitter and the valve positioners of Taylor and Moore.

Components

The essential components of a moment-balance instrument are:

1. An input element to convert a process variable to force.
2. A balancing element to convert an air pressure to force.
3. A beam mechanism on which the two forces are set.
4. A detector mechanism to detect an unbalance and cause a change in balancing force.

Arrangements

The input element in Fig. 14-1 is arranged so that it applies a force to the left-hand side of the beam.

The beam is pivoted in the middle, and on the right-hand side of the beam is the balancing component. The balancing component is a pressure-to-force converter and, therefore, can be a bellows, a diaphragm, a bellophragm or any other pressure-to-force converter. We have shown a bellows. Mounted on the beam is the baffle, which moves as the beam moves. The nozzle remains fixed. The nozzle backpressure is connected to the balancing bellows. In the diagram, we have shown a simple baffle/nozzle detector mechanism. The detector mechanism could be, and in some instruments is, a pilot valve. In most instruments, the detector mechanism is the baffle/nozzle relay detector.

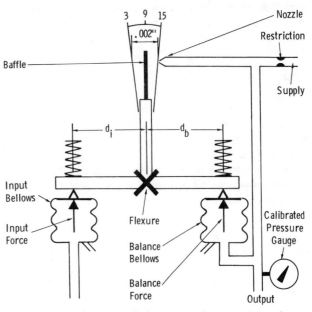

Fig. 14-1. Moment-balance mechanism, equal lever lengths.

Principle of Operation

You will recall that the purpose of the detector is to convert a small displacement to a proportional pressure. Suppose that the input signal is a pressure, and let us suppose that it is equal to zero. When it is equal to zero, the left end of the beam moves down. In this position, the baffle is away from the nozzle; hence, the nozzle backpressure is zero. Therefore, the output pressure is zero.

Suppose that the input pressure now increases to 5 psi. When it does, the baffle moves toward the nozzle. As the nozzle becomes covered, the backpressure builds up; hence, the pressure in the balancing bellows builds up. The increasing pressure in the balancing bellows causes an increased force on the right end of the beam. This balancing force tends to move the baffle away from the nozzle. The baffle will be positioned with respect to the nozzle, so that the resulting backpressure, acting on the balancing bellows, results in a force equal to the input force. In this way, the output pressure is determined by, and is proportional to, the input pressure.

In our example, we have shown that the input force will be applied at a distance from the fulcrum equal to the distance at which the balancing force is applied. If the bellows are of the same diameter, the output pressure will "almost" equal the input pressure. If we have a way of knowing what the output pressure is, we can determine the input pressure. Suppose, on the output, we install a calibrated pressure-to-quantity converter; in other words, a calibrated recorder or pressure gauge. Then, upon examination of the recorder, indicator, or any other display, we are able to determine the input pressure.

Fig. 14-2 consists of the same components as Fig. 14-1, except that the balancing bellows is twice the distance from the fulcrum as the input bellows. The operation of this mechanism is identical with the op-

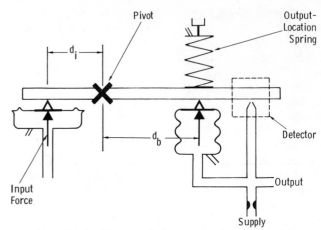

Fig. 14-3. Moment-balance mechanism, with output-location spring.

eration of the mechanism in Fig. 14-1, except that now the output pressure is proportional, not equal, to the input pressure. In fact, the output pressure is equal, "almost," to ½ the input pressure. Why is this so?

The reason is that the mechanism is not balancing forces only, but rather force times distance. In other words, the input force times the input distance (d_i) equals the output pressure times the balancing distance (d_b). Since the balancing distance is twice the input distance, the balance pressure (output pressure) need only be half as great as the input pressure.

It is customary to refer to a force times a distance as a moment. Therefore, we can say that the output moment equals the input moment. It is for this reason that we describe mechanisms wherein the forces are acting on levers as moment-balance mechanisms.

The mechanism just described is a pressure transmitter using the moment-balance principle. Again, be warned that most people will describe this mechanism as being force balance. In our discussions, the moment-balance mechanism is one branch of force-balance mechanisms.

In our example, we have said that the bellows are of equal sizes. Almost never is this the case. The important point at this time is that it is possible to balance a mechanism having different input and output pressures by changing the lengths of levers and/or by changing the bellows areas. In later work, we will discuss in some detail the variations of moment-balance mechanisms.

This mechanism in Fig. 14-3 differs on two counts when compared to Figs. 14-1 and 14-2. (Notice a beam mechanism, a pivot, an input element, a balancing element, an opposing spring, and a detector mechanism.) The first difference is that the detector is located on an extension of the beam rather than fastened to the center of the beam as was the case in our previous examples. Recognize that it is not important where the detector mechanism is located as long as it senses the beam movement. The second and more important difference in this mechanism is the spring opposing the balancing bellows. Let's see what the opposing spring does.

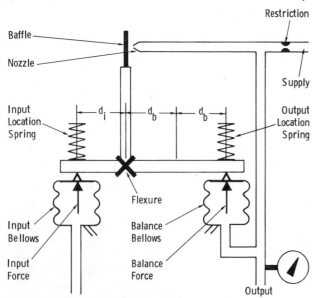

Fig. 14-2. Moment-balance mechanism, unequal lever lengths.

Assume the input signal is 0 psi. Yet, recognize that when we have zero input signal, we want a 3-psig output signal. The spring makes it possible to obtain a 3-psig output signal while there is a zero input signal.

Here is how it works. Assume the output pressure is 0 psig. Hence, the balancing force is 0 pounds. If the spring is compressed by turning the screw in, a force will be applied to the beam, causing it to rotate toward the nozzle. The backpressure will level out at that pressure which results in a balance force equal to the spring force. By adjusting the spring compression, we can preload the balancing bellows so that a 3-psig output is obtained. Notice that the input pressure signal is zero, yet we have a 3-psig output signal.

It is, of course, possible to get a variety of different outputs for zero input pressure. We have used 3 psig since that is a standard output signal level.

Alternate Arrangements

Fig. 14-4 shows a moment-balance mechanism wherein the input and balancing elements are on the right-hand side of the flexure. The operation of this mechanism is identical with the mechanism of Fig. 14-3, and the same relationships hold. The only difference is that the input element is above the beam. The input and balancing elements are found as many times on the same side of the beam as on the opposite sides of the beam.

Fig. 14-5 diagrams a moment-balance mechanism which functionally is identical to Fig. 14-4, except that in Fig. 14-5, a second beam, which we shall call a range beam, has been introduced. The reason for introducing a range beam is to make it possible to make large changes in the ratio of output pressure (hence balancing force) to the input force. The introduction of the range beam results in what we shall call a lever-type gain mechanism. We shall discuss gain mechanisms in greater detail in a later chapter.

Notice in Fig. 14-5 that we show a spring opposing the input element. The purpose of the spring is to

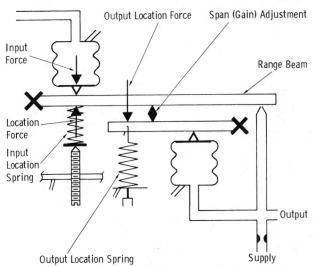

Fig. 14-5. Moment-balance mechanism with double beam.

make it possible to obtain a 3-psig output (zero output) for an input that is not zero. In other words, there are instances when we want a 3-psig output which conforms to a zero percent pen or indicator reading for an input other than zero. For example, we may want a 3-psig output when there is an input, say, of 20 inches of water.

MOMENT-BALANCE DIFFERENTIAL PRESSURE TRANSMITTER

We have discussed the moment-balance principle and have said that this principle was widely used in measuring instruments. Usually, these measuring instruments are transmitters. That is, they sense a variable and convert it to a proportional pressure. By examining the magnitude of the output it is possible to determine the magnitude of the sensed variable.

In the following paragraphs we will discuss differential pressure transmitters that use the moment-balance principle.

Components

The components of a differential pressure transmitter are:

1. A differential pressure-to-force converter (input component).
2. A beam mechanism.
3. Balancing elements.
4. A detector mechanism.

Arrangements

Fig. 14-6 shows a Taylor differential pressure transmitter in an elementary form. Nevertheless, it contains all the essential components and elements. The fundamental diagram of the moment-balance mechanism was shown and discussed earlier in this chapter. This is a moment-balance mechanism.

Observe an input element that converts differential pressure to a force that is applied to a force beam. Ar-

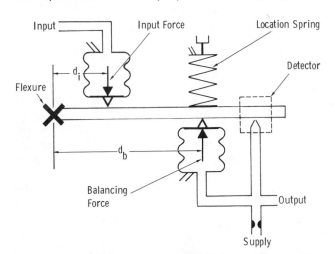

Fig. 14-4. Moment-balance with input and output on opposite sides of beam.

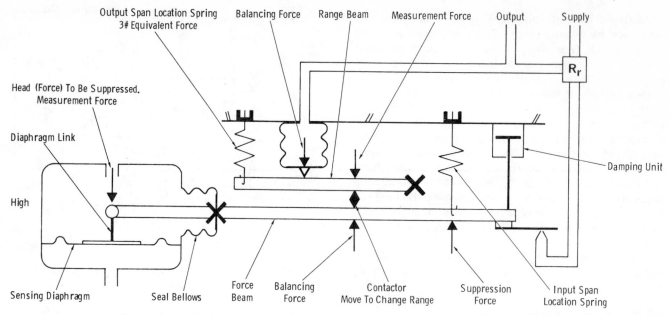

Fig. 14-6. Elementary diagram of Taylor differential pressure transmitter.

ranged immediately above the force beam is a second beam, called a range beam. Acting against the range beam is a balancing bellows that converts the output air pressure to a force that is applied to the range beam. The force applied to the range beam acting through the beam contactor is applied to the force beam. The balancing force opposes the input force.

The input component consists of a low-pressure compartment, a high-pressure compartment, and a diaphragm element. The two pressures, acting on the diaphragm, are converted to proportional forces acting against each other. The difference between the two forces is applied to the left end of the force beam. Because both compartments are under pressure, the beam moment must be taken out through a seal bellows. The instrument shown has the usual output span-location spring and input span-location spring. In ad-

dition, there is a damping unit designed to damp out the vibration of the beam. Mounted on the beam is a baffle/nozzle mechanism. A relay is also used.

Let us compare the diagram in Fig. 14-6 with a more detailed diagram. (See Fig. 14-8.) Examination of these two diagrams will show that element for element and component for component, there is no difference. Fig. 14-8 is a schematic including details not available in Fig. 14-6. Study these two diagrams. Notice that Fig. 14-8 leaves out considerable detail when compared to the actual instrument. Fig. 14-7 diagrams the differential pressure mechanism for use on liquid level. Notice the reversal of the housing.

Principle of Operation

Start at the input in Fig. 14-8. Let us assume that the high-pressure signal increases, while the low-pressure

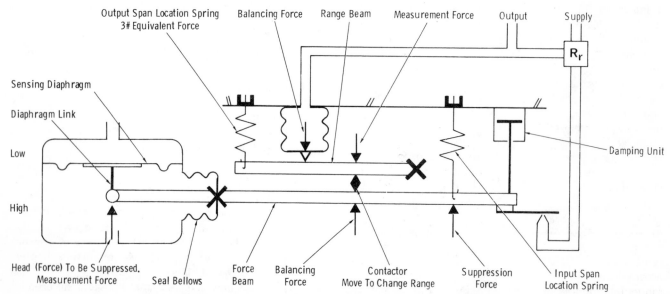

Fig. 14-7. Same as Fig. 14-6, but with pressure housing reversed.

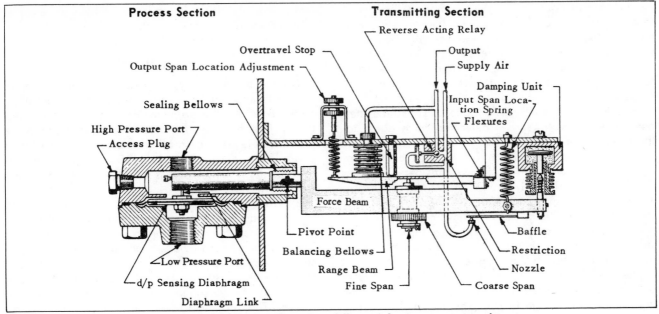

Fig. 14-8. Schematic of Taylor differential pressure transmitter.

signal remains constant. If the high-pressure signal increases, the beam will rotate about the fulcrum point, lifting the baffle away from the nozzle. The nozzle backpressure will drop off. Since the relay is reverse acting, the relay output pressure will increase. Hence, the balancing pressure will increase. The increased balancing pressure results in an increase in balancing force which, acting on the range beam and through the beam contactor, tends to move the beam; hence, the baffle is moved towards the nozzle. The instrument will be brought to balance at that point where the balancing moment, acting through the beam system, just balances the increase in input moment.

Alternate Arrangements

Let us consider a second example of a differential pressure transmitter. Fig. 14-9 is an elementary diagram of a Foxboro 13A differential pressure transmitter. It is shown in the position in which it is generally mounted; that is, with the force beam vertical. Notice that the diagram of Foxboro's 13A instrument is essentially the same as the fundamental diagram. There is an input component, force beam, a baffle/nozzle relay detector mechanism responding to the force beam movement, and a range beam. Acting against the range beam is a balancing bellows. However, there is one essential difference between the Foxboro and the fundamental diagram: the range beam is not fixed at either end. In the Foxboro instrument, both ends of the range beam are free to move. The range beam rotates about a fulcrum point that is mounted on the instrument chassis. This fulcrum can be moved to change the span of the instrument. This method of changing span differs from the method shown on the fundamental diagram in which the span changing was accomplished by moving the contactor between the range beam and the force beam, thereby changing the ratio of range beam and force beam lengths.

Notice that one end of the range beam is driven by a link attached to the force beam. The other end of the range beam is driven by the balancing force. Other than this difference in the beam system, the Foxboro and Taylor instruments are equivalent.

Principle of Operation

Let us assume that there is an increase in high-pressure signal. This will result in the upper end of

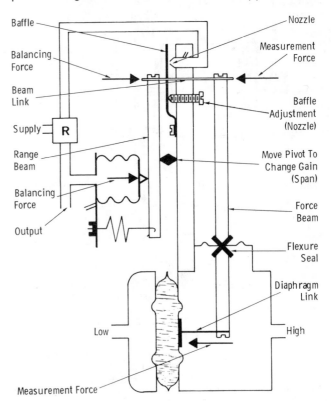

Fig. 14-9. Elementary diagram of Foxboro differential pressure transmitter.

the beam moving to the right, permitting the baffle to approach the nozzle. The nozzle backpressure will increase; the relay output will increase; the balancing force will increase. The increase in balancing force will cause the upper end of the range beam to move to the left. The balancing and measurement forces converge on the beam link and must be equal if the baffle position is to stabilize. The baffle must assume that position which will cause a balancing force equal to the measurement force.

Examine Fig. 14-10, which is a schematic diagram of the actual instrument that shows considerably more detail. Compare Figs. 14-9 and 14-10. Notice in Fig. 14-10 that the input diaphragm is a capsule. This capsule is filled with fluid, and any movement of the diaphragm surfaces results in an oil flow through a restriction within the capsule. It is in this manner that the Foxboro transmitter is dampened.

The sealing element on the Foxboro instrument is a diaphragm (labeled flexure seal in Fig. 14-9 and sealing diaphragm in Fig. 14-10), whereas in the Taylor instrument it is a bellows. Functionally, they are equivalent. Yet, it is well worth noting that this introduction of the sealing diaphragm results in a thrust on the beam. This thrust must be provided for or the sealing element would be damaged by the internal pressure. In the case of the Foxboro instrument, the sealing element also serves as a flexure. The thrust is taken care of by flexible straps mounted to the instrument chassis and the end of the beam. In the Taylor

instrument, the thrust is provided for by a flexure that also serves as the beam pivot.

ALIGNMENT

One of the most important considerations in repair and calibration of any instrument is the basic alignment. Before an instrument is calibrated, it is necessary that each of the instrument's components be properly related to each other. Notice in Fig. 14-6 that several of the components are fixed relative to the instrument chassis, whereas others can be positioned relative to the chassis.

Specifically, the input component housing, the input span-location spring reference, the balancing bellows, the output span-location spring reference, the damping unit, and the nozzle are all fixed relative to the chassis. On the other hand, the sensing diaphragm, the force beam, the baffle, and one end of the range beam can be changed relative to the instrument chassis. The problem of basically aligning an instrument consists of relating the movable components to the fixed components; in moment-balance instruments, it is essentially the relating of the two beams and the diaphragm.

In accomplishing an alignment, one component is chosen as a reference. In the case of the Taylor differential-pressure transmitter in Fig. 14-6, the basic reference point for aligning is the force-beam fulcrum point. The force-beam fulcrum point has to be aligned so that the thrust on the force beam resulting from the sealed-bellows force passes through the fulcrum. This is the static pressure alignment. If the sealed-bellows thrust does not pass through the fulcrum point, there will be a torque on the beam that will vary as the static pressure varies, resulting in a calibration error. The instrument is arranged so that by adjusting to the flexure, it is possible to move the pivot point to line it up with the center of the force beam. This then fixes the fulcrum point position.

Let us now consider the baffle/nozzle. The nozzle is fixed relative to the chassis, yet we know the baffle must be within .002 inch of the nozzle. Therefore, it is necessary to position the force beam so that the baffle is properly related to the nozzle. This is accomplished by an alignment adjustment screw (not shown in our diagram). This screw, using the baffle/nozzle as a position indicator, establishes the position of the force beam.

Proceed now to the diaphragm. Recognize that the diaphragm movement must be small if the diaphragm is to accurately convert differential pressure to force. Therefore, it is necessary that the diaphragm movement be centered about the force beam movement. This is accomplished in the following manner.

After fixing the position of the force beam, we load the diaphragm with an air pressure, pushing it against the housing. This establishes its position relative to the instrument chassis. Having done this, we fasten the diaphragm to the force beam by clamping the diaphragm link. We have now aligned the pivot point

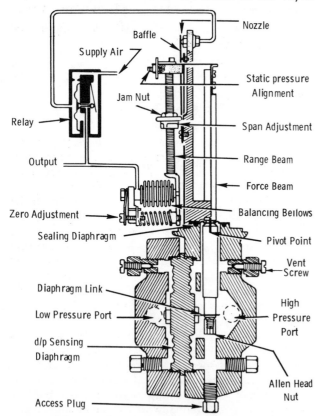

Fig. 14-10. Schematic of Foxboro differential pressure transmitter.

relative to the chassis, the force beam relative to the pivot point and nozzle, and the sensing diaphragm relative to the force beam. The components remaining to be aligned are the balancing bellows, the damping unit, and the range beam. Consider the range beam first.

The pivot end of the range beam is fixed relative to the chassis. Yet, it ought to be arranged so that it is parallel to the force beam for a 9-pound output pressure. This is accomplished by supplying a 50 per cent input signal and adjusting the zero spring so that the 9-pound output is obtained. The damping unit is aligned relative to the force beam by sliding the unit relative to the chassis so that there is no friction between the damping unit plunger and the damping unit case.

The transmitter now is basically aligned. Notice that we have related the instrument's components so that each is centered or positioned in a way that makes it possible to calibrate the instrument. Although we have considered only Taylor's differential pressure transmitter, instruments manufactured by other companies must also be basically aligned.

The basic reference alignment point may vary, depending on the peculiarities of the instrument. For example, in the case of Foxboro, the basic alignment reference is the diaphragm flexure seal. Unlike the Taylor instrument, this pivot point is fixed, relative to

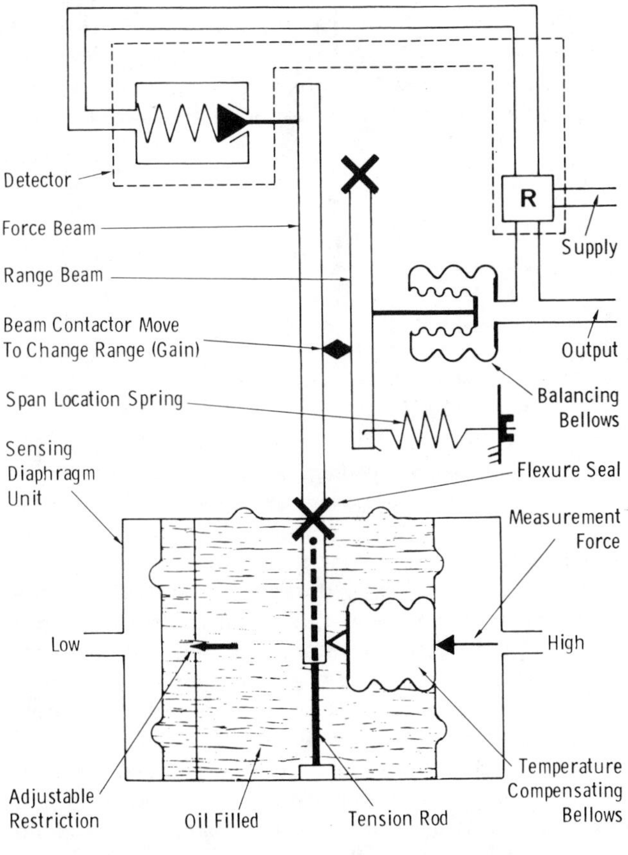

Fig. 14-11. Elementary diagram of Fischer & Porter differential pressure transmitter.

the chassis. The basic alignment here is accomplished in the manufacturing of the instrument. We, however, do have to relate the diaphragm, the baffle, and the range beam to the force beam. The diaphragm alignment is accomplished by clamping the diaphragm link in a prescribed fashion. The baffle is aligned by the baffle-alignment screw; the beams are aligned by the beam link adjustment; the bellows are aligned by adjusting the output span-location spring.

Fig. 14-11 is a diagram of the Fischer & Porter dp cell. Compare this diagram with the diagrams of other dp's to assure yourself that it is fundamentally the same. Fischer & Porter has an adjustable damping restriction and a temperature compensating element within the sensing diaphragm unit.

MOMENT-BALANCE TEMPERATURE TRANSMITTERS

The moment-balance principle is used by a variety of transmitting instruments. Among these are temperature and pressure transmitters, moment-balance controllers, and valve positioners.

In the following paragraphs, we will consider temperature-transmitting instruments using the moment-balance principle. We will find that the essential difference between differential-pressure and temperature lies in the input components.

Components

The components of temperature transmitters are:

1. The temperature-to-force converter (input element).
2. A beam mechanism.
3. Balancing components.
4. A detector mechanism.

Arrangements

The basic arrangement of a temperature transmitter is similar to that of a differential-pressure transmitter. Fig. 14-12 is an elementary diagram of a temperature transmitter. Notice that the differences in the two kinds of transmitters are almost wholly limited to the input components. For temperature transmitters, the input component is a closed system consisting of a bulb, capillary, and diaphragm element. The bulb converts temperature to pressure. The diaphragm unit converts pressure to force. This force, proportional to temperature, is applied to the force beam. The arrangements thereafter are the same as those for a differential pressure transmitter.

Fig. 14-13 is an elementary diagram of Foxboro's Type 12A filled-system moment-balance transmitter. In this diagram, there is a force beam. Operating against the force beam are the input element and the balancing bellows. No range beam is used because the instrument is essentially a fixed-span instrument. An additional element, a pressure- and temperature-compensating bellows, is also operating on the force beam.

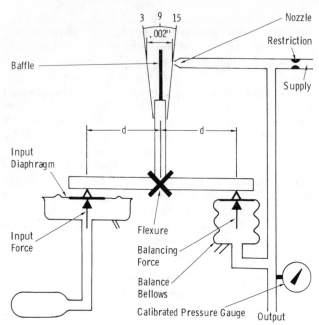

Fig. 14-12. Elementary diagram of temperature transmitter.

Principle of Operation

You will recall in our earlier discussions on filled systems that all parts of the filled system respond to temperature, yet, clearly, we only want the changes in temperature about the bulb to be sensed by the instrument. It is the temperature- and pressure-compensating bellows that compensates for any error resulting from temperature changes inside the instrument cover.

The diaphragm part of the filled system introduces a pressure compensating problem. A diaphragm is a pressure-to-force converter. Atmospheric pressure acting on the diaphragm results in variations in force. Since atmospheric pressure varies, diaphragm forces may vary even though the temperature remains constant. If the forces vary, there will be an error. The compensating bellows is arranged to compensate for changes in atmospheric pressure: as atmospheric pressure changes around the diaphragm it also changes about the bellows. The bellows is sized and positioned on the beam so that the two forces caused by atmospheric pressure changes cancel each other out.

See Fig. 14-13. For a given temperature rise, there is a proportional increase in force from the diaphragm. This force causes the beam to deflect to the left, hence, it causes the baffle to move toward the nozzle. There is a proportional increase in nozzle backpressure. This causes the relay output pressure to increase, and the increase in output pressure, acting on the balancing bellows results in a force opposing the input (diaphragm) force. The relay output, and therefore the balancing force will increase until the balancing moment, acting through the beam mechanism, balances the input moment. If the balancing pressure is measured by a pressure gauge or recorder it will be possible to determine what the input temperature is by knowing what the output pressure is.

This instrument has, essentially, a fixed span which is determined by the design of the filled system. However, it is necessary to make small span changes in order to calibrate the instrument. This is accomplished by having the balancing bellows mounted on an eccentric. As the bellows is rotated, its lever length changes, changing the feedback moment.

Fig. 14-14 is a schematic diagram of the temperature transmitter. Fig. 14-15 is a pictorial diagram. Study these and relate them to Fig. 14-12 and 14-13 to be sure you recognize the elements as they appear in the actual instrument.

Alternate Arrangements

The temperature transmitter just described is relatively simple. Shown in Fig. 14-16 is an elementary diagram of Taylor's Model 316 temperature transmitter. Notice first of all that a range beam is used in this

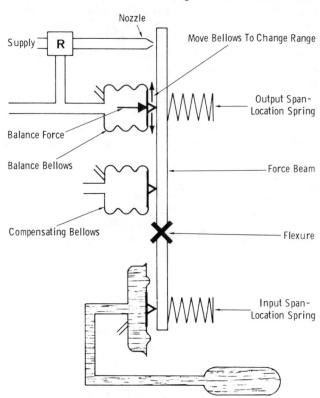

Fig. 14-13. Elementary diagram of Foxboro Type 12A temperature transmitter.

instrument. Recognize that the force originating from the input element is applied to the beam system through tension elements rather than compression elements. In other words, instead of the input-element force pushing directly against the beam, the input force pushes against a force plate which then pulls against the beams through tension links.

Let us see how this instrument operates. Suppose that the temperature increases. The increase in temperature causes an increase in force on the force plate. The force plate acting through the links pulls against the force beam and the range beam, causing the left end of the range beam to rise. This movement, acting

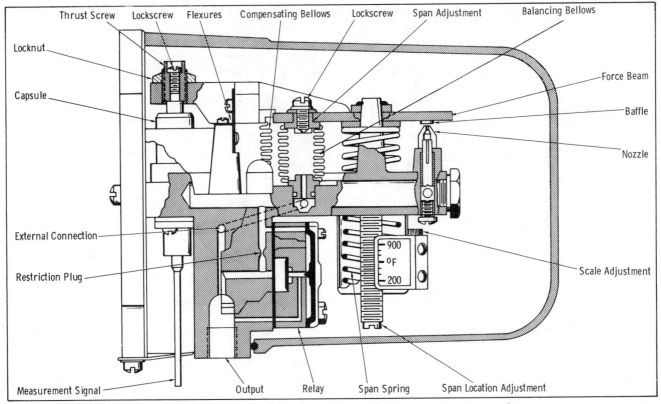

Fig. 14-14. Schematic of Foxboro Type 12A temperature transmitter.

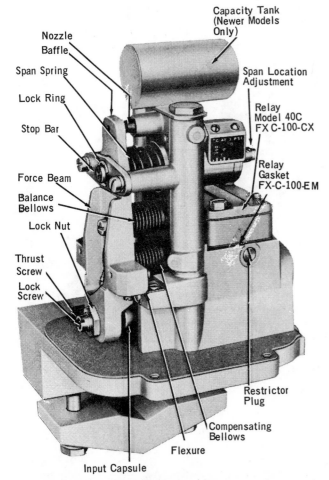

Fig. 14-15. Foxboro Type 12A transmitter.

through the link lever system of the baffle, causes the baffle to move away from the nozzle. The nozzle back-pressure drops off. The relay, which is reverse acting, causes an increase in output pressure. The output pressure, acting through the balancing bellows, results in a downward force on the force beam. This downward force tends to pull the force plate down. (Recall that the increase in temperature resulted in pushing the force plate up.) The downward balancing moment then balances the upward input moment. The instrument will balance when the particular baffle/nozzle clearance exists that results in the exact output pressure and therefore the exact balancing moment to equal the input moment.

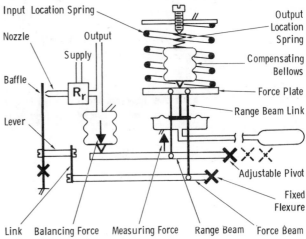

Fig. 14-16. Elementary diagram of Taylor Model 316 transmitter.

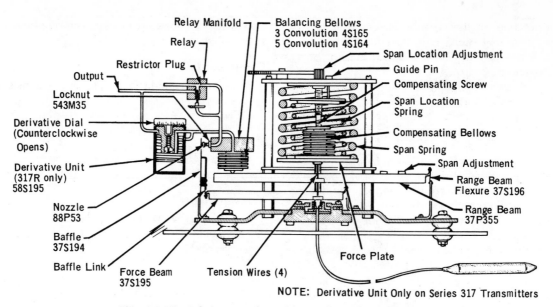

Fig. 14-17. Schematic of Taylor Model 316 transmitter.

The span of the Taylor instrument can be changed by changing the pivot point of the force beam relative to the force plate. Changing the pivot point changes the ratio of the input lever length and the balancing lever length. Changing the ratio of lever lengths is a common way of changing span although the amount of span change possible is limited. By changing the stiffness of the span location springs, it is possible to make additional span changes. Recognize that changing the span location spring only changes

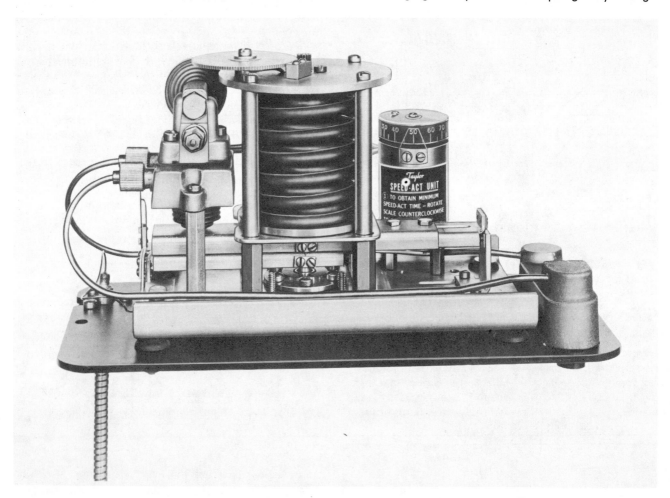

Fig. 14-18. Taylor Model 316 transmitter.

the original loading on the capsule. However, since it is a large spring and there is a selection of springs available, it is possible to obtain a 3-psig output for a variety of temperatures.

For example, suppose the temperature is 100 degrees and the output pressure is 3 psig. If we put in a suppression spring that is "twice" as stiff, we can load up the input capsule so that 200 degrees (say) would now be required before the internal pressure becomes sufficient to produce an input moment equal to the balancing moment created by a 3-psig output.

As the span location spring is changed, the force against the balancing bellows changes. As was the case in the Foxboro instrument, the Taylor instrument also has a compensating bellows. In the Taylor instrument, the compensating bellows acts on the force plate rather than directly against the force beam.

Fig. 14-17 is a schematic diagram of Taylor's transmitter. Fig. 14-18 is a pictorial diagram. Study these two diagrams until you are able to recognize and locate the essential components.

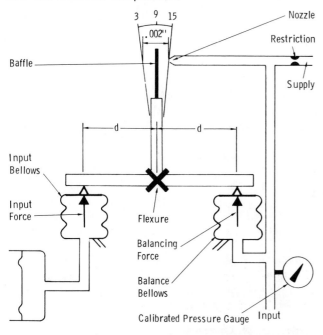

Fig. 14-19. Moment-balance pressure transmitter.

MOMENT-BALANCE PRESSURE TRANSMITTERS

In the preceding paragraphs, we considered temperature transmitters that use the moment-balance principle. In that part, we showed how temperature was converted to force, the force to a moment, and how this moment, acting through a beam system, was balanced by a moment proportional to the output pres-

sure. Now we shall consider moment-balance pressure transmitters.

Components

1. A pressure-to-force input system consisting of a pressure-to-force diaphragm element and a pressure-to-force bellows element. These two elements are connected by a capillary tube.
2. A beam mechanism.
3. A detector mechanism.
4. A balancing mechanism.

Arrangements

See Fig. 14-19. The input system is arranged in the same way as the input system used by the temperature transmitter.

Principle of Operation

The operation is essentially the same as the operation of the temperature transmitter.

SUMMARY

Other than the difference in the input element, there are no differences between pressure and temperature transmitters that use the moment-balance principle. Notice that the differences between pressure and temperature transmitters are restricted to that portion of the input system exposed to the process. Specifically, in the case of the temperature transmitter, the component exposed to the process is a temperature-to-pressure converter. In the case of the pressure transmitter, the component exposed to the process is a pressure-to-pressure converter. In addition to its primary purpose of converting pressure, there is a sealing function. The purpose is to isolate process fluids from the instrument.

Figs. 14-20A and 14-20B are diagrams of the temperature and pressure measuring elements.

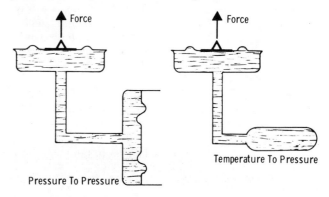

(A) Pressure element. (B) Temperature element.

Fig. 14-20. Input elements for transmitters.

Chapter 15

Moment-Balance Positioners

MOMENT BALANCE APPLIED TO POSITION DEVICES

In previous chapters, we considered moment-balance instruments whose function was to convert process variables to a proportional pressure. In common terminology, such devices are called transmitters. We shall now consider devices whose function is to convert position to a proportional pressure or, alternately, whose function is to convert a pressure to a proportional position. Position-to-pressure converters include set-point transmitters; pressure-to-position converters can be recorders or indicators.

There is an additional group of instruments that are essentially pressure-to-position converters; namely, valve positioners. These accept a low-volume air signal and convert it to a high-volume air output signal. This output is then applied to the valve actuator.

Components

1. An input mechanism.
2. A beam mechanism.
3. A detector mechanism.
4. A balancing mechanism.

Arrangements

The components are arranged in the typical moment-balance fashion. In this respect, the position-to-pressure converter is identical with other moment-balance instruments already studied. The difference arises out of the input components. In measuring instruments, the input components were devices that converted the process variable to a proportional force. Position-to-pressure converters employ an input mechanism that converts position to a proportional force. An essential element of this mechanism is a position-to-force converter. You will recall that a spring, functionally, is a position-to-force converter. The position of interest is applied to one end of the spring. The spring then converts that position to a force that is applied to the force beam.

Principle of Operation

Recall that, in moment-balance instruments, the input force, acting through its lever, is balanced by an output force acting through its lever. The detector mechanism determines when the two forces times distance (moments) are in balance. Fig. 15-1 shows the

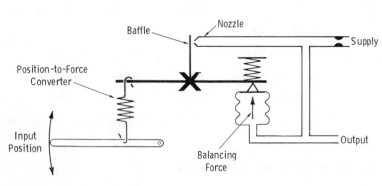

Fig. 15-1. Fundamental moment-balance mechanism with position input.

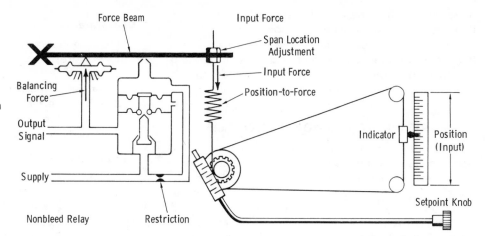

Fig. 15-2. Elementary diagram of Taylor 90J setpoint transmitter.

fundamental moment-balance diagram for a position input. Fig. 15-2 is a diagram of Taylor's 90-J series. This setpoint transmitter is essentially a position transmitter; the position of an index is converted to a proportional pressure. Setpoint transmitters are used in conjunction with controllers.

Let us see how the set-point transmitter operates. Suppose that the instrument is in balance with the indicator at some point on the scale. Let us rotate the set-point knob to move the indicator up scale. The purpose of the instrument now is to change the output pressure so that it is proportional to the new indicator position.

As the indicator is moved up scale, the lower end of the spring moves downward, which causes a downward force to be applied to the force beam. As the beam moves down, it covers the nozzle, building up the nozzle backpressure, and the relay output pressure increases. This increase in relay output pressure, acting on the balancing diaphragm, causes an increase in balancing force. When the increase in the balancing mo-

ment is equal to the input moment, the balance action will stop. At that point, the baffle has assumed a position with respect to the nozzle that results in a back-

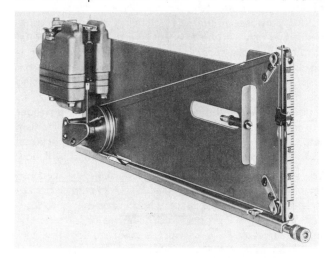

Fig. 15-4. Taylor 90J setpoint transmitter.

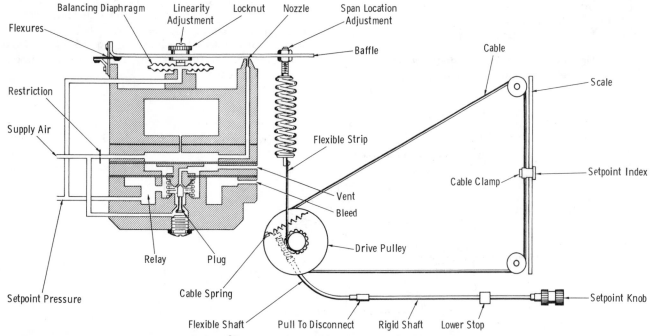

Fig. 15-3. Schematic of Taylor 90J setpoint transmitter.

pressure, which is the output pressure, and is proportional to the set-point index position.

Fig. 15-3 is a more detailed diagram which shows the actual physical relationships. Fig. 15-4 is a photograph of the instrument. Study these figures and relate them to the fundamental diagrams.

PRESSURE-TO-POSITION CONVERTERS

In the first part of this chapter, we discussed position-to-pressure converters; next, we will consider a pressure-to-position converter. In some respects, the pressure-to-position converter is the opposite of the position-to-pressure converter. The instrument we will consider is the recorder mechanism of the Taylor 90-J series. This recorder mechanism, unlike the recorders of other manufacturers, is a self-balancing instrument; or using other words, a feedback type mechanism. You will recall the recorders discussed in the first part of the chapter are feed-forward types.

The purpose of the self-balancing recorder mechanism is to drive a pen to a position that is proportional to the input pressure. In this respect, the recorder is no different from the conventional feed-forward mechanism. The difference between the self-balancing mechanism and the feed-forward mechanism is arranged so that if the pen does not assume the proper position, the air pressure driving the pen mechanism will change until the pen is at a position proportional to the input signal. How this is accomplished will now be discussed.

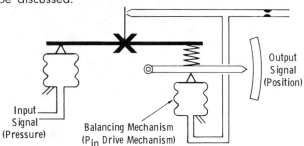

Fig. 15-5. Fundamental diagram of pressure-to-position converter.

Components

The essential components of the pressure-to-position converter are:

1. An input mechanism.
2. A beam mechanism.
3. A detector mechanism.
4. A balancing mechanism.

Arrangements

The input element, which is a pressure-to-force converter, operates against the force beam. The output of the pen drive mechanism, acting through a position-to-force converter (spring) is also applied to the beam mechanism. The difference between the input force and the balancing force is detected by a nozzle-baffle detector. Changes in nozzle-baffle position are fed to the pen drive mechanism. Fig. 15-5 is the fundamental diagram of a pressure-to-position converter. It differs from the transmitters in that the output is not the balancing pressure. The output is the change of position of the balancing component.

Principle of Operation

See Fig. 15-6. Let us assume the mechanism is balanced for a mid-scale pen position, and the input pressure to the mechanism is increased. This causes a force on the force beam which tends to cover the nozzle, resulting in an increase in nozzle backpressure. This increase in backpressure loads up the pen drive mechanism, causing a downward movement of the rolling diaphragm element. This downward movement rotates the shaft, which drives the pen. Notice, however, that as the shaft rotates, the lower end of the spring moves downward. This action results in a force being fed back to the beam. This balancing force opposes the input force. The detector will change the pressure on the pen drive mechanism until the balancing moment is equal to the input moment. Fig. 15-7 is a pictorial diagram of the actual mechanism; Fig. 15-8 is a photograph. Study this illustration to be sure you understand the mechanism.

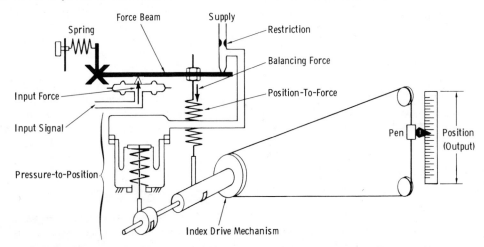

Fig. 15-6. Elementary diagram of recorder section of Taylor 90J.

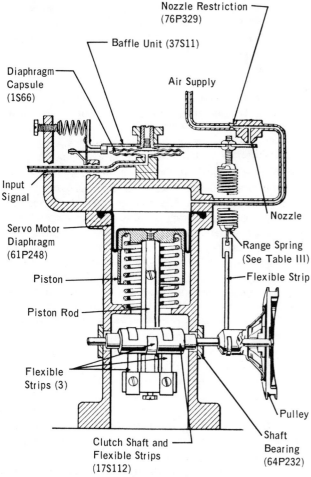

Fig. 15-7. Schematic of recorder section of Taylor 90J.

Labels for Fig. 15-7:
- Nozzle Restriction (76P329)
- Baffle Unit (37S11)
- Diaphragm Capsule (1S66)
- Air Supply
- Input Signal
- Servo Motor Diaphragm (61P248)
- Piston
- Piston Rod
- Flexible Strips (3)
- Clutch Shaft and Flexible Strips (17S112)
- Nozzle
- Range Spring (See Table III)
- Flexible Strip
- Pulley
- Shaft Bearing (64P232)

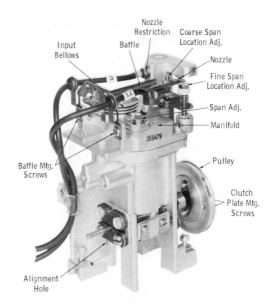

Fig. 15-8. Recorder section of Taylor 90J.

Labels for Fig. 15-8:
- Input Bellows
- Nozzle Restriction
- Baffle
- Coarse Span Location Adj.
- Nozzle
- Fine Span Location Adj.
- Span Adj.
- Manifold
- Pulley
- Clutch Plate Mtg. Screws
- Baffle Mtg. Screws
- Alignment Hole

FORCE-BALANCE VALVE POSITIONERS

We have mentioned the fact that valve positioner devices are essentially positioning devices as differentiated from measuring devices. Further, we mentioned the fact that positioners can be designed using the force-balance or the motion-balance principle of operation. At this time, we shall study force-balance positioners using the moment-balance principle. Later we will study "true" force and motion-balance positioners.

The purpose of the valve positioner is to ensure that the actuator stem assumes a position proportional to the input signal. The input signal almost always is the output of a controller, though it can be the output of a pressure regulator station. Physically, the valve positioner is mounted directly on the actuator. There is a linkage between the actuator positioner and the valve stem.

A positioner may be integral with the top works (Fig. 15-9A) or it may be "side arm" mounted as shown in Fig. 15-9B. Functionally, the mountings are equivalent, whether or not they are integral or side arm mounted.

Positioners, in addition to being used on valves, are also commonly used on piston type actuators, louvres, and on variable speed drives.

Components

1. An input element (to convert air pressure to force).
2. A force-beam system.
3. A balancing-lever system.
4. A position-to-force converter (to convert a lever position to force).
5. A detector mechanism: It is important to recognize that the valve positioner considered by itself is not a functional entity. The valve positioner not mounted on the valve is missing an essential component. That component is the equivalent of the balancing bellows of the fundamental moment-balance mechanism. The balancing element required is furnished by the valve, specifically the valve diaphragm and spring to convert pressure to position. (Notice also that the primary purpose of the valve diaphragm and spring is to drive the valve stem.)

Arrangements

The valve positioner is mounted on the valve in a way to have the valve-stem position applied to the force beam. Usually, though not always, the valve-stem position is fed back through a compound-lever system. A compound-lever system is arranged so that the gain of the system can be changed. The valve-stem position, passing through the lever system, is applied to a position-to-force converter (spring). This force is applied to the force beam opposing the input force. The detector is arranged to sense the beam position, hence, any unbalance between the input and balancing moments.

Principle of Operation

Fig. 15-10 is a fundamental diagram of an actuator positioner. Notice that basically it is identical with the fundamental diagram of the other moment-balance mechanisms. The interesting feature of the valve positioner is the fact that the balancing element is the diaphragm of the valve. The operation is identical with the fundamental moment-balance mechanism.

(A) Integral mounting.

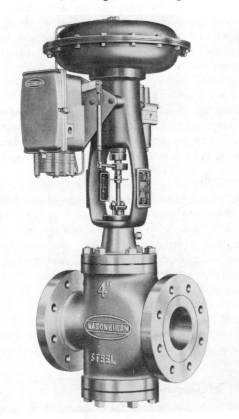

(B) Side arm mounting.

Fig. 15-9. Positioner mounting.

Fig. 15-11 shows the diagram of a Mason-Neilan valve positioner, shown connected to a valve. Let us see how this actuator/positioner operates. (Compare Fig. 15-11 with Fig. 15-10.)

Assume the positioner is in a balanced condition, and there is an increase in the input signal. The increase in the input signal will cause an increase in force that rotates the force beam counterclockwise. The detector, which in this case is a reverse acting pilot valve, responds to this movement, causing a decrease in output pressure. This decrease in output pressure, operating against the valve diaphragm, permits the valve stem to lift. The valve stem upward movement, acting through the lever system, causes the lower end of the spring to move downward, thereby increasing the balancing force. The increase in balancing force opposing the input signal force tends to move the beam clockwise. The detector will cause the output pressure to change the amount necessary to drive the valve stem to the position required to balance the input signal.

Notice that the output of the detector, which is an air pressure signal, is not equal to the input pressure signal. In fact, the output of the detector can be almost any pressure for a given input signal. It is this aspect of the positioner that makes it an important piece of equipment. In a few words, what the positioner does is to furnish that pressure necessary to drive the actuator stem to a position that is proportional to the input signal.

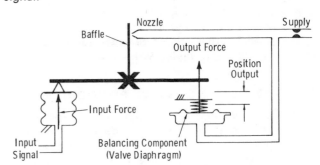

Fig. 15-10. Fundamental diagram of actuator positioner.

USES OF VALVE POSITIONERS

Valve positioners are used for the following purposes:

1. To compensate for the forcing effects of the fluids causing an unbalanced valve plug.
2. To minimize the friction effect.
3. To increase the speed of response of the control valve.
4. To split the travel of valves.

Consider the forcing effect of an unbalanced valve plug. Assume a fixed input signal pressure and assume the valve is operating in a fluid at 100 psi pressure. When the valve is closed, it is clearly possible that there will be no pressure on the downstream side of the valve. Yet, acting underneath the valve is a

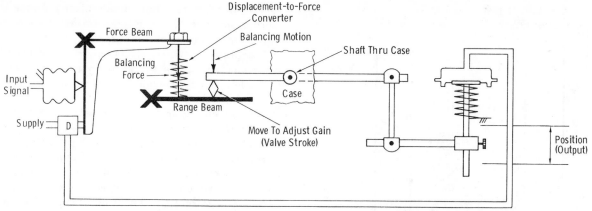

Fig. 15-11. Elementary diagram of Mason-Neilan valve positioner.

pressure of 100 psig. If the valve plug diameter is one square inch, there is a force of 100 lbs. This force lifts the stem, permitting an unwanted increased flow through the valve. Notice, the input signal has not changed, therefore, the flow through the valves should not change. The valve positioner will correct for this thrust on the valve stem in the following manner.

In our example, the input signal is constant, yet, because of a change in pressure under the plug, the stem lifts. As the stem lifts, a force is applied to the positioner force beam. The detector responds to this change in force and operates to increase the pressure on the diaphragm. This increased pressure on the diaphragm results in a downward force on the stem which drives it to its original position. Now there is a different pressure on the actuator.

The operation of the actuator positioner under high friction conditions is somewhat similar. Let us assume an increase in input signal. We know the valve stem should move, but suppose it doesn't because friction is holding it back. If it doesn't move, there is no new balancing force opposing the input force. As a consequence, the output pressure decreases until the valve stem moves. It will, in fact, drop to zero if the valve stem won't move. Usually, however, the detector will cause the air pressure on the actuator to change enough to make up for the friction forces holding the actuator stem movement back. If the input signal is in the opposite direction, that is, if it is decreased, the pressure on the valve will increase to supply pressure.

A word of caution: Actuator positioners should not be used to compensate for unnecessary friction arising from improperly maintained control valves. There is a clear possibility that an actuator positioner or a high friction valve will result in a valve that cycles, thereby causing an unstable control system.

In addition to uses mentioned above, actuator positioners are used to increase the speed of response. Recognize that the air delivery capacity of a controller is limited, and that some actuators are large and require considerable amounts of air flow to cause a change in valve-stem position. In this situation, the valve moves slowly because it takes time to build up pressure within the actuator. If a valve positioner is used, the controller output need change only the pres-

sure in the input bellows of the positioner. Therefore, the input force increases rapidly. The detector mechanism of the positioner is designed to furnish large amounts of air so that the valve will move rapidly in response to changes of input signal.

Valve positioners are widely used to split the range of valves. Usually the input range is 3 to 15 psi, and the output range is full valve travel. Frequently, for a 3 to 15 psi input, a part of full valve travel is desired. For example, on a fairly common application, it is desired that one valve move from fully closed to fully open as the input signal changes from 3 to 9 psig; and, as the input signal changes from 9 to 15 psig, a second valve moves from fully open to closed. In other words, the valve ranges have been split.

The valve positioner can do this job of range splitting because of the adjustable gain mechanism used in most valve positioners.

GAIN MECHANISMS

Fig. 15-12 shows an adjustable gain mechanism consisting of parallel levers and a movable contactor. In a parallel lever system, as used on positioners, one lever of the system is the force beam. The second lever pivots through the instrument case.

Notice that the two levers are joined by a contactor. (See Fig. 15-13.) The contactor is arranged so that it

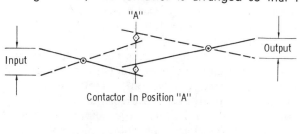

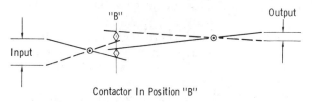

Fig. 15-12. Adjustable gain system.

95

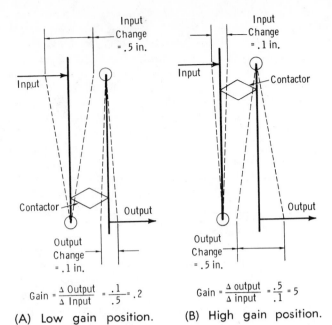

Gain $= \dfrac{\Delta \text{Output}}{\Delta \text{Input}} = \dfrac{.1}{.5} = .2$

Gain $= \dfrac{\Delta \text{output}}{\Delta \text{input}} = \dfrac{.5}{.1} = 5$

(A) Low gain position. (B) High gain position.

Fig. 15-13. Changing gain in parallel-lever system.

slides along the levers. As it is moved from left to right, the range beam length is increased, but the length of the input lever is decreased. In other words, the ratio of the range beam lever length and the input lever length is changed. This change in ratio of lever lengths changes the ratio of output-position change to input-position change. The parallel lever gain mechanism is in fact a "Z" type linkage using a very short link.

Study Fig. 15-13A and B, and notice in Fig. 15-13A that the contactor is near the input-lever pivot point, whereas in Fig. 15-13B, the contactor is near the output-lever pivot point. Let's see how the moving of the contactor relative to the pivot changes the gain. If the contactor is near the input-lever pivot point, (see Fig. 15-13A) there will be a relatively small movement of the contactor for a large input movement. Since the contactor moves a relatively small amount, and since the contactor drives the output lever, the output lever must also move a relatively small amount. In our diagram, we show the input moving .5 inch. The contactor is located so that for this .5-inch movement, the output lever will move .1 inch. The gain, therefore, is the output (.1) divided by the input (.5) or .2.

Examine Fig. 15-13B. In this figure, the contactor is near the output-lever pivot point. Even though input lever and contactor move only a small amount, this movement applied near the pivot point on the output lever produces a relatively large output movement. If the input moves .1 inch the output may move .5 inch, depending on lever lengths. In this example, the gain will be .5 divided by .1 which is 5.

As the contactor has been moved upward from one extremity to another, the gain has been changed from .2 to 5. Of course, for intermediate contactor positions, gains between .2 and 5 can be obtained.

The parallel lever system is widely used. It is necessary that it be clearly understood. This mechanism is

called an adjustable gain mechanism because it is a mechanism that makes it possible to change the ratio of the output to the input.

Recognize that the valve-stem travel is established by the range of the valve being used. The standard range is 3 to 15 psig for full travel. Other ranges are also obtainable.

The reason for "splitting" valve ranges, is to cause a full change in valve stem position for only 50 per cent change in input signal. This can be done if, for a full change in valve stem position, the resulting change in balancing force is only half of what it normally is arranged to be. If it is only half, it will balance a 50 per cent change of input signal; or, in other words, a 3 to 9 psig input signal will cause a full valve travel. Sometimes valve ranges are split in thirds.

EXAMPLES OF MOMENT-BALANCE POSITIONERS

In preceding paragraphs, we discussed the moment-balance principle applied to actuator positioners. We discussed the purpose of actuator positioners and how they operate. Now we shall consider additional examples of actuator positions, particularly as they are used on valves and piston operators.

The first example is a positioner used by Conoflow to operate its piston-type valve operator. This positioner is integrally mounted as compared to side-arm mounted. Nevertheless, the component is functionally identical with positioners already discussed.

In addition to the Conoflow positioners, we will discuss the positioners used by Foxboro and Bailey Meter to operate their piston operators.

Components

The components of these positioners are the same as those for the positioners we have just discussed.

1. An input element to convert air pressure to force.
2. A force-beam system.
3. A balancing-lever system.
4. Position-to-force converter to convert a lever position to force.
5. A detector mechanism. It is important to recognize that the valve positioner, considered by itself, is not a functional entity. The valve positioner not mounted on the valve is missing an essential component. That component is the equivalent of the balancing bellows of the fundamental moment-balance mechanism. The balancing element required is furnished by the valve diaphragm.
6. The valve diaphragm, to convert pressure to position. (Notice also that the primary purpose of the valve diaphragm is to drive the valve stem.)

Arrangements

The Conoflow positioner, unlike positioners mentioned earlier, is integrally mounted. That is, positioner

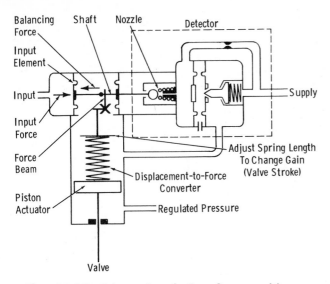

Fig. 15-14. Schematic of Conoflow positioner.

mechanisms are installed in the housing of the valve top works. Fig. 15-14 is a diagram and Fig. 15-15 is a photograph of a Conoflow positioner.

Examine Fig. 15-14 and compare it element for element and component for component, with the list of components and with the fundamental diagram. Locate the input element—a diaphragm to convert the air pressure signal to force. This force, acting through a shaft, is applied to a force beam. A force proportional to valve position is applied to the other end of the force beam. The detector, in turn, senses the force beam position through an extension of the shaft. The two forces are brought into balance by the detector.

Notice that there is no balancing lever system. Since the positioner is integrally mounted, the feedback to the force beam can be made directly without the introduction of additional levers. Elimination of the additional levers requires that different provisions be made for adjusting the gain (stroke) of the positioner from those used when the additional levers were present. The gain adjustment is made by adjusting the effective length of the spring.

The function of a spring is to convert a change in position to a change in force. For a given position, the resultant force will depend on the spring characteristic. Given a particular spring, we can change the spring characteristic by changing its length. In other words, we can change the amount of output force for a given input position by changing the effective length of the spring. Since we have changed the ratio of output to input, we have changed the gain.

The detector mechanism is the standard nozzle/baffle non-bleed relay combination. The nozzle/baffle consists of a port and ball combination, rather than the nozzle and flat baffle. Functionally, they are equivalent.

Principle of Operation

Assume that the positioner is in a balanced condition, and a new input signal comes in. This new input signal, acting on the input diaphragm, applies a new force to the force beam. Also, it moves the "baffle"

relative to the "nozzle". This changes the back pressure operating the relay. As a result, the relay output changes. This change in relay output is connected to the upper side of the piston operator. The new pressure on the piston operator causes it to move. This movement, acting through the spring element, changes the balancing force. When the balancing force equals the input force (almost), the piston actuator will come to a fixed position.

Notice, again, as was the case in valve positioners already discussed, that the balancing action is between the input force and the valve position, and that the relay output pressure, hence, the pressure on the piston, will change to that pressure which will force the piston to that position which results in a balancing force equal (within the sensitivity of the detector) to the input force.

The relay output pressure, in addition to being applied to the upper portion of the piston operator, also loads the input diaphragm. If this alone was the case, the positioner would not be functional because the relay output pressure would directly oppose the input signal pressure. Notice, however, a second seal diaphragm identical with the input diaphragm. The relay output pressure also loads the seal diaphragm. Since the diaphragms are identical, the resulting forces are identical, and since the diaphragms oppose each other, the forces oppose each other and balance out. It is in this way that the relay backpressure effect on the input diaphragm is eliminated.

To summarize, the Conoflow integral positioner functionally is identical with the positioners discussed earlier in the chapter. The differences are limited to the method of mounting, the method of changing the gain, and the nozzle/baffle construction. In the Conoflow instrument, when the positioner is integrally mounted, the gain is changed by changing the effec-

Fig. 15-15. Conoflow positioner.

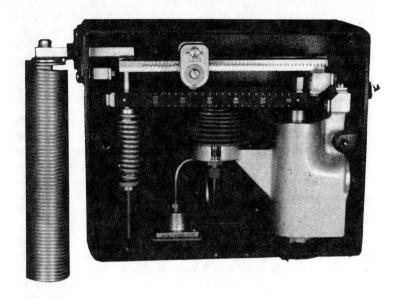

Fig. 15-16. Foxboro Poweractor.

tive length of the spring. The nozzle/baffle detector is a ball-port combination.

Our second example is the position device Foxboro uses on a piston operator. Foxboro calls it a Poweractor. The piston operator can be used to operate valves, butterflies, louvres, variable speed drives, or any other mechanical equipment that requires positioning proportional to pneumatic input signal.

Components (Foxboro Poweractor)

The components of the Poweractor (Fig. 15-16) are the typical valve positioner components already outlined. Notice the force beam and the range lever furnishing the adjustable gain. The detector is a double-acting pilot valve. The position-to-force spring is driven by the piston.

Arrangements

The Poweractor is side-arm mounted. The connection to the piston is made through an extension on the piston shaft. Connected to the end of the extension on the piston shaft is the balancing spring that converts piston position to force.

Principle of Operation

In previous discussions of the principle of positioners, we assumed a change in input signal pressure. In this example, let us assume that the input signal remains constant, but that the load on the piston changes, due perhaps to lumps of material under the roll that the piston positions. These lumps will tend to move the piston upward. (See Fig. 15-17.) As the piston moves upward, the balancing force is reduced. This reduction in balancing force will permit the force beam to rotate upwards. The detector, sensing this upward movement of the force beam, will act to increase the air pressure on the upper side of the piston and reduce the air pressure on the lower side of the piston positioner, resulting in an increased force tend-

ing to move the piston downward. (Recall that the lump tended to move the piston upward, thereby driving the piston to the position that balances the input signal.)

Of course, the piston positioner would operate in the same way as other positioners when the input signal is changed. For that matter, other positioners would operate in the same way as the positioner being discussed, when the loading on the device being positioned changes.

Our third and last example of moment-balance positioning devices is a Bailey piston positioner. This positioner is quite similar to the Foxboro Poweractor. The essential difference between the Bailey and the Foxboro positioners is that the Bailey is arranged so that it is possible to obtain a non-linear relationship between piston position and input signal. In other words, it is possible to get a nonproportional piston position

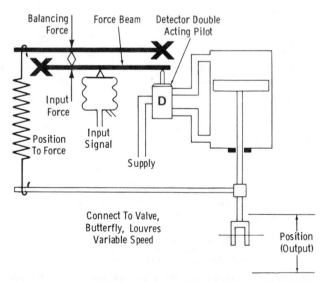

Fig. 15-17. Elementary diagram of Foxboro Poweractor.

for an input pressure signal. You will recall in our other devices that the relationship between position and input signal was proportional. That is, there was a linear relationship between piston position and input signal.

The nonlinearity feature can be extremely valuable. It is widely used when the relationship between flow and valve position itself is non-linear. If the positioning device is made nonlinear in the same way that the flow to position relationship is nonlinear, the relationship between the input signal and flow can be made linear.

Components (Bailey Piston Operator)

The components are the usual ones, with one exception. Between the piston position feedback and the position-to-force converter, is a nonlinear link—that is, a cam. Nonlinear links were discussed earlier in this volume. The nonlinear link (cam) is driven by a two-gear train. Mounted on one of the gears is a cam which is followed by the range lever.

Arrangements

A Bailey positioner is side arm mounted, usually with a piston and lever system forming a package. The device to be positioned is attached to the take-off beam. (See Fig. 15-18.) The take-off beam, in addition to furnishing take-off power, is also the lever providing piston-position feedback to the positioner. Hence, it is comparable to the lever that rotates in other valve positioners.

Principle of Operation

Let us assume that the positioner is balanced at a signal of about 3 psig, and that this signal changes to 4 psig. The new signal will result in a force on the force beam that tends to rotate the force beam upward. The detector, a double acting pilot, will sense this upward movement, and will increase the pressure on the lower side of the piston and decrease it on the

upper side. These changes in pressure cause the piston to move upward. The take-off beam will rotate clockwise. This clockwise motion, acting through the lever and gears, rotates the cam counterclockwise. The cam pushes the range lever downward, causing an increased force on the force beam. This increased force will change until it balances the increased input signal.

Suppose the positioner were balanced at 12 psig, and the signal increased to 13 psig. That is, the pressure changes the same amount as it did before. The operation of the positioner and piston will be identical with the operation just described, except now the range lever operates against a different proportion of the cam. (See Fig. 15-19.)

Suppose, that for the 1 psi change between 4 and 5 psig, the cam rotated 22½ degrees. That is ½ of the full angularity rotation of the cam. This angular rotation will result in more change in the cam follower of say ⅛ inch. This ⅛-inch change will result in the lower end of the spring changing ¼ inch. Let us examine what changes we get when the cam operates at 12 psig. When the cam rotates from 12-psi position to 13-psi position, the cam follower moves say ¼ inch. That is twice as much as before. For this ¼-inch movement, the lower end of the spring will move ½ inch. Yet, recall that the input signal changed the same 1 psi.

Notwithstanding the fact that the signal change was the same as the balancing force, the change in balancing force at the 12-psig level is twice the change in balancing force at the 4-psig level. This difference in balancing forces for the same input-signal change, will result in different piston-position changes; hence, the relationship between piston position and signal becomes nonlinear. The specific relationship is determined by the profile of the cam. A variety of cams is available.

Cams can be designed to obtain any of the required relationships between piston position and input signal. The Bailey positioner was studied as it is used on a piston actuator. The same positioner can be used on a variety of actuators driving a variety of devices.

Study Figs. 15-18 and 15-19 so that you are sure you can relate the elements and components.

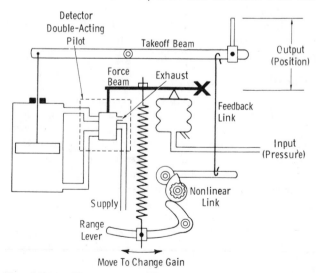

Fig. 15-18. Elementary diagram of Bailey positioner.

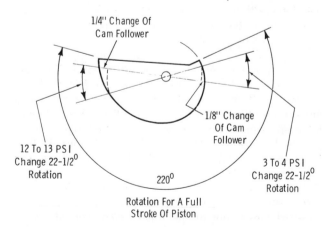

Fig. 15-19. Cam relationships of Bailey positioner.

Chapter 16

True Force-Balance Instruments

THE "TRUE" FORCE-BALANCE PRINCIPLE

In preceding chapters, we discussed a class of force-balance instruments which we call moment balance. Moment-balance instruments are characterized by forces acting at distances from pivot points. A force times a distance is a moment. The moment-balance principle was applied to instruments used in recording, transmitting, and positioning. Later, we will discuss moment-balance controllers.

In addition to moment-balance mechanisms, which are a branch of force balance, there are true force-balance recorders, transmitters, positioners, and controllers. Also, as was stated in our discussions on a non-bleed relay the true force-balance principle is used in a wide variety of relays.

The true force-balance instruments are characterized by pressure-to-force elements only. No levers are used in true force-to-balance mechanisms except the input lever of positioners.

In common language, true force-balance instruments frequently are called stack-type instruments. This expression undoubtedly arises out of the fact that the elements of true force-balance instruments are stacked one on the other much like a stack of pancakes, so that force and counterforce act along the same axis.

The discussion will be limited to examples of true force-balance mechanisms as used in transmitters and valve positioners.

Components

1. An input diaphragm (or functional equivalent).
2. A balancing diaphragm (or functional equivalent).
3. A thrust shaft.

4. A detector mechanism.
5. Input and output range location springs.

Notice the absence of any force beams or lever systems.

Arrangements

The pressure-to-force converting elements are arranged on the same axis so that the center of each of these elements lines up with the center line of the instrument. The range-location springs are also arranged on the same axis. This configuration results in a stacking of elements, each element being either clamped to a thrust shaft or applied to the thrust shaft. The detector mechanism is arranged to sense the position of the thrust shaft. The outer edges of the diaphragms are clamped between the ring-shaped pieces that space the diaphragms and form the various compartments.

Principle of Operation

Fig. 16-1 shows that the input signal is applied to the upper compartment, against the input diaphragm. The diaphragm converts this input pressure to a force that tends to move the thrust shaft downward toward the nozzle. The nozzle backpressure builds up. This backpressure is applied against the balancing diaphragm, and, acting on the balancing diaphragm, is converted to a force. This balancing force directly opposes the input signal force.

The nozzle backpressure will change to that pressure (hence, force) required to balance the input-signal pressure. When the two forces are balanced, the thrust shaft comes to equilibrium at that position in front of the nozzle that results in the required nozzle backpressure, hence balancing force.

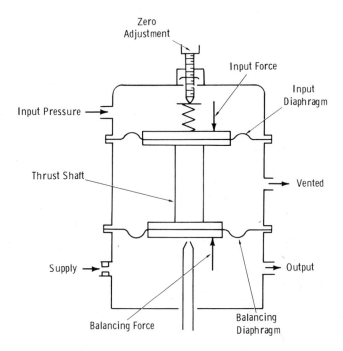

Fig. 16-1. True force-balance mechanism.

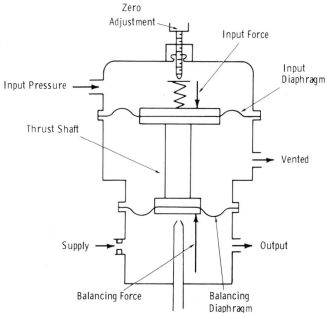

Fig. 16-2. Force-balance mechanism with diaphragm area ratio 1 to 2.

OUTPUT SPAN LOCATION

When true force-balance devices are used as transmitters, the output signal should be the standard 3 to 15 psig. The input signal is proportional to a measured variable. This means that for zero input signal, the output signal should be 3 psig.

How is this accomplished? Assume a zero input signal. To balance this zero input signal, the nozzle backpressure signal must also be zero if there are no other forces on the shaft. Yet, we want a 3-psig output for the zero signal input.

Suppose the thrust shaft is loaded with a spring so that as this spring is compressed, a force is applied to the thrust shaft, tending to move the shaft toward the nozzle. As a result of this moment, the nozzle backpressure will build up. This backpressure acting on the diaphragm will tend to force the thrust shaft upward against the force of the spring. When the balancing force equals the spring force, the thrust shaft will come to equilibrium. By adjusting the spring force, we can obtain the required 3-psig balancing pressure (hence, output pressure) with a zero input signal. This spring is an output span-location spring.

SPAN (GAIN) CHANGING

The mechanism we have just described is a one-to-one relay; that is, the output signal divided by the input signal equals one. Another way of saying it is the gain is one. Suppose a gain value different than one is wanted. In moment-balance instruments we changed lever lengths. How is this accomplished in a true force-balance instrument that has no levers?

First, recognize that the force output of a diaphragm is equal to the input pressure times the area of the diaphragm. Therefore, by changing diaphragm areas, it is possible to get different force values for a given applied pressure.

Fig. 16-2 is a diagram of a true force-balance mechanism with an input diaphragm having twice the area of the balancing diaphragm. The operation of this device is the same as the device of Fig. 16-1, except that now 1 psig of input pressure is balanced by 2 psig of balancing pressure.

Different ratios of diaphragm diameters will make it possible to obtain different ratios of output to input values. By changing the ratio of input diaphragm diameters to output diaphragm diameters, it is possible to change the ratio of output to input signals. Changing ratios of diaphragm diameters is the method used to make large changes in gain. What about small changes?

Fortunately, there is a property of diaphragms that makes it possible to obtain slight changes in output-input ratio without changing diaphragms. When speaking of the diameter of a diaphragm, we are not referring to the extreme outside diameter at the point where the diaphragm clamps to the ring components. We are, in fact, referring to what is called the effective diameter. The effective diameter not only is smaller than the actual diameter, but it varies as the center portion of the diaphragm moves relative to the housing.

Fig. 16-3 shows that when the center of the diaphragm moves downward, the convolution of the diaphragm rolls in such a fashion as to cause the section of the convolution closest to the housing to become longer than the section of the convolution closest to the center. The effect of this is to reduce the effective diaphragm diameter, hence, to reduce the effective diaphragm area. This property of a diaphragm is used for correcting minor differences, perhaps less than 2

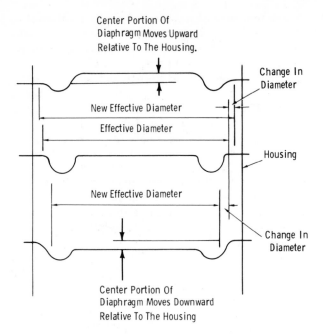

Fig. 16-3. Change in effective area of diaphragm at different operational pressures.

percent differences between output and input signals. To use other terms, the moving of the center of the diaphragm relative to the housing is a span adjustment.

The amount that the ratio of diameters can be changed is quite limited, perhaps less than two percent of the input span. This means that, unlike moment-balance differential-pressure transmitters, force-balance differential-pressure transmitters have ranges that are essentially fixed. Recall that on moment-balance differential-pressure transmitters, the input span could be changed from 25 to 250 inches of water by moving the contactor of the lever gain mechanism.

In order to make large changes in span in a true force-balance transmitter, it is necessary to make large changes in the ratio of the sensing diaphragm to the balancing diaphragm. This is accomplished by using balancing diaphragms of different diameters. The sensing diaphragm remains the same.

THE FORCE-BALANCE PRINCIPLE APPLIED

We have discussed the true force-balance principle, and have observed that the essential aspect of the true force-balance mechanism is the fact that the forces involved directly oppose each other. The unique feature of a true force-balance mechanism is the lack of levers, and the arranging of pressure-to-force- and position-to-force elements so that they directly oppose each other. In the moment-balance principle, the force involved acts at distance from a fulcrum point. Now, we will discuss the true force-balance principle as applied to differential pressure transmitters. Taylor's Model 200T differential pressure transmitter is the example that is used.

Components

1. The D/P sensing diaphragm.
2. The high- and low-pressure compartments.
3. A thrust shaft.
4. A balancing diaphragm.
5. A nozzle backpressure compartment.
6. A detector mechanism.

Arrangements

The sensing diaphragm and the balancing diaphragm are mounted on the thrust shaft. The thrust shaft is arranged within the instrument housing so that it can move a small amount. This small movement is detected by a baffle/nozzle detector located at the lower end of the shaft. The shaft end serves as the baffle. The nozzle is threaded into the housing. Turning the nozzle moves the tip of the nozzle relative to the housing. The nozzle backpressure loads the balancing diaphragm.

Mounted at the upper end of the thrust shaft is an output span-location (zero) spring. One end of the zero spring rests against the thrust shaft. The other end rests against a threaded screw. The load on the spring can be changed by adjusting the zero screw.

Two seal bellows are provided to form the high-pressure and low-pressure compartments. The seal bellows are identical and arranged to perform only a sealing function.

The sensing diaphragm is considerably larger than the balancing diaphragm, which means that the full range of balancing pressure is required to balance a relatively small range of differential pressure.

Principle of Operation

Refer to Fig. 16-4. Assume that the instrument is balanced for some input differential pressure. Assume

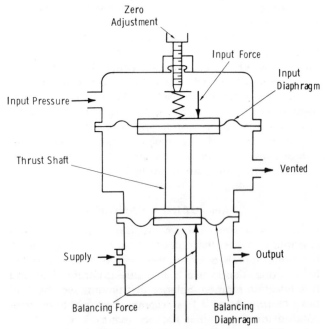

Fig. 16-4. Bellows system in Taylor Model 200T transmitter.

further that there is an increase in differential pressure. The increase in differential pressure, acting on the sensing diaphragm, results in an increased force that moves the thrust shaft downward toward the nozzle, covering the nozzle and increasing the nozzle backpressure, hence the output.

This increase in nozzle backpressure, acting on the balancing diaphragm, causes an increasing upward force. When the increasing upward force balances the change in downward force, the thrust shaft reaches equilibrium. When the forces are balanced, the output pressure is proportional to the differential pressure.

CALIBRATION ADJUSTMENTS

Suppose the output pressure did not exactly coincide with the differential pressure. In other words, suppose the instrument was not in calibration. How could it be calibrated?

For a specific example assume that as the input differential pressure changes from 0 inch to 100 inches of water, the output changes from 2 to 14 psig. Examination of these numbers will show that the output span is 12 psi, hence, correct, but the span location is off by 1 psi. To correct for this error in calibration, the span-location screw is adjusted downward to increase the spring force on the thrust shaft. This increase in spring force must be balanced out by the nozzle backpressure. The span-location screw is adjusted inward until the nozzle backpressure is 3 psig. A change of 1 psi at 2 psig will change the 14 psig to 15 psig.

Consider an example of calibration being in error on span. That is, for a 100 percent change of input, the output does not change 100 percent. To be specific, assume the input signal changes from 0 inch to 100 inches of water, but the output signal changes from 3 to 14 psig. It should change from 3 to 15 psig. In other words, the span is short by 1 psi.

To increase the span, it is necessary to change the ratio of the sensing-diaphragm area to the balancing-diaphragm area. Recall that the effective area of a diaphragm changes as the center portion of the diaphragm moves relative to the housing. The problem, then, becomes one of moving the central portions of the diaphragm relative to the housing. If the thrust shaft could be moved relative to the housing, the central portion of the diaphragm will also move.

A first look at the mechanism may lead us to believe that adjusting the span location screw will move the thrust shaft downward. This is only partly true because increasing the loading of the span location spring will move the thrust shaft an amount less than the few thousandths of an inch which will cause the baffle to fully cover the nozzle. Therefore, the amount of shifting of the thrust shaft obtainable by adjusting the span location screw is less than a few thousandths of an inch. Also notice that changing the thrust shaft this few thousandths of an inch has changed the output pressure from 3 to 15 psig. Therefore, we must conclude that the span location adjustment does not move the thrust shaft a significant amount relative to the housing.

A different way of moving the thrust shaft relative to the housing must be found. Examine the nozzle. Notice that it is threaded into the housing. Suppose the nozzle is turned away from the baffle (say) 1/32 of an inch. As the nozzle is moved from the baffle, the nozzle backpressure will decrease. As the nozzle backpressure decreases, the balancing force decreases. If the balancing force decreases, the thrust shaft will move to the same (almost) distance from the nozzle that it was prior to our changing the nozzle. By turning the nozzle away from the baffle, we have managed to move the thrust shaft relative to the housing by 1/32 inch, hence, the central portion of the diaphragm has moved 1/32 inch relative to the housing, thereby changing the effective area of each of the diaphragms.

Observe the convolutions on the diaphragm. Notice that the sensing diaphragm convolution is down, and the balancing diaphragm is up. This means that, as the thrust shaft moves downward the effective area of the sensing diaphragm gets larger as the effective area of the balancing diaphragm gets smaller. Or, more simply, the ratio of the diaphragm areas is decreased. Because of this decreased ratio of diaphragm areas, a large nozzle backpressure is required to balance a given differential pressure. This, of course, is what is required if the span is to be increased by the 1 psi that it lacked.

Unfortunately, as the nozzle is moved, the loading of the zero spring is changed because the moving of the nozzle also moves the thrust shaft. If the thrust shaft is moved, the spring force changes slightly. As a result of this interaction of zero and span adjustment, we are obligated to alternately adjust span and zero. As you will recall, this is not an unusual situation.

Fig. 16-5 is a more pictorial diagram of the Taylor 200T transmitter showing the actual configuration of components. This diagram is a considerably simplified drawing of the actual mechanism. The actual mechanism thrust shaft consists of a series of threaded members and O-ring seals that clamp the diaphragm and sealing bellows. Care must be taken to correctly assemble the thrust shaft and install it within its housing. Fig. 16-6 is a photograph of the mechanism. Study Figs. 16-4, 16-5 and 16-6, and be sure you are able to relate them.

Force-balance instruments employ a type of construction that is susceptible to both internal and external leaks. Therefore, the instruments should be carefully checked.

FORCE-BALANCE POSITIONERS

We will now consider the force-balance principle as applied to positioners. The positioners of Moore, Fisher Governor and Annin companies will be discussed. The Moore and Fisher Governor positioners are the usual side-arm-mounted type; the Annin is integrally mounted. The difference in the two methods of mounting arises out of the method of feeding back

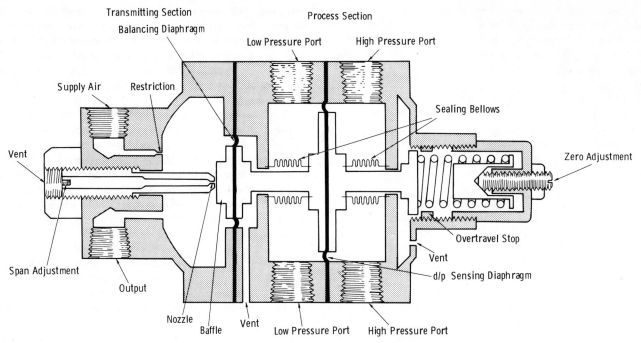

Fig. 16-5. Schematic of Taylor Model 200T transmitter.

the valve position to the positioner. Side-arm-mounted positioners require an external linkage system that feeds back the valve position to the positioner. The integrally-mounted valve positioner requires no external linkage because the feedback is within the housing.

Fig. 16-6. Taylor Model 200T transmitter.

You will recall, the point was emphasized that in force-balance devices, forces directly oppose each other; whereas, in moment-balance instruments, the forces act at distances from a fulcrum point. Do not confuse linkage that is used to route a movement to the positioner, with linkage that is an essential part of a positioner.

Components

The components of a force-balance positioner are:
1. An input device which converts the input signal to force.
2. A balancing mechanism consisting of the actuator and a feedback element that converts the actuator position to force.

3. A thrust shaft.
4. A detector mechanism.

Arrangements

All elements, other than the external lever system, are arranged on a center line. The input force is applied to one end of the thrust assembly; the balancing force is applied to the other. The detector is arranged to sense any change in position of the thrust assembly.

For a specific arrangement, consider the Moore Company positioner. Fig. 16-7 is a photograph of the

Fig. 16-7. Moore positioner.

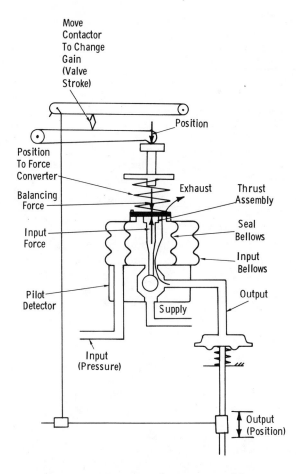

Fig. 16-8. Diagram of Moore positioner.

increase. The increased signal will result in an increased force being applied to the thrust assembly, tending to lift it. The pilot valve, responding to this lift, causes the supply port to open wider, and the exhaust to be reduced. This action increases the output pressure of the pilot valve, which moves the actuator downward.

This downward actuator movement is fed back through a parallel-lever gain mechanism. The output of the gain mechanism is applied to the top of the balancing spring and to the thrust assembly. At this point, the two forces equal each other, and the thrust assembly will come to equilibrium. Equilibrium is reached when air pressure drives the actuator to a position resulting in a force exactly equal to the input-signal force.

So far, we have not said anything about the sealed bellows because, functionally, it is not involved in the operation of the positioner. Its function is limited to providing a flexible air passage that channels the exhaust air from the pilot valve to the atmosphere via small holes through the thrust assembly.

OPERATION OF FISHER GOVERNOR POSITIONER

Fig. 16-9 is a diagram of the Fisher Governor positioner called a "Positrol." A photograph of the positioner is shown in Fig. 16-10. The positioner is side-arm mounted. The actuator position is fed back to the positioner through a parallel-lever system. In this respect, it is the same as the Moore positioner just discussed. Note, however, that one of the levers forms a 90-degree angle. Functionally, this is the same as the 180-degree angle lever used by Moore and others. The need for the 90-degree angle lever arises out of the fact that the thrust assembly is mounted at a 90-degree angle relative to the actuator travel. The thrust assembly appears to be different from that used by Moore, but notice that with both Moore and Fisher Governor, the thrust shaft is arranged so that the input

positioner and Fig. 16-8 is a schematic diagram. The Moore positioner consists of a position-to-force converter (a spring) arranged to directly load the input-signal element (a bellows). The actuator position is fed from the actuator to the top of the spring through a parallel-lever gain mechanism. The thrust assembly is a disc of metal mounted between the spring and bellows.

The thrust assembly used by the Moore positioner is extremely elementary compared to the thrust assembly of the 200T Taylor transmitter (discussed in preceding paragraphs) or to the thrust assembly of force-balance controllers and computing relays. The reason the thrust assembly is so elementary in the Moore positioner is that only two signals, hence, only two forces, are interacting. If there were a multiplicity of forces as is the case with computing relays and controllers, a more complicated thrust assembly is required.

The detector is a conventional direct-acting pilot valve. The valve plug is driven by an extension that contacts the thrust assembly.

OPERATION OF THE MOORE POSITIONERS

Assume the positioner is in balance. That is, the input force is exactly balanced by a force that is a function of the valve position. Let the input signal

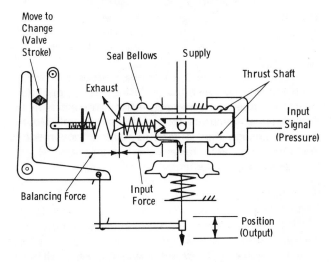

Fig. 16-9. Elementary diagram of Fisher Governor Positrol.

signal force and the balance force are applied at opposite ends of the thrust shaft.

In the Fisher Governor positioner, the input signal is applied to a bellows-in-a-can assembly. The resulting force passes through the thrust shaft and is applied to the balancing spring. The detector is arranged to detect any movement of the thrust shaft. The detector is a non-bleed pilot valve. Recall that the identifying characteristics of a non-bleed valve are a valve plug constructed so that the supply and exhaust seats "look" in the same direction, and a movable exhaust port. A sealing bellows (or diaphragm) is required so that the exhaust port can move. The output of the pilot valve is taken from between the two seats.

Fig. 16-10. Fisher Governor Positrol.

Let us see how this positioner operates. Assume the positioner is in a balanced position. If it is, both the supply port and the exhaust port will be closed. Recall that this is true for all non-bleed valves. Now let us increase the input signal pressure.

An increase in the input signal causes the thrust assembly to move to the left, lifting the supply plug from the supply port, and permitting the supply air to pass through the port. This results in an increase in pilot valve output pressure. This output pressure, acting on the actuator, moves the actuator downward. The downward movement, feeding through the lever system and compressing the spring, causes an increase in balancing force. The increase in balancing force directly opposes the increase in the input signal force. When these two forces equalize, both the supply and the exhaust ports will be closed. The pressure applied to the actuator will remain constant. The positioner and actuator are therefore in equilibrium at a new position proportional to the new input signal pressure.

Notice that the output of the pilot valve, in addition to being applied to the actuator, also fills the inside of the input-signal bellows and the seal bellows. Since these two bellows are identically sized, the forces across the bellows cancel each other out. Therefore, the change in pilot valve output pressure within these bellows does not introduce any changing force on the thrust assembly.

OPERATION OF ANNIN COMPANY POSITIONER

Fig. 16-11 is a diagram of the Annin valve positioner. The Annin valve positioner is integrally mounted, making it possible for the balancing force to be directly applied to the thrust assembly. This eliminates the need for an external lever system. In a design of this type, the change of the gain of the positioner (that is, changing the actuator stroke for a given input signal change) requires changing the spring elements.

The Annin valve positioner is designed to position a piston actuator. Furthermore, the piston actuator that is used is not spring loaded, but is air loaded. The regulator required to regulate the air pressure to supply the detector and to air load the piston is integrally mounted with the positioner. Our diagram does not show this regulator.

The positioner is mounted on the actuator housing and is on the same center line as the piston. The piston position feedback is internal; that is, within the actuator housing. The feedback element is a spring that converts the piston position to a proportional force. This force is applied to the thrust assembly. The thrust assembly is mounted between two diaphragms that permit it to move a small amount. The lower diaphragm is the balancing diaphragm; the upper diaphragm is the input signal diaphragm. Notice that the areas of the input signal diaphragm and the balancing diaphragm are different.

The detector, which is a direct acting pilot valve, is arranged to detect any small displacement of the thrust assembly. Let us see how this positioner works. As before, let us assume that the positioner is in a balanced state and that there is an increase in the input signal.

This increase in signal pressure causes the thrust assembly to move downward because the balancing diaphragm is greater in area than the input signal diaphragm. The input signal pressure causes an upward force because of the input signal diaphragm, but also it causes a downward force because of the balancing diaphragm. Since the balancing diaphragm is larger than the input signal diaphragm, the downward force is larger than the upward force. Hence, the thrust assembly moves downward.

The pilot valve, detecting this downward movement, tends to close off the exhaust port and open the supply port somewhat. This results in an increase in pilot output pressure which is applied to the under side of the piston, causing it to move upward. The

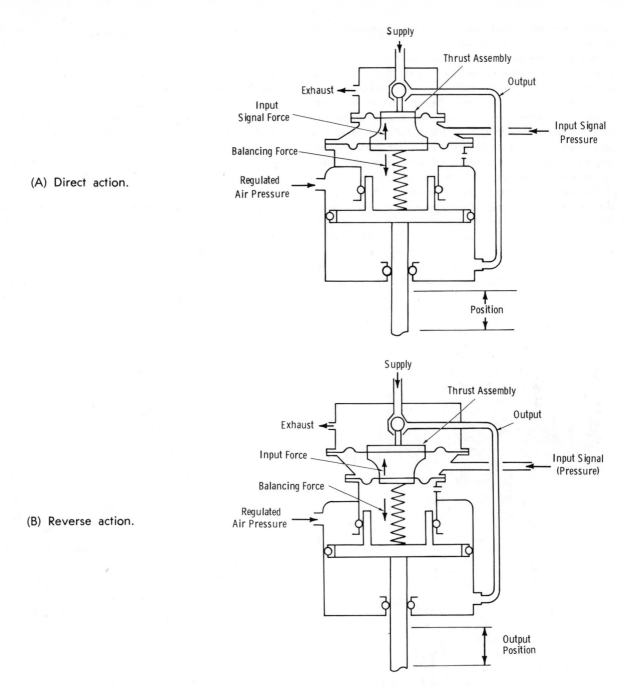

(A) Direct action.

(B) Reverse action.

Fig. 16-11. Elementary diagram of Annin valve positioner.

upward movement compresses the balancing spring and increases the force on the thrust assembly.

This increasing upward force directly opposes the increase in downward force that resulted from the increase in signal pressure. When these two forces balance, the pilot will assume a fixed position between its seats. Hence, the output pressure will become constant, and the piston will assume a position proportional to the input signal.

Again notice, as is always the case with the valve positioner, that the pilot valve output pressure will change to whatever pressure is required to force the piston to a position that results in a balancing force exactly equal to an input signal force.

The Annin Company uses a novel method for changing the action of their positioner. By action, we are referring to the direction of actuator travel for a given input signal change. If, on increasing the signal, the actuator moves upward, the positioner is described as direct acting. If on the other hand, the actuator moves downward for an increasing signal pressure, the actuator is considered to be reverse acting.

As far as the positioner itself is concerned, notice that in the direct acting actuator, for an increasing input signal there is an increasing output from the positioner. In the reverse acting actuator, for an increase in input signal there is a decrease in positioner output. Do not be confused by the fact that in the Annin valves, an increasing positioner output results in an upward actuator movement.

Annin changes the action of their positioners by reversing the thrust assembly. Recall that in our discussions, the thrust assembly was arranged so that the larger diaphragm was down. Hence, for an increasing signal, increased pressure on the larger diaphragm causes the thrust assembly to move down. If the thrust assembly is reversed so that the larger diaphragm is up, the same increase in signal will cause the thrust assembly to move upward. (See Fig. 16-11B.)

The action of the pilot valve is the same. But, in the direct acting case, the downward movement of the thrust assembly results in an increasing output pressure. When the thrust assembly is arranged so that the larger diaphragm is upward, an increasing signal causes a decreasing output signal. Figs. 16-12 and 16-13 are pictorial diagrams; relate these to Figs. 16-11A and 16-11B.

SUMMARY

In the positioners discussed, notice that with side-arm-mounted positioners a lever system is used. Nevertheless, the balancing force directly opposes the input signal force. The two forces are applied to opposite ends of the thrust assembly. The detector is arranged to detect any small displacement of the thrust assembly.

Do not be confused by the variety of physical forms that the thrust assembly has taken in the various force-balance instruments discussed. Notice that all the forces involved converge on the thrust assembly, and that the thrust assembly must be arranged so that it can respond to small differences in these forces. The detector discovers these small differences and changes forces on the thrust assembly to bring them to balance.

The usual construction is to mount the thrust assembly on a diaphragm, but, as you have already seen, bellows can also be used.

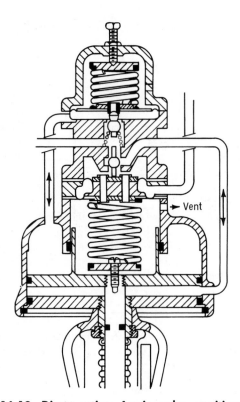

Fig. 16-12. Direct action Annin valve positioner.

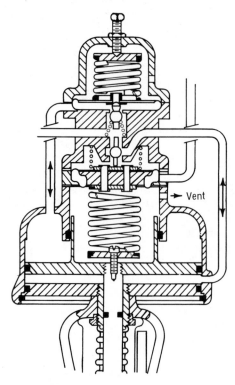

Fig. 16-13. Reverse action Annin valve positioner.

Chapter 17

Motion-Balance Principle and Applications

In previous discussions we noted that all instruments can be divided into two major branches, feedforward, and feedback or self-balancing. Self-balancing instruments, in turn, can be divided into two categories, motion-type and force-type. In Chapters 12 to 16, force-type instruments were studied, and it was shown that they can be found in two forms: true force-balance and moment-balance.

In this and following chapters, we will consider motion-balance instruments. As with force-balance instruments, motion-balance instruments also appear in two forms. The first, which is analogous to the moment balance, we shall call angle motion balance. The second form, which is analogous to true force balance, we shall call linear motion balance.

The angle motion-balance instruments will be by far the most common motion-balance instruments. Taylor's series 210 transmitter and Moore's series 173 transmitter are examples of the few linear motion-balance instruments.

THE FUNDAMENTAL MOTION-BALANCE MECHANISM

We shall in our consideration of motion-balance instruments, proceed in about the same way as we did in our consideration of force-balance instruments. We will propose a fundamental mechanism, list the essential components, and describe the operation. We will then show how this fundamental mechanism is incorporated into the design of a variety of instruments.

Elements

Elements of the fundamental angle motion-balance mechanism are:

1. An input lever which pivots on its fixed pivot.
2. A balancing lever which pivots on its fixed pivot.
3. A floating lever which rotates on two floating pivots.
4. An error detector.

Arrangements

The measurement signal is in the form of a motion to the input lever. The balancing motion drives the other fixed lever. The floating lever is arranged between the two fixed levers so that the ends of the floating levers move as the measurement and balancing motions occur. The detector is positioned to detect any displacement of the floating lever.

Fig. 17-1 is the diagram of a fundamental angle motion-balance mechanism. This mechanism is used to convert a measurement to a proportional pressure. In addition to its use in various kinds of transmitters, this mechanism also is used in controllers and valve posi-

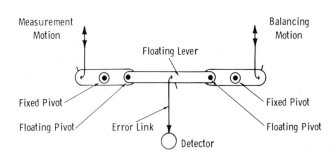

Fig. 17-1. Fundamental angle motion-balance mechanism.

tioners. The differences in these applications arise out of the way the input motion or the balancing motion originates and is used. These variations will be discussed in following chapters. Motion-balance linkage is perhaps the most important instrument mechanism.

The motion-balance lever mechanism appears in a wide variety of instruments. It is a common mechanism which is used in many ingenious ways. For example, it is used as a motion divider by Fischer & Porter in their electronic rotameter transmitter. It is also used as an adjustable ratio mechanism. Whenever there is a need to relate two signals to get one output, there is the clear possibility that variations of the three types of motion-balance mechanisms will be used. We will study motion-balance mechanisms as used in controllers in later chapters. In the next chapter, motion-balance positioners and transmitters will be studied.

Principle of Operation (Three-Lever Mechanisms)

Let us see how the fundamental angle motion-balance mechanism operates. Assume that the mechanism is in balance and there is an increase in measurement signal. The increased measurement signal will rotate the fixed measurement lever counterclockwise, thereby lifting one end of the floating lever. (The floating lever rotates about the balancing floating pivot.) As it rotates, the center portion of the floating lever is raised. The detector responds to this displacement of the floating lever by decreasing the output pressure. The output pressure is applied to the balancing bellows. This decrease in output pressure causes a change in balancing motion. This motion rotates the balancing lever counterclockwise, lowering the balancing floating pivot and with it the balancing end of the floating lever. (Recall that the measurement signal raised the measuring floating pivot, thereby raising the center portion of the floating lever.) Now the balancing motion lowers the other end of the floating lever, tending to lower the center of the floating lever.

The detector will change its output pressure until the balancing motion (almost) equals the measurement motion.

The diagram we have shown is symmetrical. The detector take off is at the center of the mechanism. This is highly idealized, but it does demonstrate how the input and balancing motions are made equal (within the range of the detector) and how the detector causes these motions to be made equal. Fig. 17-2 diagrams the balancing action. Notice the difference in lever position for balance at 3, 9, and 15 psig.

The output of this instrument is an air pressure, as was true of the force-type instruments. This air pressure is proportional to a measurement input motion, hence, the output is proportional to the input. You will recall that the function of a transmitter is to convert a measurement to a proportional pressure.

The mechanism just described is one type of motion mechanism which we shall call type 3. It is the most complicated motion mechanism in that there are three levers involved.

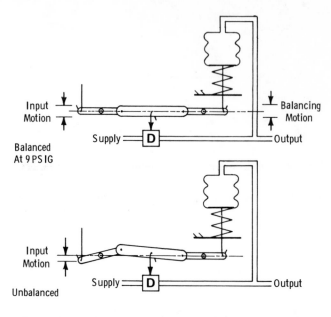

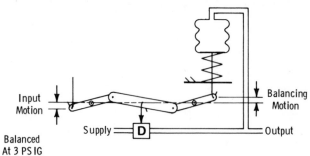

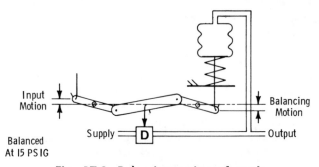

Fig. 17-2. Balancing action of angle motion-balance mechanism.

TYPE-2 MECHANISM

There is a motion-balance mechanism using two levers. Fig. 17-3 shows such a mechanism. In our discussion of Fig. 17-1, the measurement motion is applied to a measurement fixed lever. This, in turn, shifts the floating lever. If we were to connect the measurement motion directly to one end of the floating lever, we could eliminate the measurement fixed lever. Two levers characterize the type-2 motion-balance mechanism. Let us see how this mechanism is used to balance motions.

Assume the measurement motion lifts the floating lever. The detector, responding to the new position of the floating lever, will change the output of the de-

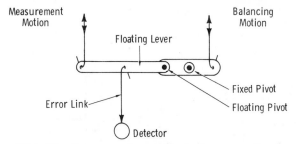

Fig. 17-3. Two-lever angle motion-balance mechanism.

tector so as to rotate the balancing lever counterclockwise, lowering the right end of the floating lever. (Recall that the original motion was to lift the left end of the floating lever.) The balancing motion lowers the right end until the center of the floating lever is brought back to its original position.

TYPE-1 MECHANISM

Let us consider a third motion mechanism. We were able to eliminate one of the fixed levers by directly connecting the measurement motion to the floating lever. It is possible to eliminate the second fixed lever by directly connecting the balanced motion to the other end of the floating lever. The detector is arranged in all three types of motion mechanisms to detect any change in position of the center of the floating lever. (See Fig. 17-4.)

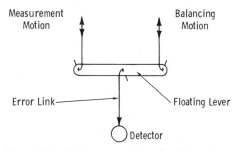

**Fig. 17-4. Detector action in Type-1
motion-balance mechanism.**

Let us see how type-1 mechanism operates. Suppose that the measurement motion lowers the measurement end of the floating lever. The detector, responding to this new position of the floating lever, will change the output pressure, which, acting through a pressure-to-motion converter, lifts the balancing end of the floating lever. When the balancing motion (within the range of the detector) equals the measurement motion, the mechanism will come to equilibrium.

ANGULAR MOTION-BALANCE TRANSMITTERS

We have discussed three types of angular motion-balance mechanisms. We noted that the essential characteristics of these mechanisms are that the two signals involved (measurement and balance) are fed in opposite directions into opposite ends of a floating lever. The detector is arranged to detect a small displacement of the floating lever.

We noted further that although the fundamental diagrams we used were symmetrical, the actual mechanisms are usually quite unsymmetrical. Frequently, the levers involved are folded 90-degree two-sided levers. It is necessary that one be able to identify the levers regardless of configuration and physical appearance. This is not always easy to do because motion-balance lever systems can be quite involved as compared to force-balance lever systems. Nevertheless, if an effort is made to first, locate the floating lever; second, locate any other levers driving the floating lever; third, locate the fixed and floating pivot points; and finally, locate the input motion and balancing motion, no difficulties will be experienced in understanding motion-balance lever systems.

We now consider examples of type 3 and type 2 motion-balance mechanisms.

Elements of Type-3 Mechanism

1. A floating lever and two floating pivots.
2. An input lever and its fixed pivot.
3. A balancing lever and its fixed pivot.
4. A detector mechanism.

Arrangements

The floating lever is arranged between the two fixed levers. The points of contact between the floating lever and the ends of the two fixed levers form the floating pivots. A detector mechanism, which frequently involves a lever system of its own, is arranged to detect any small displacements of the floating lever. The output of the detector is fed back to a pressure-to-motion converter which almost always is a bellows-spring combination. The pressure-to-motion converter drives the balancing lever.

Principle of Operation

Fig. 17-5 is a diagram of a motion-balance mechanism used in the Foxboro Model 42 transmitter. Before we discuss the operation of this mechanism, let us identify the levers involved and the fixed and floating pivots. Notice first of all, that the measurement lever is made of 2 one-sided levers mounted on the same shaft. The balancing lever, on the other hand, is oddly shaped in that there are scooped-out extensions. Do not let those odd configurations hide the fact that the balancing lever is a conventional 180-degree two-sided lever. The scooped-out ends provide clearance and mechanical stops for other elements.

Identify the fixed pivot point of the balancing lever. Observe where the balancing motion is fed into the balancing lever. Locate the point of contact between the floating lever and the balancing lever. In our diagram, it is a pinned connection between the two levers. The point of contact between the measurement lever and the floating lever forms the first floating pivot.

The detector mechanism is considerably more elaborate than the mechanism indicated in the diagrams of Chapter 14. Nevertheless, in spite of its apparent

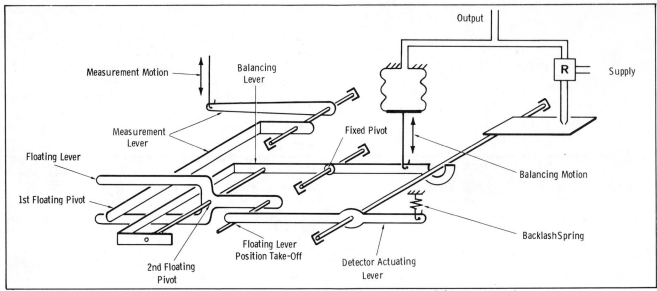

Fig. 17-5. Motion-balance mechanism in Foxboro Model 42 transmitter.

complexity, its function is simply that of detecting small displacements of the floating lever. A detector actuating lever rotates if there is a displacement of a floating lever. As it rotates, it changes the baffle-nozzle clearance. The overall effect of this lever detector system in no way changes the fact that the baffle-nozzle detector detects changes in displacement of the floating lever.

The specific arrangement of mechanisms generally results from the need for making the mechanism compact and the need for changing the direction of motion.

MOTION-BALANCE LEVER MECHANISMS

Assume that the mechanism is in a balanced condition and that the measurement changes in a downward direction. It can go either up or down, although the diagram shows it centered. This change in motion rotates the measurement lever counterclockwise, lowering the measurement end of the floating lever (the floating lever pivoting on the balancing lever). This rotates the actuating lever clockwise, thereby uncovering the nozzle. The nozzle backpressure drops off, as does the relay output pressure. The pressure-to-motion converter (a bellows in a can), responding to the drop-off of relay output pressure, lifts, rotating the balancing lever counterclockwise. The balancing end of the floating lever drops.

The dropping of the balancing floating pivot permits the detector actuating lever to rotate counterclockwise. (Recall that the measurement motion caused it to rotate clockwise.) The detector actuating lever will continue to rotate clockwise until the clockwise motion balances (within the range of the detector) the original measurement motion. Notice that the measurement and balance motions are balanced when the motions of the two floating pivots are equal.

Fig. 17-6 is a more pictorial diagram showing the mechanism; Fig. 17-7 is a photograph of the mecha-

nism being discussed. Study these diagrams carefully to be sure you are able to identify the essential elements of the mechanism as they appear in the actual mechanism.

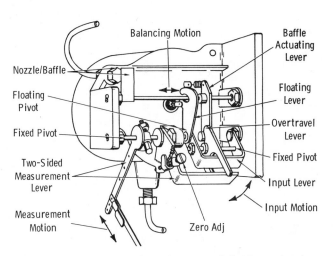

Fig. 17-6. Schematic of Foxboro Model 42 mechanism.

Elements of Type-1 Mechanism

For our second example of an angular motion-balance transmitter, we will use a liquid level displacer transmitter of Mason-Neilan. Earlier in the book, the operation of the displacer torque-tube instrument was considered in detail. We now will study how the angular motion, due to change of level, is converted to a proportional output pressure.

Let us list the essential elements in the mechanism and then identify what type mechanism is used. (See Fig. 17-8.)

1. An input motion link.
2. A floating lever on two floating pivots.
3. A detector mechanism.
4. A balancing motion link.

Fig. 17-7. Photograph of Foxboro Model 42 mechanism.

Observe the measurement coming into one end of the floating lever. The balancing motion is fed into the other end of the floating lever. (The elements so far identified are a floating lever and two floating pivot points.) The balancing motion is directly connected to the floating lever. The measurement motion is also directly connected to the floating lever. Therefore, we must conclude that we have a type-1 mechanism.

Recognize that even though there is a lever involved in the detector mechanism its function is solely that of transmitting any displacement of floating lever to the detector. Further recognize that the important thing is that the detector senses any displacement of the floating lever. It is relatively unimportant precisely what part of the floating lever the detector looks at.

Notice further that the balancing mechanism consists of a bellows, spring, and a variable spring element (a cantilever spring). As the effective length of the cantilever spring is changed, the amount of motion obtained for a given change in balancing pres-

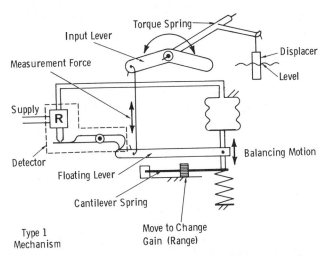

Fig. 17-8. Mechanism in a Mason-Neilan transmitter.

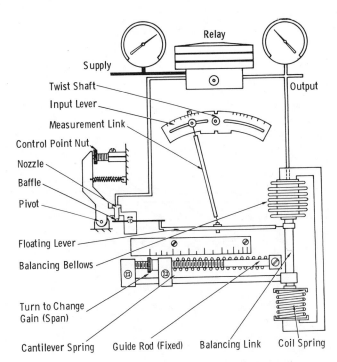

Fig. 17-9. Schematic of Mason-Neilan transmitter.

sure can be varied as the length of the spring is varied. This changes the gain (span) of the transmitter.

Principle of Operation

Assume that the mechanism is balanced and that the level decreases about the displacer. As a result of this change in level, the input-lever rotates clockwise. As a result, the measurement motion moves up, lifting the measurement end of the floating lever, and causing the baffle to move away from the nozzle. The nozzle backpressure (balancing pressure) falls off. This fall-off in pressure causes an upward balancing motion that rotates the floating lever counterclockwise about the measurement end of the floating lever.

This balancing counterclockwise motion causes the baffle to move toward the nozzle. (Recall that the original measurement motion causes the baffle to leave the nozzle.) The balancing motion will continue until it (almost) balances out the measurement motion. At that point, the baffle will have taken the position with respect to the nozzle that results in the detector backpressure that is proportional to the measurement motion.

The measurement motion now has been converted to a proportional output pressure. Therefore, the level has been converted to a proportional output pressure.

Fig. 17-9 is a pictorial diagram and Fig. 17-10 is a photograph of the transmitter. Study these diagrams to be sure you recognize the essential elements.

SUMMARY

We have discussed three types of angle-balance mechanisms. In all three mechanisms, notice that a change in measurement motion results in a corresponding change in balancing motion. The balancing motion is due to the change in detector output pressure acting on a pressure-to-motion converter. The detector output pressure changes until the balancing motion is equal to (within the range of the detector) the measurement motion.

The detector output pressure is the output of the instrument. The instrument output pressure is proportional to the measurement input motion. The motions involved are larger, perhaps, as much as ½ inch. The

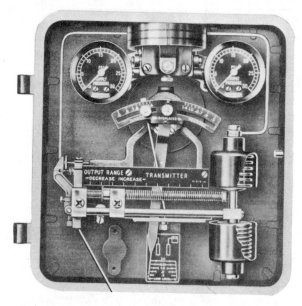

Fig. 17-10. Mason-Neilan transmitter.

motions of force-balance instruments are less than, or about equal to the motion required to fully range the detector (about .002 inches).

In this chapter, we have considered two types of motion-balance mechanisms as they are used in transmitters. The key to understanding these mechanisms is to: 1) locate the floating lever; 2) locate the fixed levers and the floating pivot points. There will be either no fixed levers, or one or two, depending on whether the mechanism is type 1, 2, or 3. The fixed levers drive the floating lever.

Knowing what elements to look for makes it relatively easy to recognize these elements as they appear in the actual instrument. Identify the essential elements before attempting to analyze the operation of the mechanisms, or much confusion will result because of the presence of the elements which are used to change direction or to transmit the position of the floating lever to the detector.

Notice that the measurement motion and balancing motion as such are completely independent of each other. In no way is the measurement motion actually "felt" by the balancing motion. It is the detector responding to these movements that causes the balancing action. Compare this action with moment-balance mechanisms. Recall that the measurement force directly opposed the balancing force because the forces involved were applied against a force beam.

In Chapter 18, we will study angular motion-balance mechanisms as they are used on valve positioners. Valve positioners frequently use a type-2, or two-lever, mechanism.

Angle Motion-Balance Positioners

THE ANGLE MOTION-BALANCE MECHANISM

In this chapter, we will discuss positioners that use an angle motion-balance mechanism. The function of any valve positioner, regardless of the kind of mechanism employed, is the same as that of any other valve positioner. All the aspects of positioners as functional entities apply to angle motion-balance positioners as well as they do to force balance positioners. That function is to ensure that the actuator position is proportional to an input signal. It is the actuator position that balances the input signal.

Components

1. An input element to convert an air pressure to motion.
2. A motion-balance lever mechanism.
3. Balancing components (the actuator).
4. A detector mechanism.

Notice that an essential component of the actuator positioner is the actuator itself. It is the actuator that furnishes the balancing motion.

Arrangements

Angle motion-balance positioners are available only side-arm mounted. The positioner is mounted on the actuator so that the actuator motion can be fed back to the positioner. The element used is usually a two-sided lever that is caused to rotate as the actuator stem moves. This lever is one of those composing the motion-balance lever system.

The input signal is fed to a pressure-to-position converter (usually a bellows/spring) that drives one end of the floating lever. The other end of the floating lever is driven by the balancing lever which in turn is

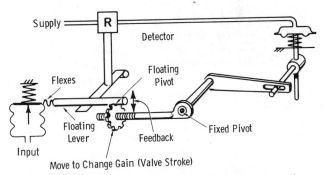

Fig. 18-1. Elementary diagram of Foxboro angle motion-balance positioner.

driven by the actuator. A detector is arranged to detect any displacement of the floating lever. The output of the detector drives the actuator.

Fig. 18-1 is an angle motion-balance positioner manufactured by Foxboro. It uses a two-lever motion-balance mechanism. The input signal is directly applied to one end of the floating lever.

Principle of Operation

Assume that the positioner and actuator are in balance and that the input signal increases. The increase in input signal will lift the floating lever (the floating lever pivoting on the balancing lever). As it lifts, the baffle covers the nozzle. The reverse-acting relay output decreases, permitting the actuator stem to move upward. This upward movement rotates the balancing lever counterclockwise, lowering the balancing end of the floating lever (the floating lever pivoting on the input). This downward movement of the floating lever continues until the downward motion balances (within the range of the detector) the input motion.

MOTION BALANCE AND MOMENT BALANCE COMPARED

Recognize that positioners are always used with actuators. Actuators are motion devices. The purpose of the actuator is to convert an air-pressure signal to a corresponding position; therefore, for a range of input signals, there is a corresponding actuator motion.

If a force-type mechanism is used, it is necessary to convert the actuator motion to a corresponding force. This was done in force-balance instruments by introducing a position-to-force converter (spring) between the actuator and the positioner. The input signal was applied to a pressure-to-force converter (bellows). In this way, the input signal and the balancing signal become forces applied to a force beam. The beam reacts to any difference in forces. The detector detects the beam movement and initiates any corrective action.

Consider now the angle motion-balance mechanism. Since it is a motion-balance mechanism, the actuator motion is directly usable. There is no need for a conversion element, hence, there is no need for a spring to be introduced between the actuator and the positioner. The actuator position is directly applied to the floating lever. On the other hand, the input signal must be converted to a motion. This is accomplished by feeding the input signal (pressure) to a pressure-to-position converter (bellows spring combination). The two signals involved are then motions. They do not react on each other. The balancing motion follows the input motion due to the action of the detector. These two motions are applied to opposite ends of the floating lever. The detector detects any movement of the floating lever.

The detectors in both angle-motion balance and angle-force balance positioners are arranged to detect small displacements of the floating lever or force beam, respectively, and to cause a balancing action so that the actuator will assume a position proportional to the input signal. The adjustable gain mechanism in both the moment- and angle-balance instruments discussed so far are the parallel-lever type. As the contactor between the parallel levers is moved, the ratio of levers changes; hence, the gain of the positioner is changed. (See Fig. 18-1.)

In the Foxboro mechanism, the floating lever does double duty in that not only does it operate as a float-

ing lever, it also operates as the second lever of the parallel-lever gain mechanism.

Fig. 18-2 is a photograph of the positioner. Study this picture to be sure you can recognize the essential components as they appear in the actual instrument.

FOXBORO TYPE "C" POSITIONER

We will now consider angle-balance positioners that do not use a parallel-lever gain mechanism.

The type "C" positioner is an angle motion-balance positioner functionally identical with the positioner just described. The type "C" positioner consists of the same components as the positioner just described. However, the specific arrangements of these components are quite different. The gain mechanism is not the parallel-lever mechanism, but is, rather, what we will call an angle-gain mechanism. For the moment, let us not concern ourselves too much with the angle-gain mechanism.

The input device is a pressure-to-position converter consisting of a bellows and a folded cantilever spring. The cantilever spring does double duty in that it is both part of the input device and part of the balancing lever.

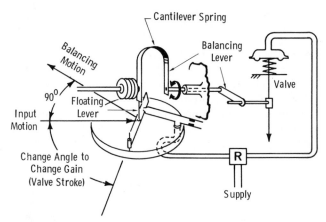

Fig. 18-3. Balancing mechanism in Foxboro type "C" positioner.

See Fig. 18-3. The balancing lever is a two-sided lever pivoted through the case. The actuator side of the balancing lever is a straight line between the bellows pivot point and the baffle actuating ball. Do not let the configuration of the cantilever spring obscure the configuration of the balancing lever.

The balancing lever is unusually arranged so that one end of the balancing lever not only is part of the balancing lever but is also the floating lever. Notice that as the input signal changes, the cantilever spring compresses, permitting one end of the balancing lever to "slide" along the axis of rotation. In other words, the input position is directly applied to the floating lever. The actuator position passes through the two-sided balancing lever, one side of which is also the floating lever.

Type "C" positioner, in addition to the unusual arrangements of components, is different in another re-

Fig. 18-2. Foxboro positioner.

spect. Notice that, unlike the mechanisms previously discussed, the two signals involved are at right angles to each other rather than parallel. Since the signals are at right angles to each other, it is necessary that the mechanisms be arranged to take this relationship into account. The result of this right-angle relationship is that the motions, rather than operating in one plane, operate in two planes. The diagram shows the two planes of operation. Mechanisms arranged to operate in two planes are ideally suited to use angle-gain mechanisms.

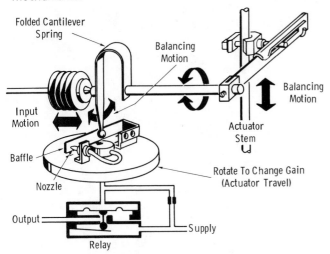

Fig. 18-4. Balancing action in Foxboro type "C" positioner.

The positioner operates as follows:

Assume the positioner and actuator are in balance and that the input signal increases. The increase in input signal moves the baffle striker in a direction that permits the baffle to cover the nozzle. The resulting increase in nozzle backpressure causes an increase in relay output pressure. The relay output pressure moves the actuator stem downward, rotating the balancing lever in a direction that causes the baffle to uncover the nozzle. (The original motion caused the baffle to cover the nozzle.)

The balancing motion uncovers the baffle until the backpressure results in a balancing motion (actuator position) that (almost) equals the input motion.

Fig. 18-4 is a pictorial diagram of the type "C" positioner. Fig. 18-5 is a photograph of the mechanism. Study these figures to be sure that you recognize the location of the essential components.

FISHER GOVERNOR POSITIONER

The Fisher Governor positioner is quite similar to the Foxboro positioner just described, in that the input motion and balancing motion are at right angles to each other. The floating lever is quite unusual in construction. A two-dimensional lever is used. All levers so far have been single dimensional. Do not let this confuse you. In essence, it is a two-sided lever with the two sides operating in different planes. (See Fig. 18-6.)

Fig. 18-7 is a diagram of the Fisher Governor mechanism. The balancing lever is unusual in that it is operated by a cam at the actuator end. You will recall in

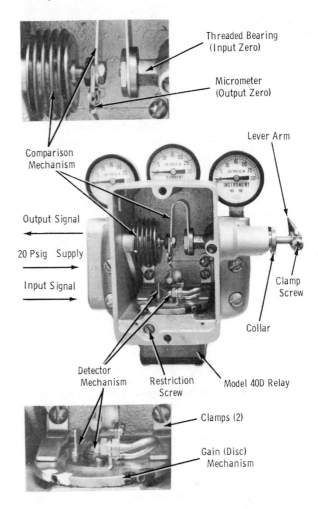

Fig. 18-5. Foxboro type "C" positioner.

our discussions of cams, that the lever length changes with angular rotation of a cam. The introduction of a cam between the actuator and the floating lever makes it possible to obtain a non-linear relationship between actuator travel and the input signal. In this respect, the

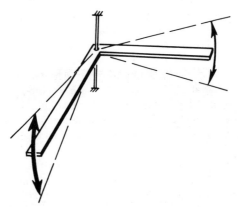

Fig. 18-6. Floating lever action in Fisher Governor positioner.

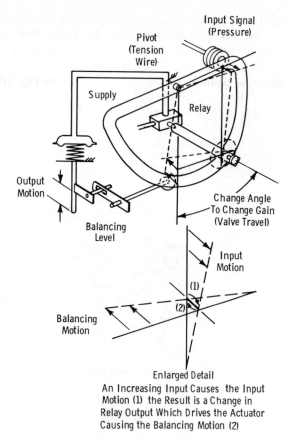

Fig. 18-7. **Balancing mechanism in Fisher Governor positioner.**

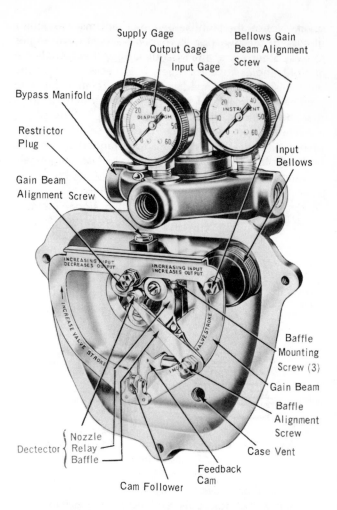

Fig. 18-8. **Fisher Governor positioner.**

Fisher Governor positioner is similar to the Bailey piston positioner.

In the discussion of the operation of the Fisher Governor positioner, do not let the presence of the cam confuse you. The floating lever, although pivoted by a tension wire, is free to float, since the balancing motion is applied to one end of the floating lever, and the input motion is applied to the other end of the floating lever, with each end acting as the pivot for the other.

The detector is arranged to respond to any movement of the floating lever. The detector take-off point can be rotated from the input end of the floating lever to the balancing end of the floating lever. It is in this way that the gain of the positioner is changed. This angle-gain mechanism is similar to the gain mechanism of the Foxboro type "C" positioner.

The operation of the Fisher Governor positioner follows: Assume the positioner and actuator are balanced, and that there is an increase in input signal. This increase in input signal lifts the floating lever. (The tension wire pivot and the balancing cam act as the pivot point). The lifting of the floating lever causes the baffle to cover the nozzle. The relay output pressure increases, moving the actuator downward. This downward movement rotates the balancing lever counterclockwise, lowering its end of the floating lever (the tension wire and bellows act as the pivot point). Remember, the input signal raised the floating lever, which causes the baffle to cover the nozzle.

The baffle will uncover the nozzle until the detector output pressure changes an amount sufficient to change the actuator position an amount equal to (within the range of the detector) the input position.

Fig. 18-8 is a photograph of the actual positioner. Study this figure to be sure that you are able to recognize the essential components as they appear in the mechanism.

ANGLE-GAIN MECHANISM

Angle-gain mechanisms are used by Foxboro and Taylor to change the gain of their positioners. In addition to their use on positioners, they are widely used in controllers, and in some instances, in transmitters. You will recall that the function of an adjustable gain mechanism is to make it possible to change the ratio of output to input.

In previous chapters, the parallel-level gain mechanism was studied. The input and output signals are parallel when used on this gain mechanism. (Remember, in the angle-gain mechanism the two signals are at right angles to each other.) In our discussions of positioners using the angle-gain mechanism, the exact operation of these mechanisms was not discussed. In this chapter, angle-gain mechanisms will be carefully studied. It is important that they be well understood because they are a key mechanism in a wide variety of instruments.

Components

1. A rotating base piece.
2. Two signal motions.

Arrangements

The baffle-nozzle mechanism is mounted on the base piece. The base piece is mounted so that it can be rotated around its center. The two signal motions are at right angles to each other and arranged to converge on the baffle.

Principle of Operation

Fig. 18-9 is a diagram of the angle-gain mechanism as used in valve positioners. As diagrammed, the baffle forms an angle of 45 degrees with the two signals. This mechanism operates as follows:

Assume an increase in input pressure. This increase results in an input motion that causes the baffle to move away from the nozzle. The nozzle backpressure drops off. The relay output pressure decreases and the actuator moves upward. This upward motion of the actuator is fed back to the baffle, causing the baffle to move toward the nozzle (recall that the original motion moved the baffle away from the nozzle). The baffle will move toward the nozzle until there is an output pressure that drives the actuator to a position proportional to the input pressure.

Assume that for a 3- to 15-psig change in input pressure signal, the input motion is ½ inch. Because the angle is 45 degrees the output motion would also have to be ½ inch. The ratio of output to input then is one, or in other words, the gain is one.

Operation—Input and Baffle at 90 Degrees

So far, all we have described is the operation of the positioner. Consider now how the gain mechanism operates to change the gain (stroke of the valve) of the actuator for a given input-pressure change. In other words, consider how it is possible to change the actuator stroke (output) to the input-pressure change (input). Fig. 18-10 is the same as the mechanism shown

in Fig. 18-9. However, the baffle and nozzle have been rotated on the base piece so that the baffle forms a 90-degree angle with the input signal and a 0-degree angle with the balancing signal.

When the baffle is in the position shown in Fig. 18-10, the positioner operates in the following manner. Assume the input pressure increases. The increased input pressure will move the baffle away from the nozzle. Since the baffle is 90 degrees relative to the input signal, a very small change in input signal will fully uncover the nozzle. The nozzle backpressure and the relay output will drop to 0 psig causing the actuator to drive to its upper stop, resulting in a full range balancing motion. However, this full range balancing motion does not change the baffle position relative to the nozzle because the balancing motion is parallel to the baffle. In other words, the detector mechanism cannot respond to the change in balancing motion.

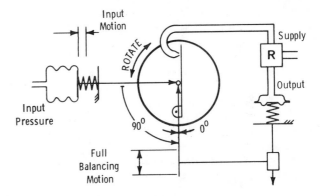

Fig. 18-10. Angle gain mechanism, 90-degree setting to input signal.

Yet, a very small change in input signal will cause the actuator to stroke through its full range. Recall that when the baffle formed a 45-degree angle with the input and balancing signal, the balancing motion had just as much effect on the detector as the input motion.

What is the gain when the baffle forms a 90-degree angle to the input signal? A very small change in input signal will cause a full change of output. Assume that the input signal changes enough to fully uncover the nozzle, hence, to stroke the actuator through its full range. Let us assume that the actuator stroke is ½ inch; then the ratio of output over input is ½ inch divided by .002 inches or, 250. By changing the baffle position 45 degrees relative to the input signal it has been possible to change the gain of the positioner from 1 to 250.

Fig. 18-11 shows the baffle positioned so that it forms a 90-degree angle with the balancing signal. When the baffle is in this position, the input signal can change from 3 to 15 psi with no effect on the baffle because the input signal motion now is parallel to the baffle. In other words, for a full change of input there is a zero change in balancing action. The ratio of output to input is 0 over ½. The 0 divided by ½ is 0. In other words, the gain of the instrument is 0

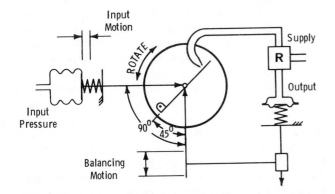

Fig. 18-9. Angle gain mechanism, 45-degree setting.

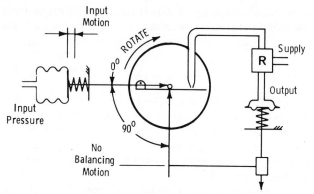

Fig. 18-11. Angle gain mechanism, 90-degree setting to balancing signal.

when the baffle forms a 90-degree angle to the balancing motion.

We have shown the baffle relative to the input signal in three positions: 45 degrees, 90 degrees, and 0 degrees. As the baffle is rotated from 0 to 90 degrees, the gain of the positioner has been changed from 0 to 250. This change in gain is quite large and adequate. Theoretically, it is possible to obtain gain changes from 0 to infinitely large gains by rotating the baffle relative to the signals a full 90 degrees. But, since some small input motion is required to fully cover and uncover the nozzle, the gain is limited by the sensitivity of the detector. As a practical matter, gains which exceed 300 may make the instrument unstable, causing a continuing cycle.

Action

In addition to the wide changes in gain that are conventionally obtained by the angle-gain mechanism, the mechanism possesses an additional important feature. Suppose we continue to rotate the baffle relative to the input signal so that the baffle forms a 45-degree angle relative to the signals.

Fig. 18-12 shows the baffle at a 45-degree angle. Compare Fig. 18-12 to Fig. 18-9, and notice that, even though in both figures the baffle forms a 45-degree angle, the baffle is in a different quadrant.

Let us follow the operation of the mechanism when the baffle is as shown in Fig. 18-12. Assume that the

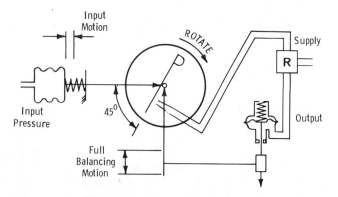

Fig. 18-12. Angle gain mechanism, action reversed compared with Fig. 18-9.

input pressure increases. This increase in pressure will cover the nozzle. The nozzle backpressure will build. The relay output will increase. The actuator, responding to this increased air pressure, will lift. Notice that the actuator in this case is arranged so that, for an increasing air signal, the actuator stem lifts.

The actuator as used in Fig. 18-9 is arranged so that for an increasing air signal, the actuator stem moves downward. In other words, the actuator actions are reversed. As the relay output increases, the actuator moves down, hence the balancing motion moves in a direction that causes the baffle to move away from the nozzle (recall the original motion moved the baffle toward the nozzle.) These two motions will come to balance when the balancing motion (almost) equals the input motion.

As was the case in Fig. 18-9, the gain of the positioner is 1. By rotating the baffle to a different quadrant, however, the action of the balancing motion relative to the input motion has been reversed. The practicality of being able to do this makes it possible to easily match a positioner to actuators having different actions. In the case of controllers, the ability to rotate the baffle to different quadrants makes it possible to change the action of the controller.

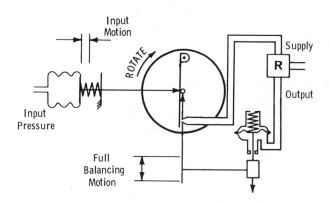

Fig. 18-13. Setting for gain of 250.

It is possible to continue to rotate the baffle so that it will form 0- and 90-degree angles relative to the input signals, as was done in Figs. 18-10 and 18-11, thereby making it possible to change the gains from 0 to 250 using a pressure to lift the actuator.

Figs. 18-13 and 18-14 show the baffle for 0- and 90-degree positions relative to the input motion. The gain will be 250 and 0 respectively. However, a balancing motion will be in a reverse direction to the balancing motion of Figs. 18-10 and 18-11. In other words, the action of the positioner is reversed.

Review the operation of the Fisher Governor positioner discussed earlier in the chapter. Study the angle-gain mechanism as shown in Fig. 18-8. Notice that the baffle "sees" all the balancing signal when it is positioned so that the take-off point lines up with the balancing signal. Alternately, it sees all the input signal when the take-off point lines up with the input signal. In other words, the gain can be changed from 0 to 250. If the baffle take-off is positioned beyond

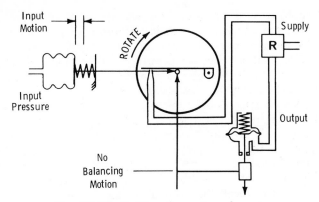

Fig. 18-14. Setting for gain of zero.

the cam and into the other quadrant, the positioner action is reversed.

By repositioning the baffle 180 degrees, it has been possible to change the gain from 250 to 0 direct-acting to 0 to 250 reverse-acting.

This mechanism has the advantage of the angle-gain mechanism in that it can make large changes in gain and can reverse the action easily by going beyond the point where the feedback enters the mechanism, to avoid reaction with the feedback circuit.

SUMMARY

In this chapter, three positioners have been discussed. The first positioner is a wholly conventional motion-balance linkage of the two-lever type. The Foxboro type "C" positioner and the Fisher Governor positioner are angular moment-balance positioners ingeniously arranged.

The floating lever used in the type "C" and the Fisher is not as straightforward in appearance as the lever system of the Foxboro angle-balance positioner of the angle-balance transmitters previously discussed. Nevertheless, a study of the mechanisms should show that all angle-balance mechanisms are essentially the same. The balancing motion and the input motion are at right angles to each other. The next chapter takes up the study of linear motion-balance instruments, where the signals involved are directly opposed.

Chapter 19

Linear Motion-Balance Instruments

LINEAR MOTION-BALANCE PRINCIPLE

In preceding chapters, angle motion-balance instruments were discussed. Recall that motion-balance instruments are available in two forms: angle motion-balance and linear motion-balance. The linear motion-balance mechanism is comparable to the true force-balance mechanism because no levers are used and because the signals involved are directly opposed to each other. Additional levers may be required to bring the motion to the balancing mechanism. The detector mechanism responds to any difference in the motions involved.

The number of linear motion-balance instruments is much more limited than the number of angle motion-balance instruments; there are only two common linear motion-balance instruments. The expectation is that linear motion-balance instruments will become more widely used.

In this chapter, the linear motion-balance transmitter of the Moore Company and the Taylor 210 series transmitter will be studied.

Elements

The essential elements of the linear motion-balance mechanism are:
1. An input element to convert the input pressure signal to a proportional motion.
2. A balancing element to convert the output pressure signal to a proportional motion.
3. A detector mechanism.

Arrangements

The input element, which must in this case be a pressure-to-motion converter, is arranged to drive one "half" of the detector. The balancing element, which

again must be a pressure-to-motion converter, is arranged to drive the second "half" of the detector. The input element, the detector, and the balancing element are all arranged on the same center line. There are no pivots or levers. Hence, the motions involved are linear. Fig. 19-1 is the fundamental diagram of the linear motion-balance mechanism. The baffle is driven by the input bellows. The nozzle is driven by the balancing bellows.

Principle of Operation

Assume the mechanism is in balance and that the input signal is increased. The increase in pressure acting on the bellows will cause the baffle to move towards the nozzle. The nozzle backpressure will increase. This increase in backpressure, acting on the balancing bellows, will expand the bellows, thereby moving the nozzle upward. (The original motion caused

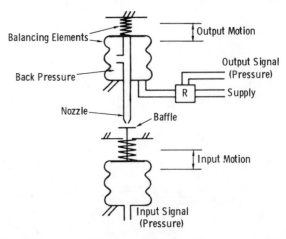

Fig. 19-1. Fundamental diagram of linear motion-balance mechanism.

the baffle to move upward). The nozzle will move until its motion (almost) equals the input (baffle) motion.

In the previous discussions of detectors, the applications were such that either the nozzle or the baffle remained fixed. As the detector is used in the linear motion-balance instrument both the nozzle and the baffle move. The differential movement between the two detector elements causes the change in backpressure.

In no way does the fact that both elements of the detector move change the essential operation of the detector. The important point here is to notice that the two elements of the detector move relative to each other. We have shown the baffle/nozzle for convenience. The other detectors can be used.

THE MOORE LINEAR MOTION-BALANCE TRANSMITTER

Fig. 19-2 is a simplified diagram of the Moore Company's linear-motion transmitter. Fig. 19-3 is a more pictorial diagram of the same instrument. The Moore mechanism uses a nozzle/baffle, relay valve, detector mechanism. The relay valve is a standard non-bleed device. The input motion can originate from a wide variety of sources. The diagram shows the input motion as an angular rotation from a bellows-type differential-pressure meter body.

The baffle/nozzle looks, superficially, like a pilot valve. In fact, Moore calls it a "pilot," but observe first of all that as the "valve plug" is moved, only one restriction is varied. (Recall that the essential characteristic of a pilot valve was that as the valve plug moved, two restrictions were simultaneously varied.) Since only one restriction varied with the movement, this part of the detector can properly be called a baffle/nozzle although it appears quite different from the typical baffle/nozzle construction.

Let's see how it operates. Assume that the instrument is in balance and that there is a change in measurement that causes a downward input motion. This downward movement uncovers the nozzle, causing

the nozzle backpressure to drop, hence, decreasing the relay output pressure. The relay output pressure is fed back into a compartment containing the balancing bellows. As the pressure in this compartment is reduced, the bellows expands. As it expands, it carries the nozzle with it. This downward movement of the nozzle toward the baffle results in a covering of the nozzle. (Recall that the original motion was a downward baffle movement that uncovered the nozzle). These two motions will be brought to balance when they (almost) equal each other. The baffle will position itself relative to the nozzle so that the resulting backpressure drives the balancing bellows an amount equal (almost) to the measurement motion. Therefore, the output pressure is proportional to the measurement.

Because of the need for both elements of the detector to move, it is necessary that the nozzle portion of the detector be mounted on a flexible element. The element used by Moore to accomplish this is a bellows. Recognize, however, that the bellows function as a flexible conduit.

The nozzle backpressure acts on the inside of both the balancing and sealing bellows. The sealing bellows and the balancing bellows have equal effective areas so that the force developed by the nozzle backpressure, acting on the sealing bellows, is cancelled

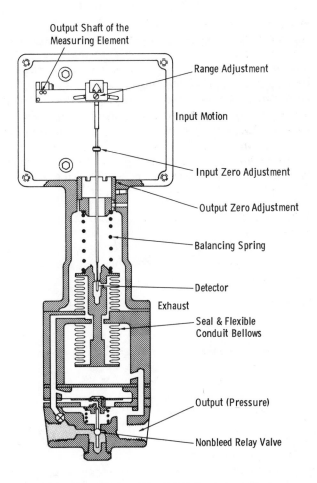

Fig. 19-3. Schematic of Moore transmitter.

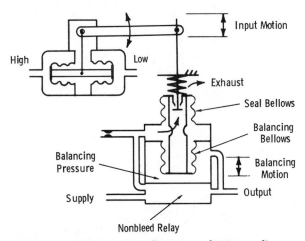

Fig. 19-2. Elementary diagram of Moore linear-motion transmitter.

out by the force developed by the same pressure acting on the inside of the balancing bellows. The only resulting motion is that caused by the force developed by the output pressure acting on the balancing bellows.

THE TAYLOR 210 LINEAR MOTION-BALANCE TRANSMITTER

The second example of a linear motion-balance transmitter is the Taylor 210 series transmitter. Fig. 19-4 is a simplified diagram of the 210 mechanism.

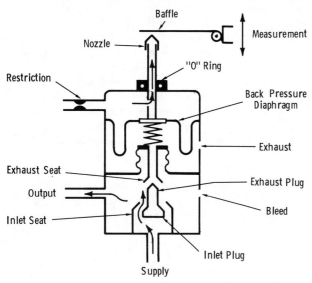

Fig. 19-4. Taylor Model 210 linear motion transmitter.

A baffle/nozzle relay-valve detector is used. The relay valve is non-bleed. In the details of construction, the relay is different from most relay valves in that the exhaust port is mounted on a bellows rather than on a diaphragm. This bellows makes it possible to obtain large movements of the exhaust port. If a diaphragm were used, the exhaust port movements would be small. The bellows, which supports the exhaust port, in addition to furnishing exhaust port movement, also acts as the balancing element. The input element is a bellophragm. Between the input motion and the balancing motion is a spring.

The bellophragm supports the nozzle and, as the bellophragm moves, so does the nozzle. The bellophragm moves as the nozzle backpressure changes. The nozzle backpressure, acting on the bellophragm, loads the relay valve through a spring. It is this spring that converts the large nozzle movements to a force that drives the relay. It is this aspect of the mechanism that distinguishes it from other relay valves.

The input motion is applied through the baffle. The baffle can be driven by a variety of input measuring assemblies. In many cases, the input is an angle motion. However, it is the linear portion of this angle motion that is detected by the nozzle. As with actuator positioners using the true force-balance principle mechanisms, do not let the lever system that is used to route the motion to the motion mechanisms confuse you.

Consider now the operation of the Taylor transmitter. Assume the mechanism is in equilibrium and that there is a change in measurement that causes the baffle to lift. The nozzle backpressure will decrease. The bellophragm will move upward, thereby reducing the force being applied to the bellows supporting the exhaust port. The exhaust port will open and that pressure will decrease, and the relay output will decrease. This decrease in relay output, acting on the balancing bellows, will cause the relay to balance at a new pressure determined by the nozzle backpressure.

Notice that both elements of the detector are driven; the baffle by the measurement, the nozzle by the balancing (output) pressure. The differential movement is what establishes the output pressure. As is the case with all motion mechanisms, the baffle "chases" the nozzle, (or vice versa). This chasing action is much easier to see in the linear motion-balance instruments and especially the Taylor 210 series.

Chapter 20

Control Valves

CONTROL VALVES

The end point of measuring and controlling instruments is the final control element. The final element is usually a diaphragm actuator driving a control valve. In the work on positioners it has been shown that the actuator is part of the positioner. If satisfactory control is to be obtained, the control valve must be in good operating condition. The control valve is subject to damage, wear, corrosion (externally as well as internally), and erosion. Therefore, control valves require a fair amount of maintenance. A great deal of process control difficulty could be eliminated by better care of the final elements.

This chapter will concentrate on air-operated control valves driven by actuators of the diaphragm type. Piston-operated actuators are in some ways superior but since they are not as widely used we shall not study them. Note however, that the study of the valves themselves is applicable regardless of the type of actuator.

Components

The control valve consists of two major components:
1. The actuator
2. The valve
The actuator is made up of a:
1. Flexible diaphragm
2. Spring (usually) and spring tension adjustment (range location adjustment)
3. Plate, stem, and locknut
4. Housing
The valve is made up of a:
1. Body
2. Plug
3. Stem
4. Pressure-tight connection

Arrangements

The actuator is arranged as follows:

The diaphragm is bolted to a dished metal head, forming a pressure-tight compartment. The controller output pressure is connected to this compartment. (See Fig. 20-1.)

The motion of the diaphragm is opposed by a spring.

The valve stem is attached to the diaphragm so that any diaphragm movement results in the same valve plug movement.

Both the motor and plug can be direct or indirect. The action of the actuator may be such that either an increase or a decrease in air may lift the stem. The design of some actuators permits them to be reversed.

The plug may be attached to the stem so that a lifting stem closes or opens the valve. Some plugs are reversible on the stem, others are not.

The determination of the valve action desired is usually based on what position the valve should take on an air failure. On one process it may be desirable to have the valve go wide open when the air fails, as, for example, in a cooling process. On other processes it may be better to have the valve close, as in a heating process. When this is decided and the type plug is established, then the actuator action may be specified.

Operation

The controller output serves as the input to the control valve if no positioner is used. The actuator converts the controller output to a valve opening.

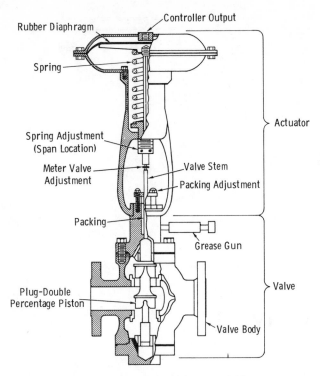

Fig. 20-1. Control valve with mounted actuator.

Suppose the controller output increases. This increase in pressure will compress the spring, allowing the diaphragm to move. The diaphragm movement is relayed to the valve plug through the stem.

Some control valves are designed so that the change in flow is a percentage of the amount flowing at that particular valve position. For example, suppose the

valve is ¾ open and 35 gpm are flowing. Then, if the valve stem moves open an additional 1 percent of its travel, the flow should increase 10 percent of 35, or to 38.5 gallons. Now suppose the valve is ¼ open and the flow is 5 gpm and suppose the stem moved open the same 10 percent. In this case, the change in flow would be 10 percent of 5, or .5 gal.

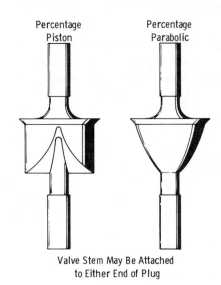

Valve Stem May Be Attached
to Either End of Plug

Fig. 20-3. Single-seated valve plugs.

The characteristic just described is called an equal percentage characteristic. This is frequently desirable because the controller output should result in a change in flow that is proportional to the amount flowing at the time the change occurred. Control valve plugs are designed to give the percentage characteristic just described. See Figs. 20-2, 20-3, and 20-4 for some formed plugs.

Other valve characteristics are also used. The most common is the linear plug which is designed so that the opening changes linearly with the stem position. The valve plug can be either parabolic or piston. The parabolic plug is designed to get the percentage characteristic. The piston plug has V notches cut into the piston walls to obtain the percentage response.

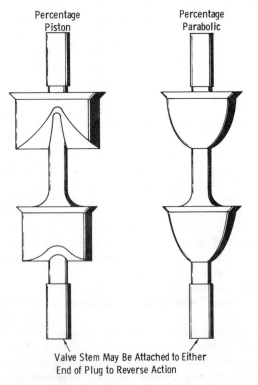

Valve Stem May Be Attached to Either
End of Plug to Reverse Action

Fig. 20-2. Double-seated valve plugs.

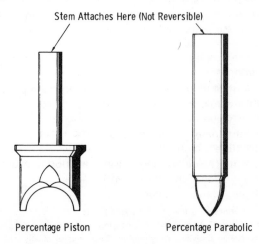

Fig. 20-4. Single-seated valve plugs.

Alternate Arrangements

Some control valves use a piston instead of the rubber diaphragm.

Instead of a spring the valve can be arranged to use an air pressure that acts as a spring.

The pressure-tight connection may be a bellows that expands and contracts with valve stem travel.

CONTROL VALVE MAINTENANCE[1]

Part I. Diaphragm Air Actuator

Air-to-Push-Down Diaphragm Actuator. The air-to-push-down diaphragm actuator (Fig. 20-5A) is a simple mechanical device. It is a completely separate unit independent of the valve body. When air pressure is applied to the top of the diaphragm, the actuator stem is pushed down. This motion or force is opposed by the compression of the spring.

How Valve Springs Are Selected. The spring is selected so that the actuator stem will start to stroke when the air pressure reaches a predetermined initial value, and will complete its rated stroke with a specified total air pressure on the diaphragm. The nominal range of a spring-diaphragm actuator is the air pressure range in pounds per square inch (psi) for rated stroke under no load. One ISA Standard is 3 to 15 psi. Another range now widely accepted is 6 to 30 psi. For a 3 to 15 psi nominal range, the rate of the spring is selected so that the stem will start to stroke when the air pressure reaches 3 psi and will complete its rated stroke when the pressure reaches 15 psi, plus or minus 5 percent. From the standpoint of maintenance and satisfactory operation, the exact operating air pressure range is not important as long as the rated valve stroke can be obtained without exceeding the maximum available loading pressure.

The criterion of good actuator performance is response to very small changes in air pressure. Alignment of moving parts is required for proper response and therefore, it is necessary to guide the actuator stem. In this actuator (Fig. 20-5A), the conformation of the diaphragm to the diaphragm plate serves as a flexible upper guide for the stem; a self-lubricated bronze lower bearing, located in the adjusting screw, serves as a lower guide.

Diaphragm Replacement. The only part normally requiring replacement is the diaphragm itself. To replace the diaphragm, relieve all spring compression by turning the adjusting screw counterclockwise. This will prevent the upper case from popping up when the cap screws are removed—especially important on actuators with a high initial spring compression. Remove the upper diaphragm case, actuator stem nut, washer and diaphragm. Install the new diaphragm and reassemble.

[1] This information (to end of Chapter) was taken from an article prepared by the Application Engineering and Service Departments of Mason-Neilan Division, Worthington Corp. and originally published in the August 1957 issue of the ISA Journal.

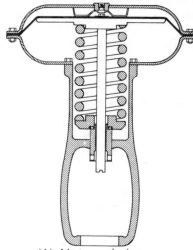

(A) Air-to-push-down.

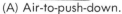

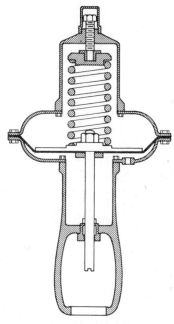

(B) Air-to-push-up.

Fig. 20-5. Diaphragm actuators.

To set the correct initial spring compression: Connect an air supply with a gauge and regulator to the air connection on the actuator. Turn the adjusting screw clockwise to compress the spring slightly. Apply air pressure and, by feeling the stem, note at what pressure the stem begins to move. Readjust the spring compression until the stem just begins to move at the minimum pressure of the air-pressure range stamped on the serial plate.

If it is necessary to make an emergency diaphragm replacement, flat-sheet stock diaphragm material can usually be used for actuators up to approximately 18 inches outside case diameter. To allow sufficient stroke without restriction, imposed by stretching the diaphragm, the diaphragm bolt-circle diameter should be about 10 percent greater than the case bolt-circle diameter.

Air-to-Push-Up Diaphragm Actuator. The air-to-push-up actuator (Fig. 20-5B) differs from the air-to-push-down unit (Fig. 20-5A) in that the spring, diaphragm, and diaphragm plate are inverted so that when air pressure is applied to the diaphragm, the actuator stem moves upward. This actuator is used where design does not permit inverting the valve body and plug. Example: angle valves and other top-guided, non-invertible designs.

Diaphragm Replacement. To replace the diaphragm, relieve all spring compression by turning the adjusting screw counterclockwise. Remove the upper diaphragm case assembly (includes spring barrel, spring, and spring bottom) actuator stem nut and diaphragm plate. Install the new diaphragm and reassemble. Readjust the spring setting using the same procedure as for the air-to-push-down unit. The diaphragm serves as a flexible upper guide, and the packing box assembly serves as the lower guide.

A gasket at the junction of the lower diaphragm case and yoke and the packing box around the actuator stem prevent operating air leakage. Since this packing box is subjected only to low air pressure, the maintenance problem is not severe. The packing-box gland should be set up lightly. If repacking is required, the actuator must be removed from the body subassembly in order to insert the preformed ring packing. The replacement ring should be covered with a thin coat of light cup grease before assembly to make possible a seal with minimum bearing pressure.

Part II. Valve Bodies and Subassemblies

Four valve-body types in common use are shown in Figs. 20-6A through 20-6D. They are shown as simplified sectional drawings for clarity.

Double-Seated, Guided Valves. Fig. 20-6A is a typical top-and-bottom guided, double V-port valve. This

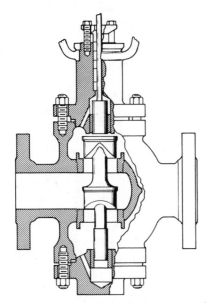

(A) Top-and-bottom guided V-port valve.

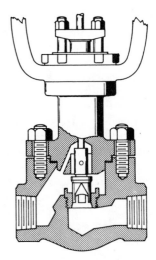

(B) Top-and-skirt guided percentage piston valve.

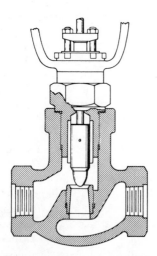

(C) Top-guided, heavy-duty, screwed-bonnet valve.

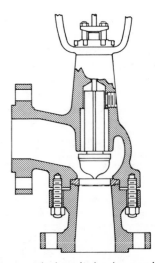

(D) Top-guided, split-body, angle valve.

Fig. 20-6. Valve bodies and subassemblies.

cast globe body is the most widely used for general service applications and is available in sizes up through 16 inches, with ratings through 600 psi ASA; and in certain sizes in ratings through 1500 psi ASA. This type of valve can be furnished with other plug types such as solid-turned parabolic, linear, and quick-opening, as well as the V-Port shown. It is also available in single-seated designs.

Single-Seated Valves. This valve includes a variety of small single-seated globe and angle bodies for general service in sizes 1 inch and smaller. It is a natural extension of the Fig. 20-6A valve into the sizes where top and bottom guiding is no longer practical. It is available in ASA ratings through 600 psi. The trim is available in an interchangeable set of five nominal sizes of ⅛ inch, ¼ inch, ⅜ inch, ½ inch and ¾ inch.

Screwed-Bonnet Valves. Fig. 20-6C shows a heavy-duty screwed-bonnet valve made in both globe and angle styles through the 2-inch size, with a 1-inch maximum orifice. The globe body is rated at 3000 psi at 450 degrees Fahrenheit and the angle body at 6000 psi at 450 degrees Fahrenheit. The valve plug has a heavy single top guide and simple turned construction. The seat ring is a threaded venturi type with a heavy hex head designed to take a standard socket wrench so that it can be screwed down tight against a copper or other metallic gasket.

Split-Body Angle-Valve. Fig. 20-6D is a split body with an integral bonnet in which the seat ring is clamped between the two body pieces. A ground metal-to-metal joint is used in place of gaskets. The seat ring is reversible so that if the original seating surface is damaged, the ring can be inverted to provide a new seating surface. This valve is produced in sizes up through 8 inches in ratings through 600 psi ASA. This split-body design is also commonly available in a straight-through flow pattern.

Angle Valve. The angle body (Fig. 20-6D) is made for heavy duty service in sizes through 6 inches. These bodies were designed principally for use involving severe operating conditions where high pressures and temperatures or erosive conditions are encountered. Where service conditions necessitate either continuous or intermittent flushing of the body, as in some oil refinery applications, a connection is provided directly under the bonnet flange. The flushing medium passes through ports around the plug bushing to help prevent the formation of coke or the accumulation of abrasive particles between the bushing and the plug. The seat ring is a venturi type and is held in place by a flared, screwed retainer.

Bonnet and Blindhead. The top-and-bottom guided invertible body style (Fig. 20-6A) has a removable bonnet and blindhead that are piloted in body recesses to very close clearances to assure positive valve-plug alignment. You must be careful in removing these parts to be sure that pilot sections, plug guides, and gasket surfaces are not damaged.

When reassembling the bonnet and blindhead, you should install new gaskets lightly coated with a good sealing compound. In an emergency, if you've been careful on disassembly, you can reclaim the original gaskets. Or, you can cut a gasket from high-grade sheet stock such as Crane No. 888 or Garlock No. 7022.

When making up the bonnet and blindhead connections, be especially careful that the nuts are tightened in diametrically opposite pairs. You should check the valve plug assembly periodically by moving it through its entire stroke to make sure that it is running free. Successful, trouble-free operation of top-and-bottom guided valves depends on good alignment throughout the whole assembly.

Air-fin bonnets are provided to reduce packing-box temperature where fluids hotter than 400 degrees Fahrenheit are valved. The effective cooling rate of the fins allows the use of standard packing material with service temperatures up to 800 degrees Fahrenheit.

Plain extension bonnets are used for low temperature service, usually below 32 degrees Fahrenheit. The extension permits the use of standard packing material because the packing-box is moved upward from the valve body to a higher ambient temperature condition. This also allows for the use of additional insulation when required.

Seat Rings. Most standard control valves are furnished with renewable seat rings made of 18-8 stainless steel, either AISI type 304 or 316. The seat rings are precision machined and piloted at maximum ring diameter into a recess in the valve body to ensure true alignment and accurate centering. A relatively heavy ring shoulder is provided to minimize distortion when the ring is set up tight in the body. The seating surfaces on the ring and in the body bridgewall are kept narrow and given a special smooth finish to ensure a tight joint. Set up threaded seat-rings using special fixtures and a lubricant such as John Crane insoluble plastic lead No. 2, used sparingly.

How to Make a Seat-Ring Wrench. Since threaded seat-rings are set up very tightly when initially installed and are sometimes in service for years before replacement, it is often very difficult to remove them. One of the chief problems in removing the rings is to find a wrench that will not jump the lugs when heavy

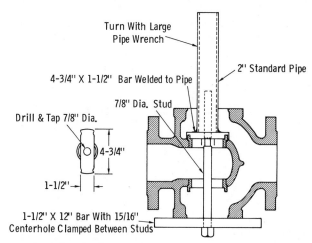

Fig. 20-7. Seat-ring wrench you can make yourself.

pressure is applied. A suggested design for such a wrench, based on the 4-inch size, is shown in Fig. 20-7. In this design, the wrench itself is prevented from rising by the tie rod running through the body. The application of heat may assist in the removal of some stubborn rings. Once you have removed the seat-ring, inspect and carefully clean the seating surface and threads in the body before you insert the new ring. We recommend that you use a light application of a sealing compound when the rings are installed. Use it sparingly, principally as a lubricant, when making up the threads.

How to Grind Seats Tight. With control valves using metal-to-metal seats, there is seldom a requirement for dead-tight shutoff. In double seated valves—the majority of all control valves—dead tight shutoff is virtually impossible at all operating conditions. Of the many possible types of seat design which could be used, the beveled seat with the same angle for both plug and seat ring is the type most commonly used.

The seating surfaces of the plug and rings are machined and are seldom smooth enough to make a tight seal. In double-seated valve designs, the distance between the seats on the plug and seat rings may vary slightly. In order to correct these two conditions, a hand operation called "lapping in" is necessary. The contact seating surfaces are kept narrow within the limits of good machining practice to give a combination that is easy to lap in.

How to Make a Grinding Tool. A T-handle and a good grade of fine grinding compound such as Glover Compound No. 2A are required for the lapping operation. You can make a T-handle simply by selecting a rod of a size that can be threaded to fit the plug and long enough to clear the body. A cross piece can be fitted to this rod by welding, or by inserting a smaller rod through the upper part of the stem. Use the bonnet or blindhead to guide the plug while lapping.

Lapping is started by daubing the compound on the seat in several spots equally spaced around the periphery of the seat ring. Put the compound on both seats at once when fitting a double-seated plug. Be careful not to get compound on the skirt of a V-Port or on the side of a turned-type plug. Compound at this point will wear the lateral surfaces. Insert the plug in the seat ring carefully until it is seated, then rotate by short oscillating strokes. After 8 or 10 strokes, lift the plug slightly from the seat and repeat. This intermittent lifting is important to keep the compound evenly distributed.

On large valves where the weight of the plug is substantial, it is advisable to mix a small quantity of lubricant, such as graphite, with the grind compound. This will slow down the cutting rate and prevent tearing of the seats. On very large valves, it is helpful to support the plug on a hoist to prevent the entire weight from resting on the seats.

Don't Lap Too Much. The amount of lapping to be done depends no the material of construction, condition of the seating surface and accuracy of machining. When continued lapping does not seem to give

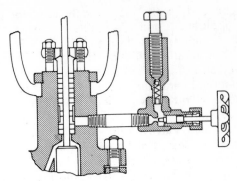

Fig. 20-8. Packing box and lubricator.

any visible indication of improvement, there is little point in continuing. Too much lapping usually results in a rough seat or small ridges on the plug or ring. These become more pronounced with additional lapping and can be corrected only by refacing one or both parts.

Valve Packing. Packing-box maintenance is one of the principal chores of routine control valve service. The packing-box must be tight, yet have a low friction. Improper care, or improper lubrication or pack material can result in leakage or excessive friction. In control valves, the packing-box is relatively deep and a lubricator and a lubricant ring are normally provided. Fig. 20-8 shows a typical packing-box section.

A typical packing material is Teflon asbestos. This is a split ring packing for ratings up to 6000 psi and 400 degrees Fahrenheit. Other packing materials, either solid or split-ring types are available, including solid Teflon.

For valves operating at high temperatures (generally above 400 degrees Fahrenheit), to improve service life an air-fin bonnet is provided to reduce the temperature in the packing-box section. For extremely low temperatures, extension bonnets are used to protect the packing-box.

Valve Lubricants. The majority of packing boxes are designed for use with a lubricator. On cast iron assemblies, the lubricator alone is furnished. It is designed with a ball check as a safety measure to prevent back flow of process fluid while the lubricator is being filled. On steel valves, a steel isolating valve is provided between the lubricator and the bonnet to give positive protection on higher operating pressures and temperatures.

Keep the lubricator filled with the specified lubricant and turned in firmly but not tightly. The lubricant is intended as an aid to the packing, not as a packing itself. Under normal service conditions, it should not be necessary to lubricate the valve more than once every two weeks or so. At that time, one or two turns of the lubricator nut should be sufficient.

There are several standard lubricants available to meet the wide range of operating conditions under which the valve may be used. The lubricants are generally divided into:

1. Those suitable for petroleum and allied chemicals.

2. Those suitable for water solutions.

Tightness of the packing is maintained by combination of lubrication and proper compression. Little by little it will be necessary to take up on the packing gland until finally all of the available compression is used up. It will then be necessary to repack.

On many ordinary services at moderate pressures and temperatures, packing life is exceptionally long and is completely satisfactory without lubrication. In such cases, the valve can be furnished without the lubricator and lubricating ring. Then, when it is finally necessary to repack, it may be justifiable merely to back off the packing gland and insert one or two rings of split packing on top of the old packing.

When it is necessary to repack, the valve must be disassembled and the stem locknuts and indicator disk removed. Turn the plug stem out through the packing box and remove the packing-box flange and gland. Remove the old packing and the lubricant ring by working from the underside of the bonnet. Insert new packing—first, approximately ½ inch of packing, then the lubricant ring, and then more packing rings to fill the packing box.

Part III. Control Valve Adjustments

Valve Reassembly. To assemble the valve body and actuator after service, proceed as follows:

1. Place the actuator on the body subassembly and secure with the clamping nut.
2. Place the packing-box flange over the plug stem and follow with the first lock-nut, the indicator plate, and the second locknut.
3. Proceed with seating of the valve plug to the valve-seat rings.

For normally-open valves using the air-to-push-down actuator, turn the plug stem into the actuator stem as far as it will go using the stem locknuts as a means of turning the stem. Lock the plug stem to the actuator stem with the locknuts and reset the indicator plate so that the indicator disk indicates maximum rated opening. Apply sufficient air pressure to the actuator to move the plug stem down until the indicator disk indicates SHUT. Turn the plug stem out of the actuator stem until the plug is seated. Relieve the diaphragm pressure and turn the plug stem about ¼-turn out of the actuator stem. Lock the plug stem to the actuator stem with the locknuts.

For normally closed valves using the air-to-push-down actuator, assembly is accomplished by turning the plug stem into the actuator stem until the plug is seated. Apply sufficient air pressure to the diaphragm to move the plug off the seat. Turn the plug stem ¼-turn into the actuator stem. Relieve the diaphragm air pressure. Lock the plug stem to the actuator stem and reset the indicator plate so that the indicator disk shows the valve to be closed.

Normally-closed valves with an air-to-push-up actuator are assembled by turning the plug stem out of the actuator stem until the plug is seated. Reset the indicator plate so that the indicator disk indicates SHUT. Apply sufficient air pressure to the actuator to lift plug off the seat. Turn the plug stem ¼ turn out of the actuator stem. Relieve the diaphragm pressure and lock the plug stem to the actuator stem with the locknuts.

Chapter 21

Controllers

Previous work has been concerned with instruments that measure, transmit this measurement, record or indicate a measurement, or respond to a controller output. This last class of instruments includes the positioners and control valves. We will now study the controllers.

Controllers, in some respects, are more complicated than the instruments we have discussed so far. The increased complexity arises out of two factors. First, the output of the controller is dependent on the relationship of two inputs. Second, the output of some kinds of controllers, in addition to depending on two input signals, is time dependent.

Recall that on all our work up to this point, the instrument considered had one input and one output. Further, there was no time dependency; that is, the instruments were designed to repeat the input as rapidly as possible. Ideally, the output signal coincided exactly both in magnitude and in time with the input signal. There is one exception. Temperature transmitters sometimes have a derivative feature. We bypassed this feature in the discussion of transmitters. It will, however, be discussed in the chapter on Derivative Mode. We will find in our discussions that the controller is arranged so that the time relationship between the input and output can be changed.

Even though controllers are somewhat more complicated, they are nevertheless composed of the same elements and components as all other instruments. Therefore, it will not be necessary to learn the operation of new elements or components.

Controllers can be categorized in the same way as measuring instruments. There are feedforward and feedback controllers. The feedback controllers can be either motion- or force-type. As is the case with measuring instruments, the force-type controller is found in two forms; true force-balance and moment-balance. To my knowledge, all motion controllers are angle motion-balance, although there exists a possibility of a linear motion-balance controller. All categories of controllers mentioned above will be carefully studied, together with the several types of controller modes. In this chapter we will propose a fundamental mechanism, which in subsequent chapters, we will revise to obtain the various controller forms that are used.

NARROW-BAND PROPORTIONING CONTROLLERS

The first controller to be considered is a feed-back narrow proportioning-band controller. For the time being, do not concern yourself too much with the meaning of narrow band.

Components

1. A measurement input.
2. A reference input called a setpoint.
3. Feed-back components.
4. A detector mechanism.
5. A lever system.

Arrangements

Fig. 21-1 is a block diagram showing the relationships between the components. Notice that there are two inputs to the controller—the measurement input and the setpoint input—and there is only one output. This means that the output is dependent on the relationship between the two input signals. The measurement input is a signal that is proportional to the measurement. It can be and frequently is the output of a transmitter. The setpoint input is a signal generated by the operator. It is the way that the operator says to

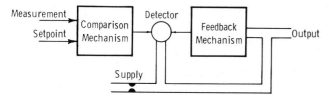

Fig. 21-1. Block diagram of controller.

the controller, "This is the value of the measurement that I want." If the controller is working properly, and if the process is under control, the measurement signal will equal the setpoint signal.

Let's examine further this first box called the comparison mechanism. Notice that even though there are two inputs to the box, there is only one output to the detector. The function of this box is to compare the measurement signal with the setpoint signal. If there is an output from the comparison box, this output will be called an error signal. The detector (which can be any of the detectors already discussed) is arranged to detect any error signal. The detector output pressure is fed back into the feed-back components (represented in our diagram as the box labeled feedback). The output of the feedback box is fed back to the detector.

As is the case in all self-balancing instruments, the purpose of the detector is to determine any unbalance between input signals—in this case the error signal and the feedback signal. If there is a difference, the detector operates to balance the two signals. The feedback signal is also the output signal; that is, the feedback signal is the signal that is applied to the final control element (usually a control valve).

Fig. 21-2 is a controller mechanism showing how the controller elements and components can be arranged to obtain a function controller. Notice that inside the box labeled the comparison mechanism are two bellows opposing each other. A measurement signal is applied to one of these bellows; a setpoint signal is applied to the second. The two bellows drive a lever. Halfway down the lever and "looking" at it, is a nozzle. The nozzle and the portion of the lever that it looks at form a baffle-nozzle detector mechanism. At the lower end of the lever is the feedback box. Within the feedback box is a bellows/spring. The nozzle backpressure is connected to this bellows. The output of the controller is the nozzle backpressure, if

no relay is used. If a relay is used, it is placed in the nozzle backpressure line, and the controller output is the output of the relay. The introduction of a relay in no way changes the essential function of the controller.

Principle of Operation

Let's suppose the instrument is in equilibrium; that is, neither of the two inputs is changing; hence, the output won't be changing. Now let the measurement signal increase. This increase in measurement signal moves the lever (the baffle) toward the nozzle. The result of this movement is that the nozzle backpressure builds up. The increase in nozzle backpressure acting through the feedback bellows moves the lever away from the nozzle. When the feedback movement is equal (within the range of the detector) to the original input movement, the nozzle backpressure will stabilize and the controller will have come to a new equilibrium position.

Let's examine the operation of the controller, leaving the measurement constant and changing the setpoint signal. Suppose we decrease the setpoint signal. A decrease in setpoint signal will permit the baffle to move toward the nozzle. The nozzle backpressure will increase. This increase in nozzle backpressure acting through the feedback bellows will move the lever (the baffle) away from the nozzle. When the feedback movment equals (within the range of the detector) the movement caused by the changing setpoint signal, the controller will come to equilibrium at a new nozzle backpressure, hence, output. Notice that the output can be changed by changing either the measurement signal or the setpoint signal.

To express the idea in a different way, suppose the measurement and setpoint pressures are both increased the same amount. If this is done, there will be no change in baffle-nozzle position because there will be no movement. The important point to recognize is that the function of the comparison mechanism is to compare two signals, and to generate an output which is proportional to the difference between the two signals. If there is no difference, the output error signal is described as a zero error signal. If the measurement is greater than the setpoint, there is a plus error signal. If the measurement is less than the setpoint signal, there is a minus error signal.

EXTERNAL FEEDBACK

The controller, much like the valve positioner, is not a functionally complete instrument. Let's now briefly consider how the controller is installed relative to a transmitter and a control valve. Fig. 21-3 shows a controller installed in some process piping. The measurement originates at an orifice. Connected across the orifice is a dp cell. The orifice-dp cell combination converts flow to an air pressure. This air pressure is the measurement signal. The setpoint signal is also an air pressure. The output of the controller is applied to a control valve actuator. The valve is installed in the same line as the orifice.

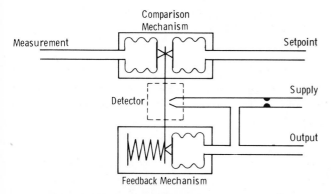

Fig. 21-2. Controller mechanism.

Let's now consider how an installed controller operates. Suppose the controller is in equilibrium, and, therefore, the control valve is in a fixed position. If the pressure upstream from the control valve increases, more flow will pass through the control valve. The increase in flow increases the differential pressure across the orifice. The increase in differential pressure is converted to an increase in transmitter output. This increase in transmitter output acting on the measurement bellows of the controller comparison mechanism will cause the baffle to move toward the nozzle. The nozzle backpressure will increase. The backpressure acting on the feedback bellows will reposition the baffle, causing a new output. This output pressure will cause the control valve to move in a direction to reduce the flow. The reduction in flow will cause a reduction in transmitter output pressure, hence, a new measurement signal. This new measurement signal will cause a new baffle-nozzle position and a new output pressure. This series of events will continue until the flow comes to equilibrium.

Recognize that, even though we have discussed the operation of the installed controller in a step-wise fashion, the balancing action is continuous. That is, as the measurement changes, the feedback changes. As the feedback changes, acting through the flow, the measurement also changes. You can see that there are, in fact, two balancing or feedback actions. One of the feedback actions is within the controller and is brought about by the feedback bellows. The second balancing action is external to the controller and is brought about by a change in measurement which, acting on the measurement bellows, results in a new controller equilibrium point. Recognize at this time that there is an external feedback action. However, do not let this confuse you because in no way does it change the fact that the controller output is required to balance a signal that is the difference between the measurement signal and the reference (setpoint) signal.

In the following discussions of controller mechanisms, we will omit consideration of the external feedback loop. We do this to simplify the discussions, and

because in no way does the external loop change the essential controller action. In our discussions on controller theory, we will re-introduce the notion of external feedback to show the reaction between controller settings and processes being controlled.

CONTROLLER GAIN

The amount the controller output will change for a given error signal depends on the configuration of the controller. More specifically, it depends on the lever length and the detector position relative to the lever. In our diagram we have shown the detector centered on the lever. This means that a change in feedback bellows position output is equally effective as a change in either measurement or setpoint bellows position (input). The relationship between input and output is called gain. If we were to change the nozzle position on the lever, we could change the ratio of output to input. Hence, we could change the gain. The notion of changing the gain of a controller is extremely important. The mechanisms of changing the controller gain are the same as were encountered in changing the gain of transmitters and valve positioners. Also, there are two additional methods of changing the gain of a controller.

The operation of a controller has been described and the point has been made that there is an external feedback loop as well as an internal feedback loop. The controller diagrammed shows a comparison mechanism, and a feedback mechanism. The fundamental operation of the controller was described as being a balancing between two signals, the error signal and the feedback signal. The feedback mechanism is a simple proportional mechanism. The comparison mechanism is composed of bellows elements with the inputs to the comparison mechanism being pneumatic signals. The detector is a simple baffle/nozzle detector.

For an opening discussion, the preceding material is adequate. Do not, however, conclude that the question of controllers has been adequately covered. In fact, the discussion so far is at best a rather simple introduction to the study of controllers. We must, before we're done, discuss in detail various kinds of comparison mechanisms and several kinds of feedback mechanisms arranged either as motion-balance or force-balance mechanisms.

Therefore, we are going to backtrack a bit and talk about a more elementary control with the purpose of establishing an understanding of controller gain.

Components

It is possible to have a controller consisting only of the following components: (see Fig. 21-4).
1. A measurement input.
2. A detector.
3. A control lever.

Arrangements

Fig. 21-5 is a diagram of a controller in a process. The controller is made up of the components listed

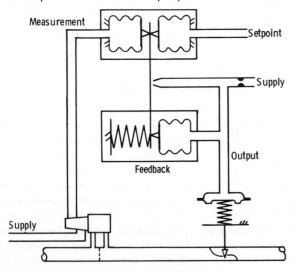

Fig. 21-3. Controller installed in process.

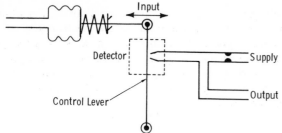

Fig. 21-4. Simple controller consisting of measurement input, detector, and control lever.

above. Note first of all, that the comparison mechanism is quite primitive compared to the fundamental controller diagrammed in the first part of the chapter. At first glance it appears that there is only one input. Second, notice that there is no internal feedback loop. There is, however, an external feedback loop.

The mechanism shown in Fig. 21-5 can be described as a blind pressure controller. It is a pressure controller because it measures pressure and is installed to control pressure in a vessel. It is called blind because it does not indicate or record the measured variable. Let's study the operation of this controller.

Operation

Suppose the measurement range is zero to 10 psig. Suppose further that the control valve has to have 9 lbs on the diaphragm to obtain 5 psig pressure in the vessel. Therefore, the nozzle must be .001 inch away from the baffle. This is true because of the sizing of the nozzle and restriction.

Suppose the up-stream pressure increased. There would be an increased flow through the control valve. The pressure in the vessel would increase as would the pressure on the controller bellows. This increased pressure in the controller bellows would move the baffle closer to the nozzle. The baffle/nozzle would in-

crease the pressure on the control valve. The valve would start closing, thereby reducing the flow to the vessel and reducing the pressure in the vessel. This reduction of pressure acting on the control bellows would permit the baffle to move away from the nozzle, reducing the nozzle backpressure and permitting the valve to open. At some point the nozzle backpressure, the valve and the vessel pressure, and the measurement would come to equilibrium. This new equilibrium point will be such as to cause the valve to be slightly more closed than it was prior to the increase in up-stream pressure.

Suppose we wanted to control the pressure in the vessel at some other pressure, say at 8 psig of water pressure. How could this be done? Notice that the detector mechanism is mounted so that the nozzle can be moved relative to the baffle. Suppose further that we move the nozzle away from the baffle. Let's follow the controller action.

The moving of the nozzle away from the baffle will cause a decrease in nozzle backpressure, hence, a more open control valve. The more open control valve will permit a pressure build-up in the vessel. This increase in pressure acting on the controller measurement bellows will move the baffle toward the nozzle, tending to increase the nozzle backpressure, hence, tending to close the valve. The controller and process will come to equilibrium at some new pressure greater than 5 psig. At what pressure? We have no way of knowing by an examination of the controller, since it is "blind." If a pressure indicating gauge were offered, we could examine the gauge and re-adjust the nozzle to obtain the desired pressure. The position of the nozzle constitutes the second controller input. It is a way of obtaining a comparison between the actual and the desired pressure.

OTHER ASPECTS OF CONTROLLER GAIN

Suppose our controller is such that a change in measurement pressure causes a bellows deflection of 1 inch. Suppose that a change of .002 inch in nozzle-baffle clearance will change the nozzle backpressure from 3 to 15 psig. Suppose further that the nozzle is centered on the baffle. Let's decide how much the measurement pressure has to change to cause a full change in nozzle backpressure, hence, valve position.

Since the measurement motion is applied to the baffle at twice the distance the nozzle is from the pivot, the measurement must move .004 inch to change the baffle nozzle clearance .002 inch. The pressure change necessary to obtain this .004 inch is .04 psi. In other words, .04 psi change will cause the valve to move from fully open to fully closed. As a practical matter this .04 inch of water is so small that the controller would continue to cycle from one limit to another, alternately opening and closing the valve. This action can be described as on and off control. Yet, the expression on and off can be misleading. A preferred expression is to say that the controller has a very high gain or is a very narrow proportioning-band control-

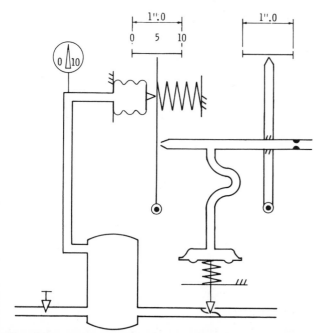

Fig. 21-5. Simple controller connected to a process.

ler. What determines exactly what the gain of a controller is?

Gain is the ratio of output to input. Referring to the above example and using percentage numbers, the output changes 100 percent when the input changes .04 per cent. The gain of the controller, therefore, is 250.

A gain of 250 is much too high for most processes. If gains of this magnitude are used, the control valve will continue to move from one limit to the other. It is necessary somehow to reduce controller gain. The inherent gain of the baffle/nozzle detector is too great. You will recall that in our discussion of the properties of the detector the high gain was a problem. Mechanisms are employed to reduce detector gain to more usable levels.

Chapter 22

Gain Mechanisms

GAIN FEEDBACK BELLOWS

In the preceding chapter we discussed an elementary controller. This controller had no internal feedback mechanisms, but, it was found that the controller had a very high gain. As a result, an extremely small change in measurement input would result in a full valve travel. This was true because the input had to change only .004 inch to fully cover the nozzle. The point was made that high gain controllers have a limited use and that there is a need to reduce the controller gain. In this chapter, we will discuss the method used to reduce controller gain.

Components

The components of a "low" gain controller are:
1. A comparison mechanism.
2. A detector mechanism.
3. A feedback mechanism composed of a bellows/spring combination.

Arrangements

The controller is arranged as was the controller diagrammed in the preceding chapter, except for the feedback mechanism. The feedback mechanism is arranged to move the control lever as the nozzle backpressure changes. (See Fig. 22-2.) The subject to be emphasized in this chapter is the feedback mechanism and its exact operation.

Operation

You will recall that it is necessary to move the baffle only .002 of an inch to cause a full change in output. Because of the lever lengths involved, the measurement must move only .004 inch to cause a full change in output. Fig. 22-1 diagrams these ideas.

Fig. 22-2 shows the control lever, a nozzle, a detector mechanism, and a bellows/spring combination connected to the nozzle backpressure. Suppose we moved the input (error signal) .004 inch. The output would change from 3 to 15 psig. This change in output acting on the bellows/spring would move the lower end of the input lever through its full travel.

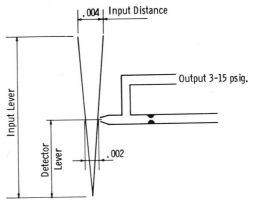

Fig. 22-1. Baffle movement for full output change.

If we start with the baffle positioned before the nozzle so that there is a 3-psig output pressure, a change in input of .004 inch will momentarily cover the nozzle, and theoretically we should obtain a 15-psig output. But, as the nozzle becomes covered, the back pressure increases. This increase in back pressure, acting on the bellows/spring, will move the baffle away from the nozzle. The feedback movement need move only .004 inch to return the baffle to exactly the same position relative to the nozzle that existed prior to changing the input. Another way of looking at the operation is to see that the feedback motion balances (within the range of the detector) the input motion.

Suppose that the bellows/spring combination were such that it would deflect a full inch for a change in pressure of 3 to 15 psig. This would mean that the input (error signal) could also change (almost) 1 inch. If we can change the input 1 inch and obtain a 1-inch change in output, the gain of the controller is 1. Therefore, the introduction of the feedback bellows made it possible to reduce the controller gain from 250 to a gain of 1.

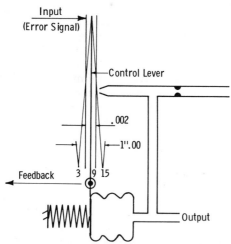

Fig. 22-2. Effect of feedback on baffle/nozzle assembly.

DETECTOR RANGE AND GAIN

You will have noticed that in the earlier discussions whenever we talked about balancing action we always qualified the balance by saying "almost." Later in the text we qualified the balance by saying "within the range of the detector." In this discussion we referred to balancing action being almost balanced within the range of the detector. It is now time to clear up the reason why it was necessary to qualify balance with the expressions "almost" or "within the range of the detector."

Suppose that the input moves 1 inch toward the nozzle. If it does, the output will change from 3 to 15 psig. As it changes from 3 to 15 psig **and if** the feedback bellows moves precisely 1 inch, the baffle position relative to the nozzle will be the same as it was prior to the input changing 1 inch. If the baffle were back in the same position, the output necessarily would have to go back to 3 psig. If the output were exactly 3 psig the bellows/spring could not have moved its 1 inch. We must agree that if the output changes from 3 to 15 psig, the baffle/nozzle clearance must change from .002 inch to .000 inch. If the baffle/nozzle clearance changes .002 inch, there must be a difference between the input and the feedback motions. This difference is equal to, in our example, twice the .002 detector range (nozzle clearance). (See Fig. 22-3.) In other words, if the input moves 1 inch the feedback motion will equal 1 inch minus .004 inch. In our earlier discussions, rather than put a numerical value on the balance, we have simply said balance "almost" or balanced "within the range of the detector."

This notion of detector range is important because all self-balancing instruments or feedback instruments, either motion-balance or force-balance type, do not return precisely to their original positions. The exactness of balance is limited by the range of the detector. We have been using .002 inch as the detector range. Remember that .002 inch is only indicative. The actual detector ranges vary from instrument to instrument.

To establish the idea of detector range more firmly, let's again examine the operation of the controller. Suppose the input were to change 1 inch. Let's suppose also that the input changes very slowly. (See Fig. 22-2.) As we move the error signals to the right, the nozzle backpressure builds up. Simultaneously with the changing of the error signal there is a changing feedback signal. As we cover the nozzle, changing the error signal, the feedback signal uncovers the nozzle. As we continue to change the error signal slowly the output eventually becomes 15 psig. But, if the output is going to become 15 psig, the nozzle must be covered. In other words, the nozzle clearance must change from .002 inch to .000 inch. Therefore, the feedback motion must be slightly less than the input motion. To be exact, the feedback motion is .004 inch less than the input motion.

Recognize that in our discussions we have assumed a geometrically symmetrical mechanism. That is, the nozzle is half way between the error signal input and the feedback signal. As a consequence, the gain is 1, because, if we neglect the detector range, the output is the same as the input. Controllers with a gain of only 1 are in some respects just as limited as controllers with a 250 gain. We would like a controller arranged so that it is possible to change the gain from, say, 250 to 1.

You will find that some of the adjustable gain mechanisms are the same as the gain mechanism used on transmitters and positioners. In addition, two other types of adjustable gain mechanisms will be considered. Perhaps at this time it would be well to point out that there are alternate expressions to gain. Among these alternate terms are sensitivity and proportional

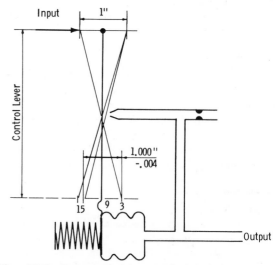

Fig. 22-3. Detector action with large inputs.

band. We will discuss these terms and their relationship in the chapter on controller theory. Be assured at this time that the mechanisms are identical, regardless of the labels used to describe them.

ADJUSTABLE GAIN MECHANISMS

We have shown that the introduction of a bellows/spring component makes it possible to obtain a controller with a gain of almost 1. We noted further that a controller with a fixed gain of 1 is of limited use. It is desirable to have a controller arranged so that it would be possible to obtain controller gain anywhere between 250 and 1. In this chapter we will discuss two mechanisms that make it possible to adjust controller gain.

Components

An adjustable gain mechanism can be one of four different types:
1. Parallel lever.
2. Angle-gain mechanism.
3. Parallelogram mechanism.
4. Pneumatic-gain mechanism.

Arrangements

The different gain mechanisms are located relative to the comparison mechanism, the feedback mechanism, and the detector in different ways. (See Fig. 22-4.) They are arranged so that by adjusting the mechanism it is possible to change the ratio of output to input. If none of the feedback motion is fed back to the detector, the gain of the controller will be, say, 250. If, on the other hand, all of the feedback motion is fed back to the detector, the gain will approach 1.

OPERATION OF THE PARALLEL-LEVER MECHANISM

Fig. 22-5 shows a parallel-lever adjustable-gain mechanism. Compare this mechanism with Fig. 22-2. Notice that it is the same except that a second lever has been introduced. This second lever drives the baffle through a contactor. Suppose the contactor is raised so that it is in line with the feedback-lever pivot point.

Also suppose that the error signal changes so that the baffle moves toward the nozzle. The nozzle backpressure will build up and the feedback bellows will move. But, since the contactor lines up with the pivot, none of this feedback movement will be felt by the baffle. For all practical purposes, we have taken the adjustable gain mechanism out of the circuit. Therefore, the controller has a very high gain. The gain value depends on the location of the nozzle and the length of the control lever.

Let's consider what happens when the contactor is located near the feedback bellows/spring. Again, assume an error signal that moves the baffle toward the nozzle. The nozzle backpressure will build up, and the bellows will move to the left, permitting the baffle to move away from the nozzle. If the contactor is at its low extremity then all the feedback motion will be fed back to the baffle. For this contact position the gain of the controller is low, perhaps 1. By changing the contactor position from one extremity to the other, we can change the controller gain from, say, 250, to 1.

The lever gain mechanism, as it is used in the controller, is the functional equivalent to the lever gain mechanism used in positioners. By adjusting the lever lengths, it is possible to adjust the ratio of output to input. This will be recognized as adjusting the gain. As the parallel lever mechanism is applied to the controllers, the ratio of feedback motion to error signal is adjusted. Because the error signal is a result of a dif-

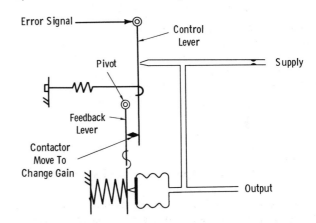

Fig. 22-5. Parallel-lever adjustable-gain mechanism.

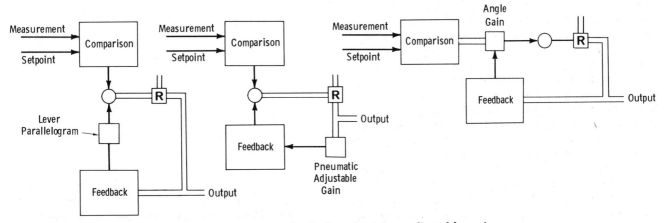

Fig. 22-4. Some methods for obtaining adjustable gain.

ference in two pressures and the output of a controller is pressure, it is possible to discuss gain in terms of the ratio of output pressure to input pressure. The important point to recognize is that the dimensions used to describe input and output are of no consequence, because the dimensions cancel out each other.

If the input is expressed in inches and the output is expressed in pounds, it would be technically incorrect to talk of controller gain. It then becomes necessary to use alternate expressions. Among these are sensitivity and proportional band. In a later chapter we will discuss these terms fully and show the relationship between them.

ANGLE GAIN MECHANISM

Let us now consider the angle gain mechanism. Fig. 22-6 is a diagram of a controller with an angle gain mechanism. We show a bellows comparison mechanism and a proportional-only feedback mechanism. Arranged between these two mechanisms is the angle

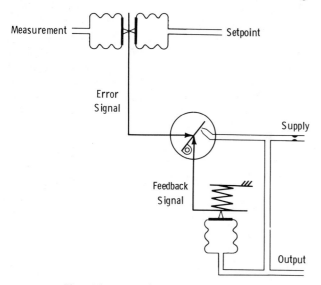

Fig. 22-6. Angle gain mechanism.

gain mechanism. Recall from previous chapters, the angle gain mechanism consists of a baffle/nozzle detector mounted on a disk arranged so that it can be rotated relative to the signals applied to it. As this mechanism was used on positioners, the two signals involved were the measurement signals and the actuator position. In the case of controllers the two signals involved are the error signal and the feedback signal. The operation of a gain mechanism is identical for both the positioner and controller applications. The purpose of the angle gain mechanism is to change the relative contribution of the feedback signal and the error signal. Using more general terms, the purpose is to change the ratio of output to input.

Suppose the baffle were rotated relative to the nozzle, so that it formed an angle of 0 degrees to the feedback signals. Fig. 22-7 shows the baffle in a 0-degree position. Let's follow the operation of the controller for this baffle position.

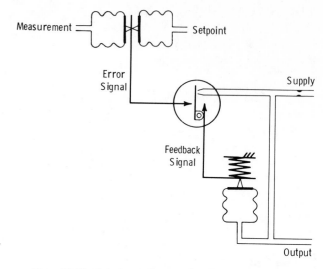

Fig. 22-7. Angle gain mechanism, maximum gain setting.

If the error signal increases, the baffle will move to cover the nozzle. The error signal required is .002 inch. Since the nozzle is covered the backpressure will increase to 15 psig. This increase in backpressure acting on the bellows/spring will result in an upward feedback motion; but, since the baffle is parallel to this feedback motion the baffle position will not be changed by the feedback motion. Consequently, as far as the baffle/nozzle is concerned, there is no feedback motion. For a 0-degree baffle position we have taken out the feedback; hence, the controller is a high gain controller, with a gain of 250, perhaps. Let's see what happens when the baffle is rotated so that it forms a 0-degree angle between it and the error signal. (See Fig. 22-8.)

Suppose the error signal increases. Since the baffle is parallel to the error signal, the error signal can travel through its full range without changing the nozzle backpressure and output. For a 0-degree baffle

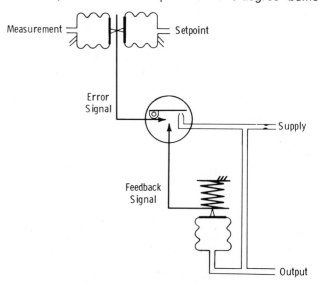

Fig. 22-8. Angle gain mechanism, minimum gain setting.

error-signal relationship we do not have a functional controller since it is impossible for the error signal to cause a change in controller output. So let us assume that, rather than a 0-degree angle position, we have a small angle approaching 0 degrees between the baffle and error signals.

An increase in error signal will move the baffle toward the nozzle, causing the nozzle backpressure to build up. Now almost all of the feedback motion gets fed back to the detector. This is true because the baffle is almost at 90 degrees relative to the feedback. The contribution of the feedback motion relative to the error-signal motion is very large. Therefore, the ratio of output to input is a number approaching 0 divided by a number, say, 1 inch, which represents the feedback motion. If the output were 0 the gain would be 0, but, since the output only approaches 0 the gain of the controller approaches 0.

Recall that when the baffle was at 45 degrees relative to the feedback and error signals, the gain was 1. When the baffle was at an angle approaching 0 degrees relative to the error signal, the gain approached 0. In other words, it is possible to get gains less than 1 in addition to gains from 1 to 250.

It is suggested that the reader review the discussion of the angle-gain mechanism in Chapter 17. As it was pointed out in Chapter 17, it is possible to change the action of an instrument by rotating the angle-gain mechanism to a new quadrant. Rather than repeat this discussion, we shall call attention to the fact that the controller action can be reversed by rotating the angle gain mechanism so that the baffle is in an opposite quadrant.

We will discuss the parallelogram and pneumatic mechanisms in following chapters. Regardless of their physical appearance, all adjustable gain mechanisms have the same function; namely, to change the ratio of output to input. They accomplish this by changing the amount of feedback signal fed back to the detector. The angle mechanism changes both the error signal and the feedback signal.

Notice that, as the baffle is rotated, the amounts of error and feedback signals applied to the detector are changed. As the baffle is rotated, the error signal applied to the baffle will be decreasing as the feedback signal being applied to the detector is increasing. The practical consequence of this observation rests in the problem of aligning controllers. We will soon start our study of actual controllers. At that time the controller alignment problem will be discussed. For now, be sure you understand how adjustable gain mechanisms are used to change the ratio of controller output to controller input.

In preceding chapters we have limited our discussion to controllers having a proportional response. Such controllers are described as proportional-only controllers. In the next chapter we will discuss a controller having automatic reset or mode response.

Chapter 23

Automatic Reset

In Chapter 22 we discussed adjustable gain mechanisms and how they are used to change the gain of a controller. In some of the following chapters, we will discuss actual controllers and relate them to the fundamental controller mechanisms. Before we do this, however, we ought to consider an additional kind of feedback mechanism that we shall call an automatic reset or reset feedback mechanism.

As is so frequently the case, a variety of different terms are used to describe the same mechanism. Whereas we will use the word reset, or automatic reset, others call it integral action.

BASIC RESET ACTION

Components

The components of a reset controller are the same as the components used in the proportional-only controller. The difference between the kinds of controller lies in the arrangement of the feedback component. The components of a reset controller are:
1. A comparison mechanism.
2. A detector mechanism.
3. A feedback mechanism consisting of a bellows/spring.
4. An adjustable restriction.

Arrangements

Fig. 23-1 is a fundamental diagram of a controller with automatic reset feedback. Compare this diagram with the fundamental diagram of the proportional-only controller. Notice that in the reset type there is a bellows/spring reversed. The bellows is at the left of the lever in the reset type and at the right of the lever in the proportional type.

The reset controller has some extremely interesting properties. On the surface, a controller arranged as shown in Fig. 23-1 appears to be quite useless.

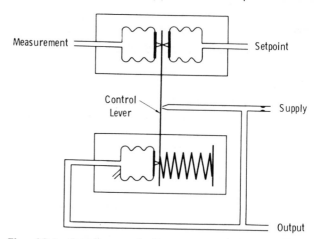

Fig. 23-1. Fundamental diagram of reset controller.

Before the discussions on reset controllers are completed the usefulness of such a controller will be amply demonstrated. The task at hand is to understand its operation and to recognize its important characteristics as a mechanism.

Operation

Let us assume that the controller is in equilibrium and postpone the question as to exactly how it was possible to get it into equilibrium. Suppose that in this equilibrium condition there are 9 psig in both the measurement and setpoint bellows and that the baffle is positioned in front of the nozzle so that there is a 9-psig backpressure applied to the feedback bellows.

Assume that there is an increase in measurement. As a result, the baffle will move toward the nozzle. The nozzle backpressure will build up; hence, the pressure within the feedback bellows will build up. This increase in pressure will cause the bellows to expand. As a result, the baffle will move toward the nozzle, causing the nozzle backpressure to increase further, and the baffle will move further toward the nozzle. As the baffle moves toward the nozzle the backpressure will continue to increase. The bellows will continue to expand and the baffle will continue to move toward the nozzle. When will this chain of events stop? Not until the backpressure equals the supply pressure.

The interaction between the baffle, nozzle, nozzle backpressure, and bellows/spring is such that when the balance is upset the mechanism will drive until the output air pressure goes to a limit. This action has been likened to a cat chasing its tail—the faster the cat runs the faster his tail goes.

Let's see how the mechanism operates when the measurement signal is reduced. Again we will start with the controller in equilibrium. As we reduce the measurement signal, the baffle will move away from the nozzle and the nozzle backpressure will decrease. The decrease of pressure within the bellows will permit the spring to move the baffle further away from the nozzle. As a result, the nozzle backpressure will decrease further. Since the pressure within the bellows is reduced, the spring will continue to move the baffle away from the nozzle. This chain of events will continue until the nozzle backpressure drops to 0 psig. Again, notice that once the equilibrium has been upset, there is no balance between the error measurement signal and the feedback motion. In fact, the feedback motion is such as to drive the instrument to complete unbalance. This type of feedback is called positive feedback because it adds to the original signal.

Recall that when we described the operation of the controller we assumed it was in equilibrium. Now it is time to answer the question as to exactly how the controller is brought into equilibrium in the first place. It is important to understand how an integral type of controller can be brought into equilibrium.

To start, apply a 9-psig pressure to the setpoint bellows and the measurement bellows. With the same pressure into these two bellows, the upper end of the controller lever will assume a fixed position. Position the nozzle far enough from the baffle so that no nozzle backpressure can build up. With no pressure on the feedback bellows, the bellows will be collapsed and the spring fully extended. There will be no pressure in the feedback bellows. Let these be the starting conditions and let us see what happens as the nozzle is moved toward the baffle.

Let's assume that the nozzle is mounted on a lever in such a way that as this lever is moved, the nozzle can be moved relative to the baffle. Fig. 23-2 shows the nozzle so arranged. We shall start with the nozzle so far away from the baffle that there is no backpressure, hence, no pressure in the feedback bellows. Let's

slowly move the nozzle toward the baffle and watch the output. Continue to move the nozzle toward the baffle until the nozzle is close enough to the baffle to cause the nozzle backpressure to start to build up. As it starts to build, move the nozzle away from the baffle. (If we don't, the nozzle backpressure starts to build and, acting on the feedback bellows, will move the baffle further toward the nozzle. We will have initiated a chain of events that will cause the output to drive to 15 psig.) If we move the nozzle away from the baffle at a slightly lower speed than that at which the bellows is driving the nozzle toward the baffle, we can slowly permit the backpressure to increase. If we do this very carefully, we can tell when the bellows and nozzle movements exactly coincide. At this point, the nozzle backpressure will stop building; hence, the bellows will stop expanding and, if we are clever enough, we will stop moving the nozzle. At this point the controller is in equilibrium.

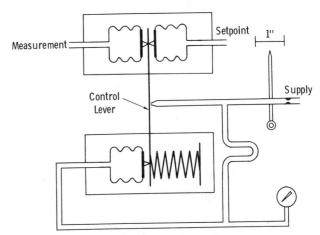

Fig. 23-2. Reset controller with movable nozzle.

CONTROLLER EQUILIBRIUM

This brings up an interesting question. Where is this equilibrium point? Equilibrium occurred when we were able to move the nozzle at the same rate the feedback bellows was moving the baffle. When the rates are the same, the clearance is fixed. Since this is the case, equilibrium is established, not at any specific pressure, but whenever the nozzle/baffle clearance is such that there is a backpressure—any backpressure.

The preceding description of how an equilibrium point can be established should help to explain integral action. Notice how the baffle tends to "chase after" the nozzle. The mechanism is such that as we move the nozzle, the baffle will also move, attempting to maintain a fixed clearance.

Consider a somewhat different way of bringing the controller into equilibrium. Fig. 23-3 is the same mechanism as shown in Fig. 23-2 except that now the output does not terminate at the pressure gauge; it is fed back to the measurement bellows. Therefore, as the nozzle/baffle clearance changes, the measurement input signal will also change. A controller connected in this fashion is said to be closed-loop connected. Consider how a closed-loop-connected controller will operate.

Do not let the fact that the measurement and setpoint bellows have been interchanged confuse you. All that has happened is that the action of the controller has been changed from direct to reverse. If the controller is to balance when closed-loop connected, it must be reverse acting.

If the setpoint pressure is 0 psig, chances are that the nozzle will be completely uncovered; hence, the pressure and the feedback pressure will also be 0. Since the measurement bellows is connected to the controller, the pressure on the measurement bellows will be 0 psig. In any case, assume that this is the condition of the controller. Now let us increase the setpoint pressure.

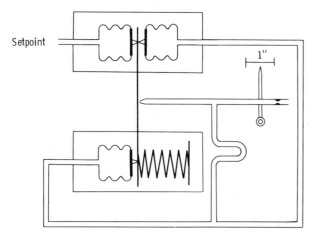

Fig. 23-3. Reset controller, closed-loop connection.

The nozzle backpressure will increase. As the nozzle backpressure increases, pressure within the feedback bellows will increase, driving the baffle closer to the nozzle. So far, the operation is the typical automatic reset action discussed earlier. Notice, however, that as the nozzle backpressure increases, the pressure applied to the measurement bellows increases. This measurement pressure causes the measurement bellows to move against the setpoint bellows. As the measurement bellows moves against the setpoint bellows it causes the baffle to move away from the nozzle. (Recall that the original change in setpoint signal caused the baffle to move toward the nozzle.) So, by closing the controller loop, we have obtained a balancing action between the setpoint signal and the measurement signal. The feedback signal still tends to unbalance the controller.

Precisely when will the controller come to equilibrium? First, let us be quite sure that the controller will come to equilibrium and later we will decide at what point the controller will come into equilibrium. If the setpoint pressure is increased, the baffle tends to cover the nozzle. This increase in pressure drives the baffle closer to the nozzle; therefore, the output pressure will continue to increase. The increase in output pressure, however, is also applied to the measurement bellows. The measurement bellows tends to

move the baffle away from the nozzle. The controller output will stop changing when the measurement pressure within the bellows is such as to position the baffle within .002 inch of the nozzle. Why do we say this? Recall in our earlier discussion when we were moving the nozzle by hand, we observed that the controller could be brought into equilibrium whenever the rate of nozzle movement was the same as the rate of baffle movement. Further, this could happen whenever the baffle was within .002 inch of the nozzle. The baffle automatically is brought within the .002-inch separation by the fact that the output pressure will continue to drive until the measurement bellows of the baffle is within that distance.

RESET OFFSET

Suppose that in order for the baffle to be driven within .002 inch of the nozzle, a difference between setpoint and measurement pressures of 4 psi is required. If the setpoint pressure is 9 psig, then the measurement pressure would be 13 psig. The fact that there is a difference in signals is all right as far as bringing the controller to equilibrium is concerned. However, as you will recall in our discussion of comparison mechanisms, we said that the measurement should equal the setpoint signal and yet, in our instrument, the measurement signal is 4 psi greater than the setpoint signal. A difference of this kind is called reset offset. How can we eliminate it?

Suppose, since measurement pressure is too high, we move the nozzle away from the baffle. If we do, the nozzle backpressure will decrease. The output pressure will decrease, and the measurement pressure will also decrease since it is the same. This is fine except that moving the nozzle away from the baffle, in addition to decreasing the pressure on the measurement bellows, will also decrease the pressure in the feedback bellows. This decrease in pressure will cause the baffle to move **away** from the nozzle. As it does, the measurement pressure will decrease, causing the baffle to move **toward** the nozzle. Therefore, since the decrease in the measurement causes the baffle to move away from the nozzle, an equilibrium between these two actions will be reached.

That equilibrium point again must be within the .002-inch baffle/nozzle clearance. When we moved the nozzle, all we did was change the position of the nozzle relative to the feedback. When we changed the nozzle position, we made it possible to bring the controller into equilibrium at a new measurement pressure. We can continue to make changes to the nozzle until the measurement pressure equals the setpoint pressure. Now that we have brought the controller into equilibrium, and further, now that equilibrium has been obtained with the setpoint and measurement pressures being equal, let's plug off the controller output and connect the setpoint signal source to the measurement bellows as well as the setpoint bellows. If we do this, the controller is said to be open-loop connected.

As we will see in later discussions, the adjusting of the nozzle relative to the feedback mechanism constitutes one of the controller alignments. Unless the nozzle is properly related to the feedback mechanism, there will be a difference between the measurement and setpoint signals. This alignment adjustment will be called the feedback-mechanism alignment.

Let us take another look at an integral controller open-loop connected. It was suggested that if it were possible to move the nozzle at the same rate as the feedback bellows movement, the baffle/nozzle clearance would be fixed and the controller would come to equilibrium. The equilibrium point could occur at any baffle/nozzle clearance within the range of the baffle/nozzle. Actually, it turns out that there is no need to move the nozzle at the same rate of the baffle and then stop. Let's look at the controller operation from a little different viewpoint. First of all, let's put an adjustable restriction, a small needle valve, say, in the line to the feedback bellows. If the restriction is closed down, the pressure within the feedback bellows necessarily will have to change rather slowly. Suppose that the pressures in the setpoint and measurement bellows are the same (this condition can readily be obtained by applying the same pressure to both bellows). With these conditions, the error signal is 0. Now, as we did before, let's move the nozzle toward the baffle until we get an increase in backpressure. This increase in backpressure will slowly be applied to the feedback bellows because of the restriction. Just as slowly, the nozzle backpressure will increase and because of the cat-chasing-his-tail-action, the feedback pressure will continue to increase until it reaches the supply pressure.

Depending on the setting of the restriction, the time it takes for the output to equal the supply pressure may be from a relatively few seconds to as much as several hours. (We will set the restriction so we have ample time to watch the output pressure drifting to the supply pressure.) As the output pressure drifts toward the supply pressure, we will make small adjustments to the nozzle, moving it away from the baffle. After each adjustment, we will look at each output pressure to see if it drifts. If it does, we will make additional adjustments to the nozzle. If the output starts to drift in the opposite direction, this means that we have moved the nozzle too far, and now it is on the other side of its .002-inch clearance. If the output stops drifting, we know that the nozzle has been properly related or aligned to the feedback mechanism. The adjusting of the nozzle to stop drifting with the controller open-loop connected serves the same purpose as the adjusting of the nozzle with the controller closed-loop until the measurement and setpoint pressures are equal.

SUMMARY

The output of an automatic reset controller will continue to drive until the baffle comes within its .002-inch clearance of the nozzle. Unless and until the baffle is within the .002-inch clearance, the output will continue to change. If there is a plus error signal, the controller will drive in one direction until the measurement crosses the setpoint, then it will drive in the reverse direction. If there is a minus signal, the controller will drive in the opposite direction. When there is a zero error signal, the controller output will be constant. This means that such a controller can come to equilibrium at any output pressure. The output will drive in one direction until the measurement crosses the setpoint. When it does, the drive will reverse direction.

If we start with a controller that is aligned, the output will drive until the measurement equals the setpoint.

In the next chapter, we will combine an integral-only controller and proportional-only controller. The result is a proportional-plus-integral controller, commonly called a two-mode controller.

Chapter 24

Proportional-Plus-Automatic Reset Controllers

GENERAL DESCRIPTION

In Chapter 23, automatic reset action was described from the point of view of a mechanism. It was shown that the feedback elements were arranged relative to the baffle so that any error signal would cause the output to drive from one extreme to the other—from supply pressure to zero pressure. Further, it was shown that the controller can be balanced at any output between 3 and 15 psig by positioning the baffle relative to the nozzle so that at equilibrium the baffle is within .002 inch of the nozzle. Consequently, the controller can be balanced at any output pressure. This is an important aspect of the automatic reset controller.

We discussed the open-loop method of connecting the controller. In comparing open-loop controller action with closed-loop controller action, we noted that the automatic reset controller can be brought into equilibrium, having the controller connected either open-loop or closed-loop. The output of a controller not in equilibrium and open-loop connected drives to either supply or zero, depending on whether the error signal is plus or minus. The output of a controller closed-loop connected not in equilibrium is different from the measurement signal. The difference is called reset offset.

In the proportional-only controller the output is always proportional to the error signal. The ratio of output to input depends on the linkage. In most cases this linkage is adjustable, making possible a full range of gains typically varying from 250 to nearly zero. You will recall in the discussions of proportional controllers that the feedback element was arranged so that the feedback motion was subtracted from the error-signal motion. This type of feedback was described as negative feedback and is the "opposite" in some respects to the automatic reset controller. In the automatic reset controller the feedback motion adds to the error signal. This type of feedback is called positive feedback.

In this chapter we shall discuss controllers having both negative feedback (proportional), and positive feedback (automatic reset).

Components

The components of a proportional-plus-reset controller are:
1. A comparison mechanism.
2. A detector mechanism.
3. A feedback mechanism with both negative and positive bellows/spring feedback elements.

Arrangements

The elementary proportional-plus-reset controller is arranged as shown in Fig. 24-1. The comparison mechanism (two bellows in our diagram) is arranged at one end of the lever. At the opposite end of the lever are the two feedback bellows/springs. Mounted between the comparison mechanism and the feedback mechanism is the detector mechanism. Notice that there is a restriction in the line to the reset bellows. Notice further that to simplify the diagram we have not shown the two feedback springs. It is clearly necessary, however, for the actual mechanisms to have either the springs or the equivalent of the springs. In some controllers the spring properties of the bellows are used.

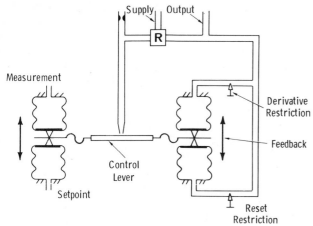

Fig. 24-1. Elementary proportional-plus-reset controller.

Operation

Let us start with the controller having the same pressure on both comparison bellows. This condition, if the controller is properly aligned, means that there is zero error signal to the detector. Let us assume further that the baffle is positioned to the nozzle so that there is, say, 11 psig backpressure. We will have the same 11 lbs in the proportional bellows and in the reset bellows. Notice that the reset restriction is closed down but not off. Assume that the error signal moves to cover the nozzle.

The output pressure will build in a normal manner, and proportioning action will take place. With time, the increase in output pressure will pass through the reset restriction and load up the feedback bellows. The loading of the feedback bellows will move the baffle closer to the nozzle, causing a further increase in backpressure. This chain of events will repeat until the backpressure reaches the supply pressure. In other words, normal automatic resetting will occur. So you see the operation of the proportional-plus-reset controller is different from the proportioning-only and reset-only controllers in that the proportioning-plus-reset controller combines the operational features of both proportioning-only and reset-only controllers. Further, the proportioning action and the resetting action are separate in time only. For short times the controller acts like a proportional-only controller; for long times the controller acts like a reset-only controller. The actual times depend primarily on the setting of the automatic reset resrriction.

Let's see how the controller operates with the reset restriction wide open. Assume the same conditions as before and assume an error signal that moves the baffle toward the nozzle.

There will be an increase in nozzle backpressure, which will be fed to the proportioning bellows. But, since there is no restriction in the reset-bellows line, the same increase in backpressure will be fed simultaneously to the reset bellows. Since the reset-bellows pressure changes at the same rate as the proportioning-bellows pressure, the two will cancel themselves out. In other words, there will be no feedback motion.

Since there is no feedback motion, the controller will act exactly like the high-gain controller discussed in Chapter 21. You will recall that in a high gain controller very small changes in error signal will cause the output to range from 3 to 15 psig. This kind of control action frequently is described as on-off. The reader is cautioned that regardless of the fact that such controllers are called on-off they are in fact narrow-band or high-gain controllers. The output appears as if it is either on (15 psig) or off (0 psig).

So far we have considered the cases where the reset restriction is almost closed and where it is wide open. Let's consider the case where the reset restriction is fully closed. Again, as we did in previous cases, assume that the controller is in equilibrium and that the error signal moves the baffle toward the nozzle.

Normal proportional action will occur, and the output will increase. Since the reset restriction is closed, the change in output will not be felt by the reset bellows; therefore, it is impossible to get any automatic reset action. For all practical purposes, by closing the reset restriction, reset has been eliminated. The controller becomes a proportional-only controller.

The three cases discussed summarize the limiting cases of the proportional-plus-reset controller. Notice how it was possible to change the controller from a high-gain proportional controller to a proportional-plus-reset controller and to a low-gain proportional-only controller, as the restriction was changed from fully open to fully closed. For intermediate restrictions, the time it took for the resetting action to swamp out the proportioning action was changed; the more closed the restriction, the longer the reset time. Finally, notice that there had to be an error signal before there was any controller action at all.

We will find in our discussion of actual mechanisms that they can be related directly, component for component, to the fundamental types discussed in Chapters 21 through 24.

Reset time is stated as "repeats" per unit of time, or as units of time per "repeat." Two examples are "3 repeats per minute" and "10 minutes per repeat." Repeats per minute and minutes per repeat are each the reciprocal of the other. Three minutes per repeat is the same as $\frac{1}{3}$ repeat per minute. A "repeat" is an additional change in output equal to the proportional response. The proportional response is that change in output which occurs in essentially zero time, and the magnitude of which is proportional to the error signal times the controller gain.

We shall now discuss an actual proportional-plus-reset controller having adjustable gain. The controller is called a Multitrol controller and is manufactured by Fisher Governor. We shall also consider an additional mechanism used to obtain adjustable gain.

FISHER GOVERNOR PROPORTIONAL-PLUS-RESET CONTROLLER

It has been pointed out that the proportional-plus-reset controller is, in fact, a mechanism wherein the two controller modes are combined, with each mode contributing to the output signal. The contribution varies with time, proportioning acting first and reset following up. The important aspects of the proportional-plus-reset controller are that it can be in equilibrium at any output pressure, and that, unless the error signal is zero (the measurement signal equals the setpoint signal), the output will drive from one limit or the other. We are going to study a proportional-plus-reset controller manufactured by the Fisher Governor Company which calls the device a Multitrol controller.

Components

1. A comparison mechanism
2. A detector mechanism
3. A feedback mechanism
4. An adjustable gain mechanism

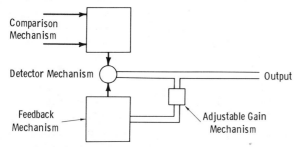

Fig. 24-2. Block diagram of reset controller with adjustable gain.

Arrangements

Fig. 24-2 is a block diagram showing the major components. In most respects it is identical with the block diagram shown in Chapter 21. Notice, however, that the adjustable gain mechanism is located between the detector and feedback mechanism. In the block diagram of Chapter 21, there is no adjustable gain mechanism. The two input signals are air pressures applied to opposing bellows. These two bellows drive one end of the controller lever. At the other end of the lever are the feedback components which also are two opposed bellows. The detector is the baffle/nozzle/relay combination. The output of the relay is the output of the controller. The output of the relay also is fed into the adjustable-gain mechanism, which is a type that has not yet been discussed. For the time being let us consider it to be a fixed-gain mechanism.

Further in this chapter the construction and operation of this mechanism will be discussed.

Fig. 24-3 is a diagram of the controller. Compare this with Fig. 24-1. Notice that except for orientation and the gain mechanism, they are identical. The Fisher Governor controller is arranged with the control lever horizontal. The diagram of the fundamental controller shows the control lever vertical. Fig. 24-4 is a photograph of the controller.

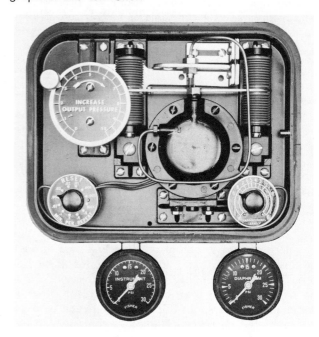

Fig. 24-4. Fisher Governor Multitrol.

Operation

The operation of the Fisher Governor controller is essentially the same as that of the fundamental controller discussed earlier in the chapter, which was open-loop connected. Now let us discuss the closed-loop-connected controller and study its operations. Recall that by closed loop we mean that the output is connected to the measurement bellows. Assume further, that the controller has zero air supply, and that there is a 9-psig setpoint signal applied to the setpoint bellows. Let us turn on the air supply and see what happens.

Since there has been no air supply, the pressure in the measurement, proportioning, and reset bellows is zero. Immediately before the air supply is turned on, the error signal is large, causing the baffle to be positioned against the nozzle. Turning on the air supply powers the nozzle, permitting the backpressure to build. The increase in backpressure drives the relay, causing the output air pressure to build. The output air pressure connected to the measurement bellows

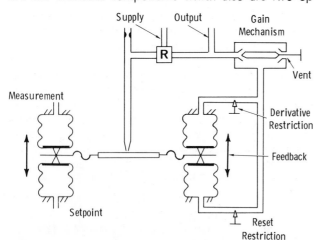

Fig. 24-3. Diagram of control mechanism in Fisher Governor Multitrol.

produces a measurement force that opposes the setpoint force, thereby reducing the error signal.

This increase in output also acts on the proportional bellows, which tends to move the baffle away from the nozzle. Very quickly the input will jump to that value which, when applied to both the measurement and proportioning bellows, will automatically balance the setpoint signal.

Now let us see what happens to the reset bellows. The increase in pressure on turning on the air supply will slowly pass through the reset restriction and enter the reset bellows. The reset bellows will return the feedback end of the lever to the position that it took when there was no air supply. This happens because having the same pressure in both the proportioning and reset bellows is the same as having zero pressure in both bellows. Therefore, we can expect that when the controller is in equilibrium, the feedback end of the lever will have assumed the same position that it had when the controller had no supply.

ALIGNMENT

When and if the pressures in the measurement setpoint bellows become equal, the comparison end of the lever will also assume a predetermined position. In our case we applied a setpoint signal of 9 psig. The measurement must also be equal to 9 psig if the error signal is going to be zero. Notwithstanding, the controller output will drive to whatever output (hence, measurement pressure) is necessary to position the baffle within .002 inch of the nozzle. The controller as such couldn't care less what the measurement signal is and whether or not it equals the setpoint signals. All the controller can do is drive the measurement until the baffle is within .002 inch of the nozzle.

Since we want a controller arranged so that it will come to equilibrium with the measurement and setpoint equal, we must position the nozzle so that it is within .002 inch of the center line of the instrument. The baffle falls on this center line. The two sets of bellows, when loaded with the same pressure, cause the controller lever to fall on the center line.

If after we turn on the air supply, the measurement pressure does not equal the setpoint pressure, we must move the nozzle until the measurement pressure does equal the setpoint pressure. When these conditions are met, the controller is said to be aligned. The test of controller alignment is whether or not the measurement equals the setpoint (if the controller is closed-loop connected) for all pressure levels of setpoint and output. One of the tasks associated with controllers is to adjust the controller so that it will pass the alignment test.

Let us look again at the controller, especially at how the components are lined up on a center line. Observe that the establishment of two points determines the total line. We cannot arbitrarily assign more than two points and expect to get a straight line. Having established two points, we "automatically" predetermine the third point.

Our controller has three points, all of which must fall on the center line. They are the feedback point, the detector point, and the comparison mechanism point. We have observed that the feedback point is fixed, after an appropriate length of time. The nozzle is fixed relative to the baffle by its mechanical position on the instrument chassis. The only point remaining unfixed is the comparison mechanism point. Therefore, the comparison mechanism must drive so that its point falls on the same line established by the detector and feedback positions. If we want the same pressure in both of the comparison mechanism bellows, we must accept the resulting bellows position. The nozzle then becomes the third point that we must put on the center line.

If this motion is understood, there will be no difficulty in understanding the alignment of this or any automatic-reset controller. The Fisher Governor controller is relatively easy to understand because it is symmetrical about a center line. In following chapters we will discuss controllers that are not symmetrical. Nevertheless, this notion of two points establishing a line is applicable.

PNEUMATIC GAIN MECHANISM

We have, in earlier work, discussed mechanical-gain mechanisms of the parallel-lever and angle-mechanism types. Fisher Governor uses what we will call a pneumatic gain mechanism. It is essentially a three-way valve arranged so that as it is adjusted, a vent port closes (or opens) as the inlet port opens (or closes). Between these two ports is an output connection. Fig. 24-5 shows a pneumatic gain mechanism. Fig. 24-3 shows the same mechanism installed in the controller circuit.

Let's backtrack for a moment. Recall that the function of an adjustable gain mechanism is to make it possible to change the ratio of output to input. The output of the pneumatic gain mechanism is the pressure between the two ports. The input to the gain mechanism is the relay output.

If we have a mechanism in which we can change the ratio of output to input, it is an adjustable gain mechanism. Let us determine if the mechanisms shown in Figs. 24-3 and 24-4 will do this.

Assume that the plug is positioned so that it closes the exhaust port. For that plug position, all of the relay output will pass by the plug and out into the feedback bellows. For this plug position, the output equals the input; hence, the gain is 1. Let's turn the adjustment

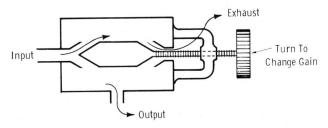

Fig. 24-5. Pneumatic gain mechanism.

to slightly open the exhaust port. Doing this will close down the input port slightly and part of the input signals will be exhausted to the atmosphere. As a consequence, the output pressure will be less than the input pressure. Or in other words, the ratio of output to input will be changed. So you see that even though the mechanism is essentially a three-way valve, by adjusting relative port openings we can change the ratio of output to input. Therefore, such a mechanism is an adjustable gain mechanism.

A pneumatic gain mechanism is an important type of gain mechanism and is widely used in the "stack type" force-balance controller; however, we will not discuss this type of controller at any length in this manual.

SUMMARY

We have noted that the Fisher Governor controller, except for its adjustable gain mechanism, is identical with the fundamental proportional-plus-reset controller. We will find in subsequent chapters that even though other controllers appear to be more complicated, they can be directly related to the fundamental controller. Unlike the Fisher Governor controller the gain mechanisms to be encountered are mechanical.

Chapter 25

Derivative Mode

DERIVATIVE IN CONTROLLERS

In previous chapters we discussed proportional control and reset control, and then combined the two to form a proportional-plus-reset controller. A proportional-plus-reset controller manufactured by Fisher Governor Company was discussed. We observed that there was a restriction in the line to the proportioning bellows. We assumed in our discussions that the restriction was wide open and therefore could be neglected. This restriction will be discussed in this chapter. As is so often the case, the derivative controller to be discussed is described by various terms. We shall use the term derivative, but many people use rate action. Foxboro uses the term "hyper reset."

Components

Only one component is required in addition to the components of a proportional or proportional-plus-reset controller to obtain a proportional-plus-derivative or a proportional-plus-reset-plus-derivative controller. That component is an adjustable restriction. Frequently, a variable capacity is added to stabilize the output.

Arrangements

The adjustable restriction (or the variable capacity) is placed in the line to the proportional bellows. Fig. 25-1 is a diagram of a proportional-plus-derivative controller. Notice, the only difference between this diagram and the diagram of the proportional-only controller is the presence of the restriction in the line to the proportioning bellows.

Operation

If we assume that the reset restriction is wide open, the operation of the proportional-plus-derivative controller is identical with the operation of any proportional-only controller. If, on the other hand, we close the derivative restriction, we eliminate the proportioning feedback motion. Therefore, the controller will act like a high-gain controller. By adjusting the restriction from fully open to closed, we have changed the characteristics of the controller from those of a proportional controller with feedback to a controller with no feedback.

On the surface, it may appear that we are changing the gain of the controller. This is partly true, as we shall see.

Let us study the operation of the controller with the derivative restriction closed down but not shut off. Assume an error signal that moves the baffle toward the nozzle. The nozzle backpressure increases, and the output will increase. Because the derivative restriction is almost closed, the increase in output will not be immediately felt by the proportioning bellows. Therefore, for a small period of time the controller will act like a high-gain controller. Let's wait a few minutes. The increase in nozzle backpressure will work past the restriction and load up the proportioning bellows, permitting the proportioning bellows to operate in its normal way. The increase in pressure in the proportioning bellows will move the baffle away from the nozzle, decreasing the output.

If we wait long enough, the pressure within the proportioning bellows and the output pressure will equalize across the derivative restriction. When that happens, the output will be directly proportional to the error signal. Since there is no difference in pressure across the restriction, the circuit acts as if the derivative restriction were not there.

The derivative restriction "holds back" the proportional feedback motion, thereby causing the output

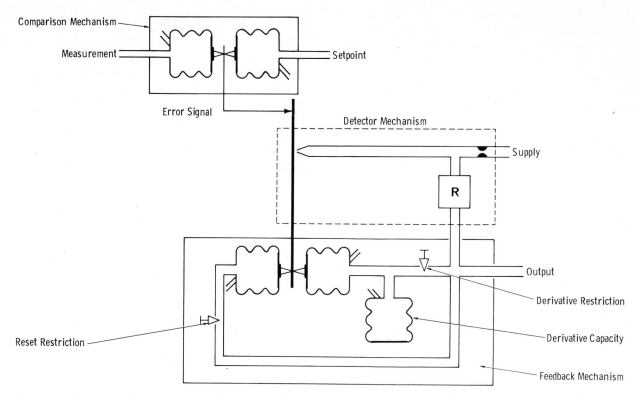

Fig. 25-1. Proportional-plus-derivative controller.

to change an amount greater than it would change if the restriction were not present. For the time that the derivative restriction is in the circuit it does increase the controller gain.

As was the case with automatic reset, the effect of the derivative is time dependent. Given enough time, the derivative has no effect. In Fig. 25-2, we show a plot of output pressure versus time. Notice that the output pressure on a change of error signal increases almost immediately to well beyond the amount that proportional-only would cause. But, with time, the output reduces to the amount that would be obtained with a proportional-only controller.

DERIVATIVE IN TRANSMITTERS

The use of derivative action is not limited to controllers. Certain transmitters, especially temperature

transmitters, incorporate derivative action. In those cases a restriction is placed in the line to the feedback bellows. Fig. 25-3 is a diagram of a temperature transmitter with derivative. The operation here of the derivative in transmitters is quite similar to the operation in controllers.

Suppose the measurement changes. Since the derivative restriction slows the rate at which the balancing bellows can act, the balancing motion (or force) is delayed in time. As a consequence, the output of the transmitter is greater than the change in measurement.

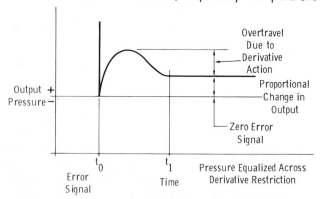

Fig. 25-2. Output in proportional-plus-derivative controller.

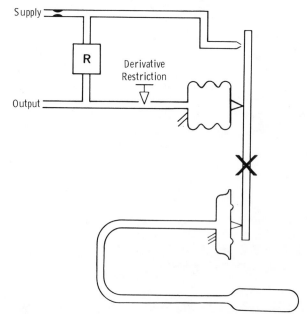

Fig. 25-3. Temperature transmitter with derivative.

152

Given sufficient time the transmitter will come to balance at an output pressure that balances the new measurement signal. Temporarily, however, the output travels an amount much greater than would be expected, compared to the input.

The reason for arranging the transmitter so that the output overtravels the input will be clarified in our discussions of derivative controller motion. For the present, we need only say that it enables the controller to handle rapid process changes more quickly.

SUMMARY

We have seen the nozzle derivative-mode controller. All we need to do is temporarily prevent the normal proportioning or balancing action by introducing restriction in the line to the proportioning or balancing bellows. By adjusting this restriction we can change the time it will take before normal proportioning or balancing action occurs. The effect of this is to cause the output to overtravel.

Chapter 26

Foxboro's Model 40

GENERAL DESCRIPTION

Chapter 24 was devoted to the proportional-plus-reset controller manufactured by Fisher Governor. This controller was related to the fundamental proportional-plus-reset controller discussed earlier in the text. It was determined that the Fisher Governor controller is quite similar, geometrically, to the fundamental controller. The alignment of the controller consisted of relating the comparison, feedback, and detector mechanisms about the center line.

In this chapter, we shall consider a second proportional-plus-reset controller, the Foxboro Model 40, proceeding somewhat differently than we did in our study of the Fisher Governor controller. We will start with the complete controller and relate it to the fundamental diagram.

Arrangements and Components

Fig. 26-1 is a photograph of the Foxboro Model 40 controller. Let us first attempt to determine whether this controller is a proportional-only, a proportional-plus-reset, or a proportional-plus-reset-plus-derivative controller. If it is a proportional-only controller, there will be no adjustable restrictions in the controller circuit, and the feedback mechanism will consist of a bellows/spring. If it is a proportional plus-automatic reset controller, there will be one adjustable restriction and two bellows in the feedback mechanism. If the controller is a proportional-plus-reset-plus-derivative controller, there will be two adjustable restrictions and two bellows in the feedback mechanism.

Having this information is sufficient to answer the question that will establish the number of modes. As with any controller, we will have to determine the location of elements composing the comparison mecha-

nism, the detector mechanism, and the feedback mechanism. In addition, we must determine if there is an adjustable gain mechanism and what kind it might be.

An examination of Fig. 26-1 shows two scales in the front of the instrument in addition to the scales marked supply and output. One of the scales is circular; the other is a strip gauge. These scales make it appear as if there were two adjustments. This evidence is a good indication that the controller has an adjustable-gain mechanism and a reset restriction.

If the controller has reset, the feedback mechanism should consist of two bellows opposing each other. Fig. 26-2 is a photograph that shows the feedback mechanism. Notice that there are two bellows, there-

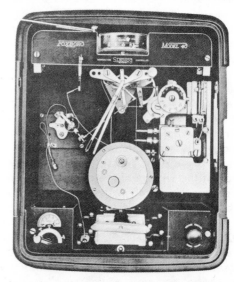

Fig. 26-1. The Foxboro Model 40 proportional-plus-reset controller.

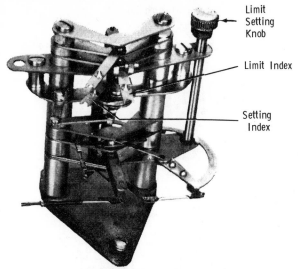

Fig. 26-2. The feedback mechanism of Foxboro Model 40 controller.

fore, we can conclude that the subject instrument is a proportional-plus-reset-plus-derivative controller. Also notice in Fig. 26-2 that the gain mechanism is an angle-type gain mechanism. We make this conclusion because as the gain dial is rotated, the nozzle and baffle rotate about an axis. Our conclusion is supported by the fact that the error-signal link is at right angles to the feedback motion. This configuration implies an angle-type gain mechanism.

We have located the points where the error signal and the feedback signal converge on an adjustable-gain mechanism. The error signal originates at the comparison mechanism. So if we follow the error link, we will be directed to what might be a comparison mechanism. What kind of comparison mechanism? This mechanism certainly is not made up of bellows. Clearly, it consists of linkage. To determine if we have a comparison mechanism, we must establish whether or not the linkage mechanism offered meets the test of the comparison mechanism. Recall that the purpose of the comparison mechanism is to compare a measurement signal to a setpoint signal. If there is no difference, the output of the comparison mechanism is zero or, in other words, there is a zero error signal. If the measurement is greater than the setpoint, there is a plus error signal. If the measurement is below the setpoint, there is a minus error signal. Increasing the measurement a predetermined amount or decreasing the setpoint the same predetermined amount should result in the same error signal.

A study of the linkage of the comparison mechanism of the Foxboro Model 40 will show that it is a type-2 motion-balance linkage. Recall that the type-2 motion-balance linkage consists of a fixed lever and a floating lever. On all motion-balance linkages there are two inputs, and the output is taken from the floating lever. In the case of the Foxboro controller, or for that matter any controller using a linkage-type comparison mechanism, the two inputs are the measurement and the setpoint signal.

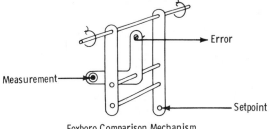

Foxboro Comparison Mechanism

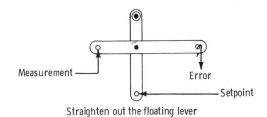

Straighten out the floating lever

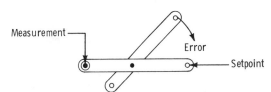

Rotate the levers counterclockwise so that the lever lines up.

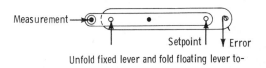

Unfold fixed lever and fold floating lever to-

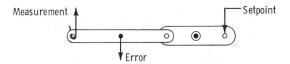

Get the fundamental type 2 motion-balance mechanism.

Fig. 26-3. Relationship of fundamental to actual detector mechanism in Foxboro Model 40 controller.

From your knowledge of the motion-balance linkage, assure yourself that if the two signals are moved simultaneously, there will be no change in output. On the other hand, a change in measurement signal or a change in setpoint signal, providing they are the same, has the same effect on the output. If the measurement signal increases, the error signal will have one polarity; if the measurement signal decreases, the error signal will have the opposite polarity. Fig. 26-3 is a series of diagrams showing the relationship of the actual mechanism to the fundamental mechanism.

Our examination of the controller has shown that the comparison mechanism is a linkage-type mechanism, that the feedback mechanism is a two-bellows mechanism having both positive and negative feedback, hence, reset and proportional modes. The gain mechanism is the angle-type gain mechanism. The detector is the baffle/nozzle and relay combination. The relay is mounted under the proportional-band dial.

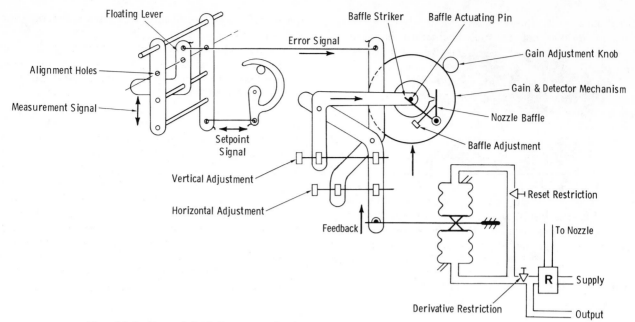

Fig. 26-4. Essential elements and adjustments of Foxboro Model 40 Controller.

Fig. 26-4 shows all the essential elements and adjustments. Certain of these elements, particularly those arranged around the gain mechanism, have been distorted. Functionally, the diagram is the equivalent of the actual mechanism.

Operation

Let us increase the setpoint signal and see how the controller operates. An increase in setpoint signal will raise one end of the floating lever to the left, hence, the error signal is to the left. The error signal positions one end of the control lever. The other end of the control lever is positioned by the feedback signal. (Do not let the fact that the control lever consists of three levers pinned and locked together obscure the essential control lever. The essential lever is a straight line between the application of the error signal and the feedback signal).

The leftward movement of the upper end of the control lever moves the baffle striker to the left, permitting the baffle to cover the nozzle. The nozzle back-pressure increases and the relay output pressure increases. This increase in output, acting first on the proportional bellows, causes an upward movement of the feedback bellows, hence, an upward feedback signal. This upward feedback signal lifts the control lever vertically, simultaneously lifting the baffle actuator pin. Since the striker forms an angle with this vertical movement the baffle striker is permitted to move to the right, uncovering the nozzle. (Recall that the original error signal caused the baffle to cover the nozzle.) The actuating pin, hence the baffle, will come to equilibrium at that baffle/nozzle clearance that results in an output pressure which, acting through the feedback mechanism, balances the error signal.

But this change in output also acts on the reset bellows and will ultimately cause the feedback mechanism to return the feedback signal to precisely the same position it had prior to changing the setpoint signal. As a result of these interactions the normal reset drifting will set in. The output will continue to drive in an effort to maintain a feedback signal. The reset bellows, in a way of speaking, will undo this effort.

Since our original error signal was in the direction to cause the baffle to cover the nozzle and since the relay is direct acting, the output will drive, due to reset action, to supply pressure. Recall that the only way we can prevent the output from driving in a reset controller is to reduce the error signal to zero.

The error signal can be reduced to zero only if the measurement moves to the setpoint. If the output of the controller were connected to a control valve in process, as the control valve moved, the measurement would change until it reached the setpoint. When it does, the output of the controller will stabilize the control valve will assume a fixed position, and the measurement will line out at the setpoint, provided that the controller is properly aligned.

CONTROLLER ALIGNMENT

If the measurement is to line out at the setpoint, the controller must be aligned correctly. By aligned, we mean the comparison mechanism, the feedback mechanism, the detector mechanism, and the gain mechanism must all be properly related to each other. Let's see how this is done.

Before considering the aligning of the several mechanisms with each other, we must first align each mechanism within itself. Having done this, we then relate the individual mechanisms to each other so that when the measurement and setpoint are together, at any place on the scale, the output will not drift and it will be possible to rotate the gain dial without changing the output.

Let's start with the comparison mechanism. The alignment of the comparison mechanism is accomplished by inserting an alignment pin through the holes provided in the mechanism linkage. Having done that, if the setpoint and measurement indexes do not agree, the micrometer on the setpoint index is rotated so that measurement index agrees with the setpoint index.

Consider now the feedback mechanism. When the pressure is zero the pressure in both bellows is the same, and the bellows will assume a fixed position. Since the pressures in the individual bellows cancel each other out, it makes no difference what the pressure level is. The bellows will return to the same fixed point when the pressure equalizes. As a consequence, the point at which the feedback signal is applied to the control lever is fixed. There are no adjustments available to change this point. This point becomes one of the fixed points of the three necessary to establish the "alignment center line" of the controller. This leaves two other points to consider.

When we align the comparison mechanism with the alignment pin we fix a second point because the error signal length is not adjustable. Now two points of the necessary three have been fixed. If the controller is to be brought into alignment, the only remaining point is the detector position. The nozzle position of the detector is fixed, but the baffle is adjustable. The adjustment of the baffle makes it possible to align the detector relative to the comparison and feedback mechanisms. The remaining mechanism needing alignment is the gain mechanism.

Gain Mechanism Alignment

The definition of whether a gain mechanism is aligned is whether or not it is possible to change the gain when there is a zero error signal, without having the output change with the gain adjustment. Let's think about this a minute. If there is no error signal, we should be able to change the gain without the output changing because zero times any number is still zero. It will be possible to change the gain of an angle-type gain mechanism without the output changing if and only if as we change the gain dial we do not change the baffle/nozzle clearance, because if we do the output must necessarily also change.

The baffle/nozzle clearance won't change if the baffle actuating pin is centered on the axis of rotation of the gain mechanism. If it is on the axis of rotation, the baffle striker will just ride around the pin and the baffle will remain in a fixed position relative to the nozzle.

To test for gain-mechanism alignment rotate the gain mechanism. Maintain a zero error signal. Observe the output. If it changes, the actuating pin is not centered. If we are to center the actuating pin, we must be able to move it both vertically and horizontally. Examine the diagram. Notice that as the vertical adjustment is rotated, we move one end of a 90-degree shaped two-sided lever horizontally. However, the other side of the lever that carries the actuating pin moves essentially vertically. This constitutes our vertical adjustment.

Consider now the horizontal adjustment. In your mind's eye disconnect the error-signal link and hold the feedback end of the lever in a fixed position. Change the horizontal screw. As it is turned, the error-signal end of the control lever will move horizontally. But, let's now re-connect the error signal link. Recognize that the comparison end of the error-signal link is fixed. This means that the error signal end of the control lever is fixed. The feedback end of the control lever is also fixed. Therefore, as we adjust the horizontal adjustment, the middle of the controller lever tends to bulge either to the right or the left depending on which way we turn the horizontal adjustment screws. As it bulges, it moves the actuating pin horizontally. By adjusting these vertical/horizontal screws, we can position the baffle-actuating pin so that it is centered on the axis of rotation of the angle-gain mechanism.

Alignment Principles

As is so often the case with instrument adjustments, there is a certain amount of interaction between the adjustments. In addition, there is another complicating factor. That complication arises out of the fact that the detector mechanism is used to determine if the gain mechanism is aligned. Yet, when we start, we do not know if the detector itself is aligned. In other words, the very thing we use to determine if the gain mechanism is aligned, may not itself be aligned. This is not an uncommon problem in alignment and it is not limited to the alignment of the gain mechanism and the detector mechanism. We have comparable problems in aligning feedback mechanisms and comparison mechanisms.

When encountering this kind of problem, the remedy is to alternately make a correction in the alignment of each of the two interacting mechanisms. In our case, it means we would alternately make corrections to the baffle and to the gain mechanism adjustments. For a detailed description on an exact line of procedure, refer to the applicable IMO (Instrument Maintenance Outline). A good rule to remember is one adjustment can adjust for only one condition. You cannot use an adjustment to achieve two alignment objectives.

SPECIAL ASPECTS

The Foxboro Model 40 controller differs from other controllers in some aspects that are well worth pointing out. First, notice that the derivative restriction is in series with the reset restriction. In other words, the change in backpressure must pass through the derivative restriction before it can pass through the reset restriction. A controller so arranged is described as a series controller and differs from the parallel controllers previously diagrammed.

For our purposes, there is no essential difference between a series and a parallel controller. The difference arises in the frequency response of the controllers.

A second aspect involves the measurement micrometer. Unlike most linkage-type instruments, it is possible to change the measurement micrometer without introducing errors in the controller alignment. This is true because the micrometer adjustment is arranged so that the change is made on the measuring side of the comparison mechanism rather than on the display or index side.

SUMMARY

We have oversimplified the derivative mechanism. The actual controller, in addition to the derivative restriction, also has a small stabilizing bellows installed within the proportioning bellows. We shall, in our discussions on derivative, omit the stabilizing bellows. We do this because, from the point of view of a mechanism, the function it serves is to stabilize the deriva-tive action and it does not enter into alignment or change the way a controller operates.

A good understanding of the angle-gain mechanism and how it is aligned is important not only because of its use in the Foxboro Model 40, but because there are several other controllers using similar mechanisms. The general requirement of centering the baffle actuating pin on the axis of rotation is a requirement of all instruments using angle-gain mechanisms.

The alignment principles outlined in this chapter apply equally to all controllers. In the next chapter we will consider a proportional-plus-reset controller, manufactured by Minneapolis-Honeywell and described by them as the Air-O-Line controller. You will find that this controller, other than for a change in arrangements to obtain automatic reset, is quite similar to controllers already discussed.

Chapter 27

Honeywell (Brown) Air-O-Line Controller

GENERAL DESCRIPTION

The Foxboro Model 40 is a motion-balance controller using a linkage comparison mechanism, an angle-gain mechanism and a baffle/nozzle/relay combination as the detector. Although we have limited our discussion to the proportioning-plus-reset-plus-derivative controller, other mode combinations are available.

In this chapter we will study Honeywell's controller, which is also a motion-balance controller that uses a linkage comparison mechanism. We will find that the feedback mechanism, though functionally equivalent to the mechanism previously discussed, is ingeniously arranged and is unique in the industry.

Components and Arrangements

Fig. 27-1 is a pictorial diagram of the Honeywell controller. The derivative unit, made up of a resistance and a variable capacity, is placed between the relay output and the proportioning bellows. If the derivative restriction is wide open, the controller becomes a proportioning-plus-reset controller only. The controller diagrammed appears as it is arranged in the Brown Electronic measuring instruments. It is almost identical with the Air-O-Line controller as used in any of Honeywell's measuring instruments.

We have said that the controller is a proportional-plus-reset controller. Therefore, we must expect to find a comparison mechanism, an error detecting mechanism, and a two-bellows feedback mechanism with a restriction in the line to the reset bellows. Since it is also an adjustable-gain controller, we should expect to find an adjustable gain mechanism. We shall study the several mechanisms and discuss how they are each aligned with the other. Let us start with the comparison mechanism.

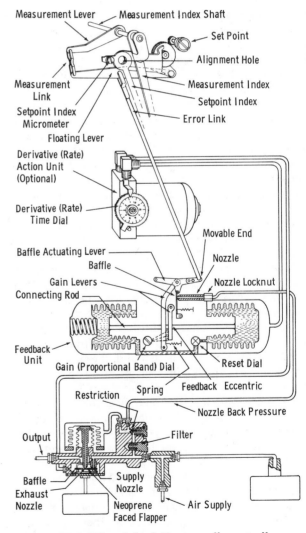

Fig. 27-1. Pictorial of Honeywell controller.

Alignment

The comparison mechanism is a linkage-type mechanism as differentiated from the bellows-type mechanism. As we did in the case of the Foxboro Controller, let us determine what type linkage the mechanism is.

You will recall that there are two input signals and one output signal from a comparison mechanism. The output signal is the error signal and is taken off the floating lever. The two input signals are the measurement and setpoint. If the mechanism consists of three levers it is a type-3 mechanism; two levers, type-2; one lever, type-1. Study Fig. 27-1 and locate the floating lever. Observe that one end of the floating lever is supported by a link and a lever that is driven by a shaft. The shaft rotates as the measurement changes. Study the other end of the floating lever. Notice a series of gears. Notice further, that as the gears rotate, a lever is caused to rotate. This lever is attached to the setpoint end of the floating lever. Since we have located three levers, we can properly conclude that it is a type-3 linkage comparison mechanism.

How is this mechanism aligned? It can be considered to be aligned if for a zero error signal the setpoint index coincides with the measurement index. Recall that in aligning any controller, one mechanism is selected as the reference and all other mechanisms are related to it. As was the case in the Foxboro Model 40, the Air-O-Line unit is aligned around the comparison mechanism. The comparison mechanism itself is related to the instrument chassis. This is accomplished by inserting an alignment pin through an alignment hole in the instrument chassis. The setpoint or the measurement is changed so that the alignment pin is able to enter the hole vacated by the error-signal link. If the measurement and setpoint indexes do not agree, the setpoint micrometer is adjusted to bring them into agreement. The comparison mechanism is now aligned and the error link can be reconnected.

Let us proceed now to the adjustable gain mechanism. Determine what kind of gain mechanism is used and then consider its alignment. Notice that it consists of levers. Notice further that as the gain dial is rotated, a contactor between the two levers is moved. Therefore, we can properly conclude that the gain mechanism is a parallel-lever gain mechanism. Recall that the parallel-lever gain mechanism has only one input signal applied to it and one output signal from it. In other words, as the gain dial is changed, the amount of output is varied. The input remains fixed. Examine the diagram and satisfy yourself that there is only one input and one output to this gain mechanism and that as the dial is changed the ratio of output to input is changed. The input to the gain mechanism is the feedback signal. The output is the lever movement as detected by the nozzle.

Consider now the alignment. Recall that the requirement for any gain mechanism alignment is that it be possible to change the gain with no change in output, provided the error signal is zero. There will be no change in output as the contactor is moved up and down if the levers are parallel. Therefore, the alignment problem is one of making the levers parallel.

The levers are driven by an eccentric pin mounted on a rod that connects the feedback bellows. As the nozzle backpressure changes, the relay output will change and the feedback will drive. The driving of the feedback mechanism acting on the gain mechanism levers, will cause them to move either to the left or to the right. Any lever movement will be detected by the baffle/nozzle and will be reflected by a change in nozzle backpressure. What we must do then is make whatever adjustments are necessary so that there will be no lever movement as the gain is changed. Our possibilities are either to adjust the nozzle or to adjust the actuating pin on the feedback-mechanism connecting rod.

We can adjust the nozzle by turning it on its threaded base. We can adjust the feedback point by rotating the eccentric actuating pin mounted on the connecting rod.

Recall in earlier discussions that an automatic reset mechanism always drives so as to bring the baffle (or nozzle) within the baffle/nozzle clearance. In a way of speaking, the feedback mechanism will search out the position it must assume to bring the baffle to the nozzle. If this is true and if we decide the way to align the gain mechanism is to adjust the eccentric, we have two contradictory statements. The statements contradict each other because if we adjust the eccentric we thereby momentarily re-position the lever, moving the baffle in front of the nozzle. But as far as the feedback mechanism is concerned, it has taken the position that puts the baffle in its correct position in front of the nozzle. Now, by changing the eccentric we have moved the baffle. What happens? The nozzle backpressure changes. The change in nozzle backpressure acting on the feedback mechanism drives the feedback mechanism so as to return the baffle to exactly the same position it had prior to our changing the eccentric. Because the baffle has the same position, the parallel levers must have the same position.

As we move the eccentric in an effort to move the levers to the left, the feedback mechanism drives to move the whole eccentric and the levers so that they are exactly back to the same position they had prior to our changing the eccentric. Therefore, we must conclude that adjusting the eccentric won't align the gain.

Suppose we move the nozzle away from the baffle a small amount. The reset mechanism will then drive to bring the baffle back within the nozzle clearance. To do this, it must move to the right, permitting the baffle to drive within the baffle/nozzle clearance. Since the top of the controller lever has moved to the right (the bottom is fixed) we have changed the inclination of that lever. And, through the contactor, we have changed the inclination of the second lever. Since one end of it is also fixed, we have succeeded in changing the degree of parallelism between the two levers. We can properly conclude that by adjusting the nozzle we have changed the degree of parallelism between the gain mechanism levers. Therefore the nozzle adjustment is the one to be used to align the gain mechanism.

The last mechanism needing alignment is the feed-back mechanism. We have established two points on the controller center line: namely, the comparison mechanism and the error-detector mechanism. Recall that the feedback mechanism will drive so that its take-off point falls on the controller center line. For the feedback mechanism to be aligned, it should be positioned so that its take-off point is on the center line when there is the same pressure in both bellows. The take-off point can be adjusted by rotating the eccentric on the connecting rod. Examine the controller output. If the output drifts, the feedback mechanism is attempting to bring its take-off point to the center line. Make adjustments with the eccentric until the drift stops. When the drift stops, we know that the take-off point is on the controller center line.

The controller center line, in the case of the Air-O-Line controller, is a simple straight line originating at the alignment hole in the instrument chassis, passing by the nozzle tip, and terminating at the feedback eccentric. The gain mechanism levers will be parallel to the center line.

To reverse the action of this controller, the error link is moved from one end of the baffle actuating lever to the other end. This changes the polarity of the error signal as seen by the detector; hence, it changes the polarity of the controller output for a given measurement setpoint deviation. For a detailed alignment pro-cedure of the Brown Air-O-Line controller, see the applicable IMO.

SPECIAL FEATURE

Honeywell uses a non-bleed relay in its controller. This relay was discussed in the chapter on relays. The

Fig. 27-3. Pictorial of control unit in Honeywell Air-O-Line controller.

feedback mechanism is unique. Notice that, unlike other controllers, the relay output does not pass through the reset restriction. Oil flows through the reset restriction. This oil is confined within a compartment composed of the proportioning bellows and a seal bellows, a reset bellows and a seal bellows, and the line connecting the two bellows systems. Let us study the operation of this feedback mechanism.

Starting with the reset restriction closed, and recognizing that a fluid is noncompressible, we must conclude that the connecting rod will follow the proportioning bellows as the nozzle backpressure positions the proportioning bellows. The spring opposing the proportioning bellows is mounted against the reset bellows, but again since the fluid is incompressible as the proportional bellows is loaded, it is opposed by the spring. The whole assembly then moves to the left, compressing the spring as the relay output increases. Now open the reset restriction. If there is a difference in pressure within the two bellows compartments, oil will flow through the restriction in an effort to equalize the two pressures. The normal reset drift will set in.

In the next chapter we will study a third motion-balance controller (Taylor Fulscope) using a linkage-type comparison mechanism. Fig. 27-2 is a diagram of the Brown Air-O-Line controller. Study this diagram and relate it to that of Fig. 27-1. Fig. 27-3 is a photograph of the controller showing the actual physical relationships. Study the photograph and relate it to Figs. 27-1 and 27-2.

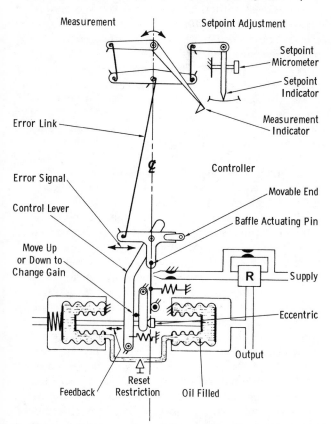

Fig. 27-2. Diagram of Brown (Honeywell) Air-O-Line controller.

Chapter 28

Taylor Proportioning-Plus-Reset Controller

TAYLOR FULSCOPE CONTROLLER

In the preceding chapter we discussed the Brown Air-O-Line controller and found that other than for the construction details of the feedback mechanism, the controller was directly comparable to all other controllers so far discussed that use a linkage-type comparison mechanism. We shall consider only one more example of proportioning-plus-reset controllers using linkage-type comparison mechanism. This is a controller manufactured by Taylor Instrument Company and called by them the Fulscope controller. We shall find that this device is quite similar to others already discussed; the major difference between it and the others is the gain mechanism.

Components

1. A comparison mechanism
2. A detector mechanism
3. A feedback mechanism
4. An adjustable gain mechanism

The comparison mechanism is a linkage type; the detector mechanism is a baffle/nozzle/relay detector; the feedback mechanism is a "bellows in a can" which functionally is the equivalent of the two opposing bellows mechanisms. If derivative (a restriction and a variable capacity) is furnished, it is placed in the line to the proportioning bellows.

Arrangements

The comparison mechanism is mounted so that its major center line coincides with the axis of rotation of the measurement index. The detector, unlike those previously discussed, is arranged so that the nozzle portion of the detector "looks" directly at the floating lever of the comparison mechanism. An examination of the mechanism will show that there is no error link. Nevertheless any error in position of the floating lever is detected by the nozzle. Another way of looking at it is that the error link is very, very short in that the baffle portion of the detector directly mounts on the floating lever, rather than being driven by the floating lever by a link. The feedback mechanism is mounted off to one side. The output of the adjustable gain mechanism positions the nozzle. (See Fig. 28-1.)

Let us look at the comparison mechanism a little more closely. Fig. 28-2 is a diagram of the Taylor controller. Notice that one end of the floating lever pivots on a geared disk which can be rotated. As it rotates, one end of the floating lever is raised and lowered. This is the setpoint input signal. Driving the other end of the floating lever is an actuating pin that mounts on a lever. This lever is positioned by the measurement, thus forming the second input to the comparison mechanism. The comparison mechanism can be considered to be a type-2 or a type-3 motion-balance linkage. If the large geared disk is considered to be a lever it is a type-3 comparison mechanism.

For the feedback mechanism Taylor uses the bellows-in-the-can construction. Recall that a bellows in a can is the functional equivalent of two opposing bellows. The problem with all bellows-in-the-can mechanisms is how to take the bellows position out of the can. Taylor accomplishes this by introducing a seal bellows within the feedback bellows, thereby making it possible to connect a link to the movable end of the bellows assembly. An introduction of one seal bellows, however, introduces its own problem. If the bellows is to be brought into equilibrium, a different pressure is required within the bellows than is required outside. The solution to this problem is the introduction of a second seal bellows of the same diameter as the first

Fig. 28-1. Two views of Taylor Fulscope controller unit.

on the other side of the bellows. If this is done, the effective areas of the inside and outside of the bellows are the same, hence, the bellows will come to equilibrium with the same pressure on both sides.

A proportioning spring is mounted within the second sealed bellows, and attached to this spring is an adjustment. As this adjustment is changed, the loading on the spring changes. This in turn changes the initial position of the bellows.

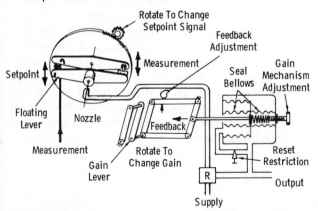

Fig. 28-2. Diagram of Taylor Fulscope controller.

Operation

The operation of this controller is basically the same as the operation of all other controllers. Because the individual components are somewhat differently arranged, let us see how this controller operates. Suppose that the measurement signal moves upward. This will permit the right-hand end of the floating lever to lower. The lowering of the floating lever moves the baffle closer to the nozzle, increasing the nozzle back-pressure. Because the relay is reverse acting, the relay output decreases. This decrease in pressure permits the bellows to expand, causing a feedback movement to the right. This feedback movement permits the gain mechanism to drop, causing the baffle to move away from the nozzle.

Notice that this decrease in pressure also acts on the reset bellows. Normal resetting action will occur as long as there is an error signal. The resetting can be stopped only if the measurement is returned to the setpoint. Measurement can be returned to the setpoint through a change in the external controller loop. The output from the controller repositioning a final element will cause a change in measurement until the measurement returns to the setpoint.

Parallelogram Gain Mechanism

The parallelogram gain mechanism is a one-input, one-output mechanism. In this respect it is comparable to the parallel-lever mechanism. Fundamentally, the parallelogram is a four-bar linkage arranged in a

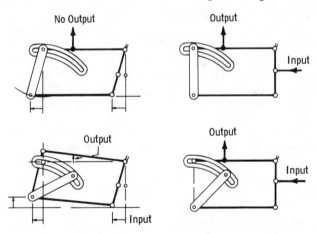

Fig. 28-3. Action of parallel gain mechanism.

parallelogram. (See Fig. 28-3.) One point of the linkage is fixed to the instrument chassis. The opposite point is supported by a lever that can be rotated relative to the parallelogram. If the lever lines up with the vertical edge of the parallelogram, there will be no output from the parallelogram, even though there is a change in input. In your mind's eye, picture an input movement. As the input moves, the three lower levers composing the parallelogram will simply swing on the fourth lever. There will be no change in the position of the fourth lever; therefore, there will be no change in output.

The feedback signal moves to the left. The bottom lever of the parallelogram will also move towards the left. Since the left end of the lever is supported by the adjustable gain lever, the direction of its travel is determined by the travel of the gain lever. Because the gain lever forms the 45-degree angle, the left movement applied to it will cause it not only to swing to the left, but also to swing up. This upward movement raises the parallelogram. The raising of the parallelogram is the output.

As the angle of the gain lever relative to the parallelogram is increased, there is more parallelogram upward movement for a given input moment to the parallelogram. As the angle of gain lever relative to the parallelogram is reduced to zero, the output for a given input is reduced. In fact, at zero angle the output, regardless of the input, is zero.

Alignment

The overall problem of aligning this controller is the same as with all other controllers. Several mechanisms must each be aligned within themselves and then to each other. The basic Fulscope alignment reference is the comparison mechanism. However, this alignment was accomplished by the use of an alignment pin that was inserted through the chassis. The comparison mechanism was adjusted until the alignment pin could be entered into a reference hole in the floating lever. In the Taylor controller the nozzle/baffle is used to determine if the floating lever is centered. The problem, however, is how to determine whether the nozzle itself is properly aligned.

You will recall that we encountered this same kind of problem in the alignment of the gain mechanism of the Foxboro Model 40. The method to use when aligning two components is to alternately make alignment corrections on each of them, thereby, in a step-wise fashion, bringing them simultaneously into alignment. This is the typical "half and half" adjustment.

The comparison mechanism is aligned by alternately reversing the action of the mechanism, examining the output, making corrections to the setpoint micrometer and then to the nozzle position. The action of this controller is reversed by rotating the floating lever so that the setpoint end of the lever is moved to the opposing side. This is accomplished by rotating the large geared disk that supports the pivot on which the floating lever is mounted.

For the gain mechanism to be aligned, it must be possible to rotate the gain without a change in output when the measurement and setpoint are given. This will be possible (in the case of the parallelogram) only if the movable end of the parallelogram is centered on the axis of rotation of the gain lever. If it is centered on the axis, changing the angle will not change the position of the movable end of the parallelogram. Since the angle-gain lever is not adjustable, we need only to position the parallelogram horizontally to cause the movable end of the parallelogram to line up with the axis of rotation. Therefore, we need only one adjustment. This is accomplished by the adjustment which loads the spring. Adjustments are made until it is possible to rotate the gain knob without a change in the output.

The gain mechanism and the comparison mechanism have been aligned. Now we must align the feedback mechanism. If the feedback mechanism is aligned, the output will hold constant if the error signal is zero. The output will hold constant providing the nozzle is within its clearance relative to the baffle. If it is not, the feedback mechanism will drive in an effort to bring it within its clearance. If the output drives, we must change the nozzle position relative to the feedback mechanism.

An eccentric is furnished that changes the nozzle position relative to the feedback position. This adjustment is comparable to the eccentric on the connecting rod of the Brown Air-O-Line controller. Unlike the Brown, the eccentric is on the nozzle side of the gain mechanism. In the Brown controller, the eccentric was on the feedback side of the mechanism. Adjustment of this eccentric will result in a new baffle/nozzle position for a given feedback mechanism position, thereby stopping the reset drift.

There is a practical problem in using this adjustment, however. It is extremely difficult to precisely adjust the eccentric; therefore, it is extremely difficult to stop the drift using the eccentric adjustment alone. The solution is to use the eccentric for coarse adjustment and to make minor adjustments using the gain mechanism. Admittedly, using the gain mechanism adjustment to correct the feedback alignment introduces small errors in the gain mechanism alignment. As a practical matter, these errors in gain mechanism alignment are not serious.

The discussion of the alignment of the Taylor Fulscope controller should serve to reinforce some alignment principles. For a detailed alignment procedure for the Taylor Fulscope, see the manufacturer's literature or the applicable IMO.

In the next chapter we will study a motion-balance controller using a bellows-type comparison mechanism rather than the linkage mechanism used in the Foxboro Model 40, Brown Air-O-Line, and Taylor Fulscope. Interestingly enough, the controller can be furnished with a linkage-type comparison mechanism. Our discussion, however, will be limited to the bellows-type input. The controller is manufactured by Fischer & Porter. We shall refer to it as Fischer & Porter's Mark III controller.

Chapter 29

Fischer & Porter's Model 45 Controller

MARK II AND III CONTROLLERS

In preceding chapters, we have discussed several controllers. We have emphasized the need for relating the several controller subassemblies to each other. Except for the Fisher Governor controller, the controllers discussed used a linkage-type comparison mechanism. In this controller the measurement and setpoint were compared, using linkage. We will in this chapter discuss a controller using two opposing bellows that perform the comparison function.

A controller using this type of comparison mechanism will be called a pneumatically-connected controller. The pneumatically-connected controller is used to indicate that the measurement and setpoint signals are air pressure signals.

The major advantage of the pneumatically-connected controller is that it makes is possible to locate the individual pieces of instrument equipment at some distance from each other. Since they are connected pneumatically, the individual instrument may be located at any convenient point as long as the necessary tubing is run to each instrument of the loop. Pneumatically-connected controllers in common language are frequently called plug-in controllers or miniature controllers. Pneumatically-connected controllers may or may not be plug-in; for example, the Fisher Governor controller is not plug-in. Controllers are all approximately the same size.

The disadvantage of the pneumatically-connected controller is the resulting increase in maintenance cost. This increased cost is offset in part by an increased on-stream time. To this potential increase of on-stream time, the instrument in the loop must be calibrated to a standard and the controller must be aligned for all input-output levels and all gain settings. If it is not, it is not possible to take advantage of the plug-in feature without extensive retuning.

In later chapters we shall consider several pneumatically connected controllers. We will, in this chapter, study Fischer & Porter's current controllers. Interestingly enough, this controller is offered with either a bellows-type comparison mechanism or a linkage-type comparison mechanism. The feedback mechanism, the gain mechanism, and the detector mechanism are the same for either type comparison mechanism. The Fischer & Porter controller, in addition to being link-connected or pneumatically connected, has been offered with three different models. We shall discuss the current model, describing it as Mark III. It differs from the Mark II primarily in that adjustments are offered for aligning the comparison mechanism. The Mark II does not have comparison-mechanism alignment adjustments.

Components

The components of the Fischer & Porter controller are the usual ones. There is one additional component not used in other controllers: a second restriction. The restriction is located between the relay-output and nozzle-backpressure systems. As the relay output pressure changes, the amount of air furnished to the nozzle changes. As a consequence, the amount of nozzle baffle clearance required to change the output from 3 to 15 psig is reduced markedly. This restriction is called regenerative-feedback by Fischer & Porter. The presence of the regenerative-feedback restriction affects the response characteristics of the controllers. The overall functioning of the controller is identical with controllers previously discussed.

Arrangements

The feedback mechanism consists of two sets of bellows placed in a can and connected by a rod. Mounted on the rod is a platform. (See Fig. 29-1.) Pivoting on this platform is a control lever. The feedback motion is in line with the bellows. As the bellows connecting rod moves, it carries the platform and the control lever.

Fig. 29-2. Gain mechanism.

The error signal is at right angles to the feedback mechanism and as it changes, the control lever rotates. On the control lever is a baffle striker which positions the baffle in front of the nozzle.

The comparison mechanism consists of two opposed bellows. The output of the comparison bellows is a displacement that drives the error link.

The detector is a baffle/nozzle nonbleed relay combination with the modification mentioned above. The baffle is bent 90 degrees, forming a right angle rather than the straight angle as with baffles previously encountered. The baffle has this angle because of the orientation of the nozzle relative to the other controller mechanisms.

The gain mechanism is an angle-type gain mechanism quite similar to the angle-gain mechanism of Foxboro's Model 40. Fig. 29-2 is a photograph of the gain mechanism. (The comparison mechanism has been removed so that the gain mechanism can be seen.) Fig. 29-3 is a pictorial diagram of the controller. Study these figures and relate them to each other and to the controllers discussed in previous chapters.

Operation

See Fig. 29-1. Suppose the measurement signal increases. The error link will move to the right, rotating the control lever. As the control lever rotates, the baffle striker moves to the right, permitting the baffle to cover the nozzle. The nozzle backpressure will build up, as will the relay output. The relay output is applied to the proportioning bellows (and at some time later to the reset bellows) lifting the control lever. Depending on the angle of the baffle relative to the feedback movement, more or less of the feedback baffle movement will be applied to the baffle, causing it to move away from the nozzle. (Remember, the measurement signal caused the baffle to move toward the nozzle.)

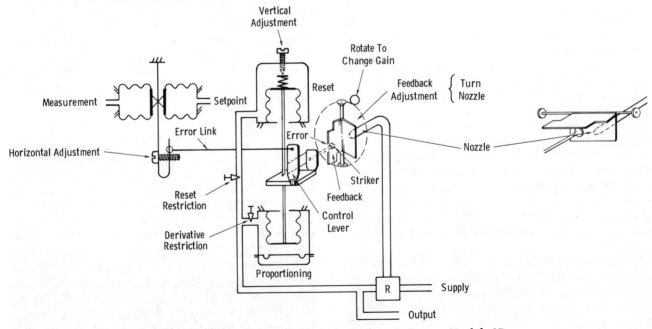

Fig. 29-1. Controller mechanism, Fischer & Porter Model 45.

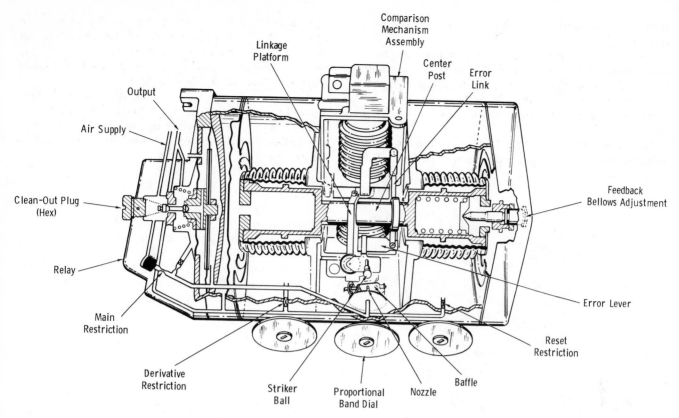

Fig. 29-3. Cutaway view of controller mechanism.

The controller output will drive to that pressure that brings the feedback signal into equilibrium with the measurement signal. Of course, the actual feedback movement, hence pressure, required for a given error signal movement will depend on the gain setting.

At some later time the change in relay output pressure will pass by the reset restriction and will load the reset bellows. When the pressures in the reset and proportioning bellows are equal there will be no feedback signals. If there is an error signal, the controller output will drive to one limit or the other. This will be recognized as the normal resetting action.

If the derivative restriction is closed down so that some time elapses before the change in relay output is applied to the proportioning bellows, the initial feedback action will be retarded. The result is controller output "over-traveling." That is, the output would change more than it would change if the normal proportioning response were not impeded by the derivative restriction.

Alignment

The alignment of the Fischer & Porter controller consists of relating the comparison mechanism, the feedback mechanism, the gain mechanism, and the detector mechanism to each other. So that for all levels of input, for all levels of output, and for all gain settings, the output will not drift if the controller is open-loop connected. Or, if the controller is closed-loop connected, there will be no offset between the setpoint and measurement (output) for all levels of input and for all gain settings.

Consider the gain mechanism alignment. For the gain mechanism to be aligned, it should be possible with zero error signal to rotate the gain from low to high without the output changing. This will be possible only if the striker is centered on the axis of rotation of the gain disk. The nozzle is centered on this axis. To align the gain mechanism then, it is necessary to have available adjustments to move the striker vertically and horizontally.

Since the nozzle is also adjustable, and since it is used to tell whether or not the gain mechanism is aligned, we must also align the nozzle. Since these two alignments interact, we are confronted with the typical half-and-half adjustment of open-loop connection. After first making an adjustment to the horizontal adjustment, reverse the action and correct for half of any change in output by adjusting the nozzle. If these adjustments are repeated until the output doesn't change when the action is reversed, the striker is centered on the horizontal centerline. Simultaneously the nozzle is brought into alignment with the feedback mechanism. By rotating the baffle so that it is at a 90-degree angle to the connecting rod, and by also adjusting the vertical adjustment, the striker then can be centered on the vertical centerline on the gain mechanism.

Consider now the comparison mechanism alignment. Recall that as long as the measurement and setpoint signals are equal there should be no error signal regardless of the signal level. This means that as the pressure in both bellows is changed from 3 to 15 psig, the output of the controller should not change. If it does, the comparison mechanism is not properly aligned.

The reason for error signals at one pressure level when there is no error signal at a different pressure level is that the effective area of the bellows changes with internal pressure. Usually bellows are manufactured and matched by the manufacturer to avoid this problem.

Fischer & Porter, in their Mark II controller, offer adjustments for aligning the comparison bellows. This is accomplished by changing the lengths of the two bellows. We have briefly outlined the procedure for aligning the controller when it is open-loop; it may also be aligned closed-loop. For detailed alignment procedure, see the applicable IMO's.

In the next chapter we will consider a second pneumatically coupled controller: the Taylor Trans-scope. We will find again the controller consists of the same sub-assemblies. The difference is almost wholly limited to the geometry of the controller.

Chapter 30

Taylor Transcope Controller

TAYLOR CONTROLLER

The Taylor Transcope Series Controller is pneumatically connected and in many respects is quite similar to the Foxboro Model 40 and the Fischer & Porter controller discussed in the previous chapter. As is so often the case, the difference between this controller and others of the same type is almost wholly limited to the geometry of the controller.

Components

The components are the usual components of an automatic reset controller: a comparison mechanism, a feedback mechanism, a detector mechanism, and an adjustable gain mechanism.

Arrangements

The comparison bellows, unlike those in other controllers, do not directly oppose each other. Functionally, however, the arrangement used by Taylor is the equivalent of directly opposing bellows.

Refer to Fig. 30-1. The setpoint and measurement bellows are at extremities of a beam pivoted in the middle by a tension-type wire pivot. This arrangement is the functional equivalent of a comparison mechanism consisting of two directly opposed bellows.

The feedback mechanism is similar to the comparison mechanism. The proportioning bellows and the reset bellows are located at the extremities of a second force beam. This second force beam is at right angles to the comparison mechanism and pivots on the same tension line.

The output from these two beams is an actuating pin mounted on the beams and centered on the pivot. Contacting the actuating pin is the control lever. One end of the control lever is the baffle. The angle between

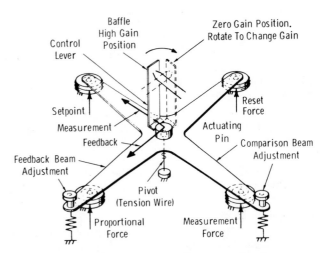

Fig. 30-1. Beam and bellows mechanism, Taylor Transcope controller.

the comparison beam and the feedback beam can be changed. Hence, the relative contribution of the feedback signal to the error signal as detected by the nozzle can be changed.

Operation

Suppose the measurement signal increases. An increase in measurement signal will permit the baffle to move closer to the nozzle (as with the baffle shown in Fig. 30-1) and the backpressure will build up. The relay output will increase, causing an increase in the proportioning force. An increase in proportioning force will lift the proportioning end of the feedback beam, but since there is a zero-degree angle between the baffle and the feedback mechanism, none of the feedback signal will be applied to the baffle. For the baffle position shown in Fig. 30-1, the gain of the controller is extremely high.

Suppose the baffle were rotated relative to the beams so that it formed a 45-degree angle. Let's now consider its operation. Again assume an increase in the measurement signal. This increase will permit the baffle to move closer to the nozzle. The relay output pressure will increase. This increase in pressure acting on the proportioning bellows will move the actuating pin, thereby causing the baffle to move away from the nozzle (remember the original movement was toward the nozzle). When the feedback motion equals the error signal motion the controller will come to equilibrium.

Suppose, however, the controller is open-loop connected. That is, there is no way for the controller output to change measurement signals. Yet, in our example, we have assumed that the measurement signal increases and is now different from the setpoint signal. Since there is a difference between the measurement and the setpoint, there is an error signal to the detector. As we have already noted, this error signal resulted in an increase in output pressure which, acting on the proportioning bellows, tends to return the baffle back to its original position.

What about the reset bellows? The same increase in pressure will at some later time, depending on the setting of the reset restriction, also be applied to the reset bellows. As the reset bellows pressure approaches the proportioning bellows pressure, the feedback signal will approach zero. When the pressures in the proportioning bellows and the reset bellows are the same, the feedback signal is zero. Of course, what happens is as long as the error signal persists, the controller output pressure will continue to drive in an effort to position the proportioning bellows so that there is a feedback signal to balance the error signal. But, the same increasing controller output ultimately acting on the reset bellows will cancel out the proportioning. This will be recognized as the normal reset action.

As was the case for any angle-type gain mechanism, it is possible to change the gain from less than 1 to

several hundred. Also, by rotating the gain mechanism so that the baffle/nozzle is in a different quadrant, the action of the controller can be changed.

Controller Alignment

The Transcope controller has three adjustments available for alignment purposes. These adjustments are the feedback mechanism adjustment, which is a spring on the feedback beam; the comparison mechanism adjustment, which is a spring on the comparison beam; and the nozzle position adjustment, which is accomplished by rotating the threaded nozzle.

As is always the case with pneumatically connected control, the controller can be aligned either open-loop or closed-loop. Whether the controller is aligned open-loop or closed-loop, does not in any way change the basic alignment requirements. These requirements are that (1) with a zero error signal the measurement and setpoint agree (if the controller is closed-loop) or the output does not drift (if the controller is open-loop); (2) with a zero error signal it should be possible to rotate the gain dial from high gain to low gain, without the output changing; and (3) the error signals should remain zero for all pressure levels to the comparison mechanism.

It will be possible to rotate the gain mechanism without changing the output only if the striker is centered on the controller center line. To center the striker, we need a "horizontal adjustment" and a "vertical adjustment." These adjustments are the two springs on the beam mechanism. By adjusting these two springs it is possible to center the striker on the controller center line.

As is so often the case, the detector is used to determine whether or not the gain mechanism is aligned. But since the nozzle is adjustable it also may be out of alignment. This, then, introduces the classical half-and-half adjustment where half of the error is eliminated by adjusting the nozzle and the other half of the error is eliminated by adusting the beam. These

Fig. 30-2. Taylor Transcope controller mechanism.

adjustments are alternately made. They are the horizontal adjustment of the gain mechanism and nozzle position or feedback mechanism alignment.

The second spring is the vertical adjustment. If for all levels of pressure to the comparison mechanism, the error signal does not remain constant, the comparison mechanism is not aligned. It is possible to align the comparison mechanism by changing the distance of the bellows from the pivot point because the bellows are mounted on eccentrics. This alignment correction is better done in the factory and is not recommended in the field. For a detailed alignment procedure, see the applicable IMO.

Fig. 30-2 is a photograph of the controller. Study Figs. 30-1 and 30-2. Relate them to each other and to the other controllers.

Chapter 31

Foxboro Model 58 Controller

FOXBORO CONTROLLER

The Foxboro Model 58 controller is a pneumatically-connected controller. Unlike the controllers studied so far, it is a force-balance controller. You will recall that in our study of transmitters we classified them either as motion-balance or force-balance. We found that force-balance instruments could be either moment-balance type or true force-balance type and that motion-balance instruments could be either linear motion-balance or angle motion-balance. We indicated that the same kind of categorizing was possible with controllers.

True force-balance controllers are constructed so that the forces directly oppose each other. There are no levers involved. This type of controller is frequently referred to as a stack controller.

Though we haven't mentioned it before, the controllers previously discussed are angle-type motion-balance controllers. They are motion-balance because the feedback signal and error signal do not directly load each other. They are angle-motion type because the motions act at distances from a pivot. In other words, levers are involved.

The Transcope controller deviates somewhat from our previous definition of motion-balance in that the motions involved are extremely small and do not differ substantially from the motions involved in the typical force-balance instruments. But, since the feedback signal and the error signal do not load each other, we can properly consider the Taylor instrument to be an angle-type motion-balance controller.

We will find in our discussion of the Foxboro Model 58 controller that the error signal and the feedback signal directly force each other. It is the difference between these two force signals that drives the baffle.

Components

The Foxboro Model 58 controller consists of the typical controller components: a comparison mechanism, a feedback mechanism, a detector mechanism, and an adjustable gain mechanism.

Arrangements

The comparison mechanism consists of two bellows applied to a plate. The feedback mechanism is also two bellows applied to the same plate. This plate, notwithstanding its appearance, is a two-dimensional lever (control lever). The plate, in turn, is located below a reference plate that essentially is part of the instrument chassis and serves as a reference for all the controller components. Mounted in this reference plate is the nozzle. The nozzle is arranged to "look" at the position of the force plate (control lever), which is driven by the four bellows. That part of the force plate under the nozzle is the baffle. Between these two plates is a bar-type fulcrum. This fulcrum can be rotated 90 degrees. At one extreme, it centers on the feedback bellows; in the other, it centers on the comparison bellows.

As the fulcrum rotates from its centered feedback position to its centered comparison-bellows position, the relative contribution of the feedback signal to the error signal is changed. Fig. 31-1 is a diagram of the controller, showing the arrangement of the components. Fig. 31-2 diagrams the gain mechanism.

The gain mechanism used in this controller is a parallel-lever gain mechanism. Do not let the fact that

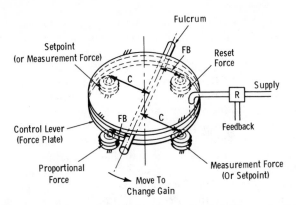

Fig. 31-1. Mechanism of Foxboro Model 58 controller.

the lever system is two-dimensional obscure its essential characteristic. Notice that as the fulcrum is moved, the lever lengths of the two pairs of bellows relative to the pivot are changed. In other words, even though the bellows remains fixed, the lever lengths over which they act change as the fulcrum is rotated.

Operation

Suppose that the controller is in equilibrium and the measurement signal increases. An increase in measurement signal will lift the force plate toward the nozzle. The nozzle backpressure will increase, the output will increase, and the proportional force will increase. Since the proportional bellows is on the opposite side of the fulcrum, the proportional force tends to move the baffle away from the nozzle. Since the feedback lever is shorter than the comparison-lever, there

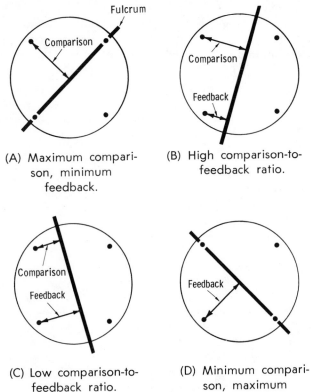

(A) Maximum comparison, minimum feedback.

(B) High comparison-to-feedback ratio.

(C) Low comparison-to-feedback ratio.

(D) Minimum comparison, maximum feedback.

Fig. 31-2. Different settings of gain mechanism.

must necessarily be a greater pressure change on the proportioning bellows than the pressure change on the measuring bellows, if the forces are to balance. The important point here is to recognize that the feedback force directly opposes the measurement force, and since the lever lengths can be different, the air pressures can be different.

Let us examine the operation of the controller, with the fulcrum positioned so that the feedback lever lengths and the comparison lever lengths are the same. They will be the same when the fulcrum forms a 45-degree angle relative to the bellows center lines.

Assume that there is an increase in measurement. The increase in measurement will move the baffle closer to the nozzle, causing an increase in output. This increase in output, acting on the proportioning bellows, will result in a force opposing the change in measurement force and will tend to move the baffle away from the nozzle. (The change in measurement force moved it towards the nozzle.) The output will change until the forces on the force plate come into equilibrium.

Suppose, however, the controller is connected open-loop, or suppose, because of the peculiarities of the control loop, that the measurement is not changed as the controller output is changed. In other words, suppose there is a difference between the measurement and setpoint pressures, hence, a difference in force. This difference in force is an error signal.

When the measurement changes, the output changes and the proportioning bellows at the feedback mechanism tend to restore the baffle to its position prior to the change in measurement. However, this same change in output is also applied to the reset bellows. Depending on the reset restriction, the pressure in the reset bellows will ultimately equal the pressure in the proportioning bellows. When this happens the feedback-force signal will go to zero and there will be no counterbalancing force to the error-signal force. Therefore, the output will continue to change in an effort to balance out the error signal. This will be recognized as normal reset action.

As a consequence, the controller output will drive to one limit or another unless the error signal is eliminated. The error signal can be eliminated only if the measurement pressure becomes the same as the setpoint pressure.

Since the gain mechanism is somewhat unique, it will be worthwhile to study it further. Fig. 31-2 is a diagram showing several positions of the fulcrum relative to the bellows. If the fulcrum lines up with the feedback bellows, as at (A), there can be no feedback signal because the force plate cannot be moved. The controller is an extremely high-gain controller. If, on the other hand, the fulcrum is rotated so that it lines up with the comparison mechanism, as at (B), there can be a large difference between the measurement and setpoint pressures, but none of this difference in pressure will be detected by the nozzle because the measurement and setpoint bellows cannot move the force plate. As the fulcrum is rotated between these two limits as at (C) or (D), the comparison lever length gets shorter as the feedback lever gets longer. Hence, the amount of feedback signal required to balance a given error signal changes. This of course represents a change in gain of the controller.

Alignment

There are two alignment adjustments. These are springs that load the force plate. One spring is on the center line of the comparison mechanism bellows; the other is on the center line of the feedback bellows.

The alignment test for the Model 58 controller is identical with the alignment test for any other pneumatically-connected, adjustable-gain, automatic-reset controller—that is, does the measurement agree with the setpoint for all lever of setpoint pressures (if the controller is closed-loop) and for all gain settings? It is recommended that this controller be aligned closed-loop connected.

Fig. 31-3. Foxboro Model 58 controller mechanism.

It will be possible to change the gain without the output changing only if the force plate is parallel to the reference plate. If it is to be made parallel, two adjustments are required. If, on the other hand, the comparison is to be aligned, the effective area of the bellows must not change with the internal pressure. Any small difference in an effective area can be corrected by making adjustments to the spring.

If, however, in order to align the gain mechanism, the two plates are made parallel by adjusting the springs, it will not be possible to also align the comparison mechanism by adjusting the same springs. It is not possible to correct two faults with only one adjustment. Either the gain alignment or the comparison-mechanism alignment must suffer. If both mechanisms are not in alignment, trouble is indicated in the bellows or in the gain mechanism.

It is fairly important to recognize that a misaligned controller indicates faulty components. This is true regardless of the controller. A controller once aligned, should not go out of alignment. Depending on the individual controller design and manufacturing policies there may be no alignment adjustments to perhaps 12 alignment adjustments. The lack of alignment adjustments in no way changes the function of the controller; hence, it in no way changes the definition of whether or not the controller is aligned. Therefore, the number of adjustments do not change the test that should be made in a controller to determine if it is in alignment. If a controller is found out of alignment, the number of adjustments in no way changes the fact that there is trouble in individual components of the controller. These troubles should be located and corrected. There should be no need to continually realign controllers any more than there is reason to continually re-calibrate measurements. For a specific alignment procedure, see the applicable IMO's.

Chapter 32

Control Theory

Some understanding of the theoretical aspect of automatic-control theory is desirable because such an understanding is helpful in analyzing and understanding instrument devices that implement the control theory. In this chapter we shall study the three types of responses (modes) from the viewpoint of the operator.

On and off control is not discussed as such because "on and off" control in pneumatics is a high-gain, proportioning controller.

PROPORTIONING RESPONSE

Suppose we are required to heat a stream of water with a steam heater. The water flows through a coil outside of which is steam. The heat of the steam passes through the coil walls and into the water so that by controlling the amount of the steam to the heater, we can control the temperature of the water leaving the heater. To measure the temperature of the water, a strip chart temperature recorder with a range of 0 to 100 degrees centigrade is used. The range of the recorder is 0 to 100 degrees centigrade. The water temperature is to be held at 50 degrees centigrade.

Assume that we start under the condition that the valves are half open and the temperature of the water is 50 degrees centigrade. If the temperature increases to 60 degrees centigrade (a 10-percent change), we might choose to close the valve to a 40 percent open position (a 10-percent change). If the temperature increases to 70 degrees (a 20-percent change), we might choose to close the valve to a 30 percent open position (a 20-percent change). Or, suppose that the temperature drops to 40 degrees (a 10-percent change), we might choose to open the valve to 60-percent open (a 10-percent change).

If we make the adjustment just described, we will be making an adjustment proportional to the change in temperature. A 10-percent change in temperature causes us to change the valve opening 10 percent. Or in other words, the magnitude of the change in valve position is in proportion to the magnitude of the change in temperature. This type of response is called proportioning response.

In the case just described the ratio of temperature deviation to valve change is 1 to 1. So if the temperature reading of the water were zero, we would have a wide open valve. And if the temperature were 100 degrees, we would have a closed valve. Or a 100-percent change in temperature reading would result in a 100-percent change in valve position. These ideas might be represented as shown in Fig. 32-1.

Proportional Band

In the case just discussed the conditions were that the valve moved 100 percent of its travel to change the temperature 100 percent. This is never the case in an actual situation.

In the actual situation the valve may need to move only part of its travel (say 50 percent) to change the temperature 100 percent. In this case the ratio of temperature change to valve change would be 100/50 or 2.

Perhaps in an actual case the valve may move 100 percent of its travel and the temperature might change only 50 percent. The ratio of temperature change to valve change would be 50/100 or 1/2.

In the first example we find the ratio to be 1 to 1. In this case the controller can be said to have a proportional band of 100 percent. In the case where the ratio is 2, the band is said to be 200 percent. When the ratio is 1/2, the band is described as being a 50-percent proportional band. Proportional band may be described as the ratio of measurement change to valve position change (or change in controller output) taken as a percent.

As we have already seen, in most controllers there is an adjustment that will change the amount the valve will move for a given change in measurement. We have called this the gain adjustment. This adjustment

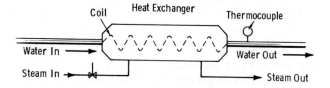

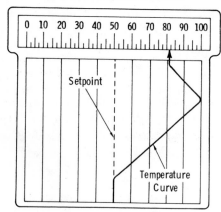

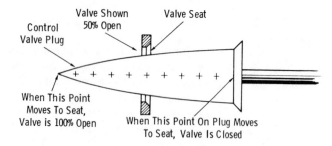

Fig. 32-1. Elements of temperature control system.

is also called the proportional band, throttling range, or sensitivity adjustment. Controllers with such adjustments are called adjustable proportional-band controllers. Adustable gain mechanism has been described in several chapters. The need for such an adjustment arises out of the necessity of "matching the controller (which includes the valve) to the process." This means that different processes require different valve movements for the same measurement deviations. The valve movement required depends on a wide variety of considerations; for example, the size of the equipment, the kind of material being processed, the rate of processing, the size of pipe lines, or desired pressures, and temperatures. In general it might be said that there are as many different valve responses required as there are chemical processes.

Gain, Sensitivity, Proportional Band

These three expressions are used to define the proportional response. In prior work, gain was described as the ratio of output to input. Proportional band is defined as the ratio of the measurement change to the change of output, expressed as a percent. For example, if the change in measurement relative to the setpoint is 10 percent of the chart (or scale) and the controller output changes 1.2 psi, then the proportional band is 100 percent. Why? Because 1.2 psi is 10 percent of output and the ratio is

$$\frac{10 \text{ percent}}{10 \text{ percent}} = 1$$

and 1×100 percent = 100-percent proportional band.

Consider a second example. Suppose the output changed 12 psi for a 10-percent change in measurement setpoint deviation. A change of 12 psi represents a 100 percent change in output.

$$\frac{10}{100} = .1$$

$.1 \times 100$ percent = 10 percent proportional band

A last example. Suppose that for a measurement setpoint deviation equal to 100 percent of the chart the output changed 6.0 psi (50 percent).

$$\frac{100}{50} = 2$$

2×100 = 200-percent proportional band.

Gain is defined as the ratio of output pressure change to measurement change. We have used gain throughout this book. Technically gain is a dimensionless number; that is, the units used to express output must be the same as the units used to express input, so that the units cancel out. Therefore, gain is usually applied to pneumatically-coupled controllers and in this case the ratio would be psi of output change to psi of change in the transmitted measurement, and the psi's cancel out, leaving a dimensionless number. For example, if the transmitted measurement pressure changed 1 psi and the output pressure changed 3 psi, the gain would be 3/1 or 3.

Sensitivity is defined as the ratio of output pressure to change in measurement, where the measurement is expressed as inches of pen travel. For example, if the pen moves 2 inches on the chart and the output changes 1 psi, then the sensitivity is 1 psi per 2 inch or .5 psi per 1 inch.

To relate sensitivity to gain, the following expression applies:

$$\text{Sensitivity} = \frac{12 \text{ psi} \times \text{gain}}{\text{chart width}}$$

To relate proportional band to gain use the following:

$$\text{Proportional band} = \frac{1}{\text{gain}} \times 100 \text{ percent}$$

To relate proportional band to sensitivity use the following:

$$\frac{PB}{100} = \frac{12 \text{ psi}}{S \times \text{chart width}}$$

Where,
  S is the sensitivity,
  PB is the proportional band.

Regardless of the particular notation and terminology used, the important point is to recognize that the different terminology describes the same thing: the relationship between the input and output.

INTEGRAL RESPONSE

Using the process described earlier, suppose that the temperature increased from 50 degrees to 60 degrees as shown in Fig. 32-2. If we were operating the process, we would readjust the valve, closing it in an effort to bring the temperature to the setpoint. After waiting a suitable period of time, we might observe that the temperature dropped but was not yet on the setpoint. If this were the case, we might close the valve further and wait to observe the results. Finally, after a number of valve adjustments (T_1, T_2, T_3 on Fig. 32-2) the temperature could be made to coincide with the setpoint and no further adjustments required.

What we have done is readjust the valve whenever the temperature is away from the setpoint. When the temperature was too high, we closed the valve a small amount. When the temperature was too low, we opened the valve a little.

Remember, the first temperature change that appeared on the chart at T_0 occurred with no change in valve position. Therefore, there must have been a change in the process. Some of the changes in the process which could cause this temperature rise are changes in the steam supply and/or changes in the water throughput. The steam pressure might have increased, and even though the valve position remains the same, more steam would flow through it because of the increased pressure. Or, suppose the rate at which water were flowing through the heater were reduced. Then the temperature of the remaining flow of

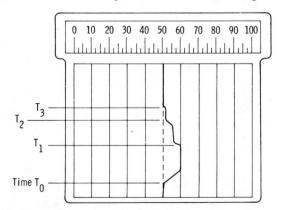

Fig. 32-2. Effect of experimental adjustments in process control system.

water would increase since the same steam feed heats a reduced amount of water. Conversely, if the water usage were increased, then the temperature would fall; or, if the steam pressure dropped, the temperature would fall. So it can be seen that if the temperature is to remain the same without valve adjustments, process conditions must also remain the same. Yet, in actual practice, process conditions never remain precisely the same.

If the process being discussed were "automatically" controlled with a proportioning controller, the valve would automatically change to compensate for a temperature change. This is so, but is it sufficient to bring the pen back to the index?

Suppose the requirements for hot water have been increased. The effect would be to reduce the water temperature (say to 40 degrees). The valve would open due to proportioning response, and, as a result, the temperature might return to 50 degrees. If it does, the valve will be returned to 50-percent opening; but remember, the 50-percent opening can no longer be sufficient to heat the new water load because it was just sufficient to hold the original water load at 50 degrees. Therefore, it is impossible for it to heat the increased load with the opening that just heated the original water load to 50 degrees. Therefore, we must conclude that if the load changes, the measurement cannot return to the setpoint unless:

1. The load on the system returns to the original condition, or
2. We raise the index, causing the valve to open an amount sufficient to heat the additional water to 50 percent and then shift the physical setpoint index mechanically so that it coincides with the setpoint.

If we do this, we have mechanically aligned the controller for new balance conditions that suit the new load. Such a readjustment is called **manual reset.**

For a continually changing process a manual reset may not be sufficient. The utility of the reset mechanism described in earlier chapters will now be shown.

We found that if the measurement were away from the setpoint, the control valve must be continually repositioned until the measurement returns to the setpoint. The proportional response is not adequate to return the pen all the way back to the setpoint. A review of the basic reset mechanism will show that **unless** the error signal is zero (measurement and setpoint are together), the controller mechanism will cause the valve to drive to fully open or fully closed. This driving will stop only when the measurement and setpoint are together. If the automatic reset mechanism is used, we have a controller which responds proportionally due to the proportioning part of the mechanism, and also responds whenever the measurement is away from the setpoint. The magnitude of this reset response is determined by:

1. How far the measurement is away from the setpoint, and
2. How long the measurement is away from the setpoint.

Or, in other words, the magnitude of the reset response is determined by the setpoint and measurement deviation multiplied by the time that the deviation exists.

Using mathematical terms, the magnitude of the reset response is related to the area under the measurement curve with the position of the setpoint being the base line (deviation × time); that is the reason for referring to this type of response as integral response. In mathematics one definition of integration is the determination of the area under a curve.

It should be remembered that the reset mechanism uses a restriction. This restriction, which is adjustable, establishes the rate at which a corrective action will take place for a given measurement/setpoint deviation. If the restriction is wide open, the rate of correction is so fast that the control valve will be driven alternately from fully open to fully closed. If the restriction is closed, no reset response will be obtained.

There are two aspects of integral response that are a continual source of bother to those not too familiar with integral-response control. Much consternation arises out of the fact that it is impossible to have a gain value and an integral-response value such that even though the measurement is moving towards the index, the controller output can be driving the valve in a direction that will ultimately cause the measurement to overshoot the setpoint. The direction of reset response will change; the output will reverse only when the measurement crosses the setpoint. For example, if in our process the temperature were swiftly approaching 50 degrees from a starting point of 60 degrees, the integral action would continue to close the valve until the measurement was 50 degrees.

A second aspect arises when a process is shut down. If the process is shut down there is no way for the changing valve to bring the measurement back to the setpoint. Nevertheless, the controller continues to move the valve, and if the shutdown is long enough, the valve will be driven to either fully open or fully closed. Depending on the reset-restriction setting, it may take as much as several hours for the valve to be returned to its normal operating position. It is for this reason that a process using a proportional-plus-reset controller generally must be started up "nonautomatically." There are available proportioning integral controllers that are arranged to cut out the integral response for startup on batch-type operations.

To Summarize

1. The integral response is a function of the distance between the setpoint and measurement multiplied by the time that each of these differences exist. (Area under the measurement curve).
2. The effect of integral response is to cause the valve to move until the measurement and setpoint are together, regardless of the actual output pressure.
3. The integral response will reverse its effect on the valve only when the measurement crosses the setpoint.

4. During shutdown, a proportioning-plus-reset controller causes the valve to drive fully open or fully closed, depending on the reset adjustment and the duration of the shutdown. If this drive is excessive, the process must be put on hand control or a special batch-type controller must be used.

DERIVATIVE RESPONSE

The last type of control response to be considered is called derivative response. This mode of control is referred to by Foxboro as hyper reset, and by Taylor as preact. Others call it rate action.

Curve 2

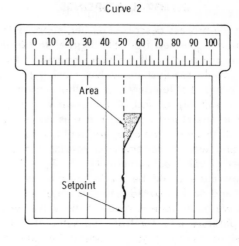

Curve 1

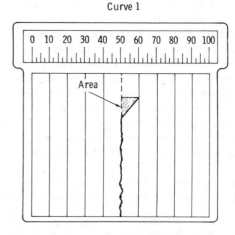

Fig. 32-3. Temperature curves showing different rates of loss of control.

We shall call this type of response derivative response. This term implies the mathematical derivation of the word. Our treatment, however, will not be mathematical.

Again using the process described earlier, suppose that a pair of temperature curves as shown in Fig. 32-3 was obtained.

An examination of the curves shows that at the time we observe the temperature, it has increased by 10 degrees. Therefore, the proportioning response for Curve 1 and Curve 2 would be identical.

Since the area under curve 1 is a bit less than the area under curve 2, the total reset response would be somewhat less for curve 1 than curve 2.

However, we know intuitively that curve 1 represents a process going out of control more rapidly than the one represented by curve 2. If it is to be brought back into control, a larger change in valve position must take place. Curve 2 represents a process going out of control at a much slower rate so that less rapid change in the valve position would be required to control the temperature.

In other words, it would be desirable to have a control response which recognizes the rate at which the temperature is changing from the setpoint. Or putting it another way, a control response that would recognize the slope of the curve might be useful. Mathematically, the slope of the curve can be defined as the time derivative, hence, the reason for calling this control response a derivative response.

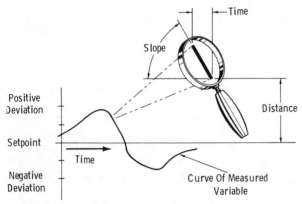

Fig. 32-4. Interpretation of a response curve.

The rate of response of the derivative control is established by the derivative restriction. The effect of the derivative control is to give the valve a "boost" in the right direction so as to respond quickly to the rapid change in temperature and to "flatten" it out. That is, to cause the control valve to overtravel for a short period of time. The valve overtravels much in the same way that an operator would close down the valve a few extra turns for a couple of minutes. Whenever the curve is flat there is no derivative response, regardless

of the actual position of the pen on the chart. There is no derivative response because derivative control reacts only to the slope of the curve. A "flat" curve has a zero slope, hence, the derivative response is also zero.

Since the derivative control responds to the slope of the curve, it might be said that the derivative control has the ability to "anticipate" what the measurement will be at some future time. Though his view is not strictly valid, it migh be helpful in developing a "feel" for derivative control. Remember, if the slope is zero, that is, if the measurement curve follows the setpoint, there is no derivative response.

COMBINED 3-MODE RESPONSE

So far we have considered three control responses. The method employed was to assume a certain type of measurement/setpoint deviation and then propose a type of valve correction required to bring the measurement to the setpoint. Curves were used to demonstrate the need for the three types of response. To summarize, consider the random curve of Fig. 32-4. This curve could represent any variable (measurement).

A very small portion of the curve can be described by specifying three things:

1. How far is the portion of curve from the setpoint?
2. What is the time duration of this portion of curve?
3. What is the slope of this portion of curve?

A skilled chemical plant operator intuitively recognizes these three specifications and makes a control adjustment in light of the total situation as he observes the curve. Control mechanisms also are able to recognize the three specifications listed as follows:

How far is the portion of curve from the setpoint? It has been shown that the proportioning mechanism does this part of the job.

Specifications 1 and 2 multiplied represent the area under the portion of curve. The integral response mechanism responds to those specifications.

What is the slope of the curve? The derivative mechanism responds to the slope.

Therefore, the total response of the control mechanism consists of the sum of the three individual responses of proportioning, reset, and derivative acting simultaneously.

Chapter 33

Process Control

Up to this point we have focused on the instrument mechanisms used for measuring and controlling. Control theory is outside the scope of this book. Nevertheless, a brief introduction might be helpful. It is well to remember that the only justification for instrumentation is to make it possible to make some more chemicals cheaper and safer. As a consequence, all instrumentation must be evaluated in light of the chemical job that needs to be done.

Instrumentation influences the process, but the process to a far greater degree influences the instrumentation. It is, perhaps, valid to say that instrumentation does not have an identity of its own. That is, instrumentation at best can only reflect the process to which it is applied. The practical consequence of this viewpoint is that the process dynamism must be understood before the instrumentation can be judged. For example, a temperature recorder/controller may be completely unsatisfactory on one process but on a second the same equipment may do an excellent job. An instrument is only "good" or "bad" in relation to what we want it to do.

WHAT DOES CONTROL MEAN?

The word "control" means many things to many people. Control as applied to electric motors usually refers to the electrical gear which starts and stops the motor. A control laboratory is a laboratory where chemicals are tested with the object of determining whether the chemicals meet specifications. The accounting department refers to certain accounting practices as cost control. The warehouse people talk about inventory control. Each group has a control concept.

The people in industrial instrumentation have their own definitions of control; the operating people have

their definitions. In spite of the diversity of applications of the term control, there is one basic idea that is expressed by control as used by all the people in the various activities. This idea is simply that control implies the ability to predict what will happen in the future because the ability to alter factors that affect future events are available. We are in control of our automobile if we can predict what will happen in the future. The extent of the control is limited timewise to the next few seconds. The degree of control is also limited by factors that can't be predicted. For example, we may have a blowout which might cause the automobile to go out of control.

The automobile driver, the warehouse supervisor, the cost accountant, the control chemist, and instrument engineers require two pieces of information before they can implement control. They all must measure. The warehouseman cannot control inventory unless he knows how much stock he has on hand. The control chemist must take measurements on the chemicals being analyzed. The cost accountant must know how much it is costing to do certain jobs.

But a second factor is also absolutely necessary for control. All too frequently this factor is lost or neglected. That factor is a precise definition of the object of control. For example, the control chemist may take many precise and involved measurements that result in specific information on the quality of a chemical. Yet, it is impossible for him to make any decisions on quality control unless he is given a set of quality specifications. Given these, he can compare his measurement with the specifications, thereby permitting him to exercise the control function of accepting or rejecting the chemicals examined. The cost accountant may accumulate very good cost figures, yet he must also have a set of acceptable cost figures to compare with.

The warehouseman may know precisely and continuously what stock he has on hand. But, this information alone without information on what and how much stock he should have makes it impossible for him to control his inventories.

In all these activities, it is necessary to measure what we are controlling and it is equally necessary to compare that measurement with what we want. The control action must always be based on the difference between the two.

"OPEN-" VERSUS "CLOSED-LOOP" CONTROL

There are two types of control response—one is termed open-loop, the other closed-loop. The meaning of each, and the differences, may best be conveyed by using the analogy of a man driving his automobile. There are two ways to drive an automobile on a road. One way would be for the driver to look down the road and decide where he wants to go (measure) and then to observe where he is, and comparing these, decide how he shall adjust the wheel and throttle (control). Having done this, he could close his eyes and travel a distance toward his goal and then open his eyes and repeat the above actions, exercising "open-loop" control.

The second way to drive an automobile would be for him to simultaneously determine where he wishes to be on the road and where he actually is (measure), and comparing these, adjust his wheel and throttle (control) so as to cause his automobile to go where he wants it to go. In this case, the driver continuously measures, compares, and controls. At no instance is the chain opened. The loop of events—measure, compare, and control—is closed. Hence the term closed-loop control.

The "open-loop" method of controlling an automobile perhaps is used more often than we may care to admit; and on a straight road with no side traffic, this method might work. Under these conditions the degree of success perhaps is established by the degree with which we can predict nothing will happen that will require a control action. For as long as we can predict that no other automobile will get in our way, that no pedestrians will get on the road, that the road is straight and free of pot holes, that our automobile won't have blowouts or otherwise fail mechanically—for as long as we can predict these conditions, we can drive "open-looped" and still be entirely in control. However, as a practical matter, the ability to predict is limited to a time span of a very few seconds; it is limited in degree by the number of factors we have knowledge of. As a consequence, "closed-loop" control is the only practical method for driving an automobile.

CONTROL IN A PRACTICAL PLANT

If the ideas of the first part of this discussion are all applied to the actual plant, some conclusions can be very swiftly made:

1. Measurements that are not used to establish a yardstick for the comparison step in control, or which do not result in a control action, need not be made at all.
2. Measurements that are in error, perhaps, are worse than no measurements at all.

The definition of the extent and degree of control, together with the overall controllability of a process, determine what instruments will be used and how much and how well this instrumentation must work. As a general statement, the "faster" a chemical process is, the greater the difficulty in holding that process in control.

A chemical process is in control if we can predict what it will be doing at points in the future. It is possible to predict what will happen if there is equipment that will result in changes being made to the process when and if the process tends to go out of control. In one of the examples it was shown that the location of an overflow pipe was all the equipment needed to maintain control of a liquid level in a tank. Usually the control problems are much more complicated and varying amounts of instrumentation and human attention are required. These combinations of human attention and instrumentation may be broken into three groups as follows: (See Fig. 33-1.)

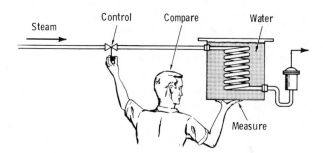

(A) Mostly human—very little instrumentation.

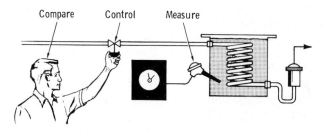

(B) Human plus measuring instruments.

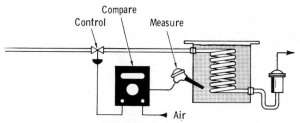

(C) Measuring and control instruments with very little human supervision.

Fig. 33-1. Three types of control.

1. All human, with very little instrumentation.
2. Human plus measuring instruments.
3. Measuring and control instruments with very little human supervision.

It is interesting to observe just how these three groupings effect control in the following control procedures:

1. The operator measures the temperature by feeling the pipe. He then compares this measurement with what it should be; then, depending on the comparison, he controls the valve.
2. The operator determines the temperature by examining the instrument that measures the temperature. He then compares that temperature with the correct temperature. Then depending on the comparison he controls the valve. If the operator never takes his eyes off the instrument or his hand off the valve and if he never stops making the comparison of measured temperature and desired temperature, he is effecting closed-loop control. If he periodically checks the chart and adjusts the valve, he is effecting open-loop control.
3. The measurement is made by the recorder, the controller compares the measurement with the setpoint, and controls the valve in accordance with that comparison. Since this is a continuous cycle of events without interruption, it is described as closed-loop control.

Material Balance (or Energy Balance)

To maintain a process in control, it is necessary to match the rate at which material (and/or energy) is fed to the process with the rate at which the process "uses" material (and/or energy). To do this it is only necessary to cause the control valves to take a position such that the material (and/or energy) is being "used up" by the process. On the surface this seems to be a rather simple job. If we could get perfect measurements without any delays, if the processes were free of inertia and lags, and if the controllers and control valves acted without delays, it would be an extremely simple job.

Lags

Unfortunately, there are time and transfer delays in getting a change in process measured and corrected. After it is sensed, there is a limit to the sensitivity of the measuring instrument such that the process change has to be sufficiently large to cause a response in the measuring instrument. It then takes time to get the measurement response to the recorder controller. The controller requires time to do its job and still more time is required to get the controller output to the valve. When the valve does respond to the controller, output time is required for the controller fluid to move into the process. More time is required before the process equipment responds to the change in feed rate. Finally, the change in process, after passing through the various phases of the process, is sensed by the instruments. By this time, it may very well be too late because what the new valve position has caused to happen may no longer be the correct thing for the valve to do.

These time requirements for the individual actions are called lags. The time it takes the heat to flow through the tube wall is called a "transfer" lag. The time it takes for the change to be recorded is called a measurement lag. The time it takes to get the signal to the control valve is called a control lag. The time it takes to get the material flowing through the valve to the process is called a distance-velocity lag.

Capacity

Since the basic control problem is to match the valve movement with the movement of the process, and since, due to lags and instrument sensitivities, it is a fairly difficult job to accurately match the valve travel to the changes in process, one might swiftly conclude that processes which can tolerate relatively large errors in valve positioning are the easiest to control. Such is the case.

Let us consider the heating process as shown in Fig. 33-2. Suppose the hot water storage capacity is quite large compared to the amount of water we take out of the heater. If it is, a very large amount of steam will be required to change the temperature of the large quantity of water. If the valve controlling the steam flow is fairly small, it might be possible to allow the valve to go wide open for a substantial period of time before the temperature changes; or, alternately, we might use the hot water at a faster rate for periods of time, with small changes in temperature. The large quantity of water acts as a "fly-wheel" and the relatively small steam supply affects the "flywheel" only if it acts over fairly long periods of time.

As a consequence, we might properly conclude that this process is easy to control.

Suppose the process were one of holding a level in a tank. Assume the input to the tank is large and the tank is small. We are given the problem of holding the level constant by changing a valve opening, permitting more or less fluid to flow from the tank. The valve is sufficiently large to discharge all the fluid that may enter the tank.

To effect good control it is necessary that the flow out be almost exactly equal to the flow in. Any difference will result in a change in level. Suppose the supply suddenly increases, then the control valve must suddenly open more. If it is slow to respond, the level

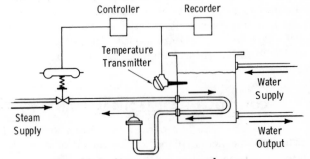

Fig. 33-2. Hot water control system.

will increase substantially. If the valve overtravels, the tank may run dry. In other words, the capacity of the tank is small compared to the capacity of the supply. In the heater example, the capacity of the steam supply is small and the heater capacity is large.

The process might be split in "halves," one half called the supply side and the half using materials or energy being called the demand side. The capacity of the equipment to use energy or material is called the demand side capacity. The capacity of the input is called the supply side capacity. If these expressions are used in connection with the heater example and the tank-level example, we might say that the heater example was one with a small supply side capacity and a large demand-side capacity, whereas the tank-level problem was a process with a small demand-side capacity and a large supply-side capacity. In general, processes with large demand-side capacities are easy to control as compared to processes with small demand-side capacities.

Index

NOTES